CROSSWORDS WORD SEARCHES LOGIC PUZZLES & SURPRISES!

MIND STRETCHERS

MOSS EDITION

EDITED BY STANLEY NEWMAN

Reader's Digest

The Reader's Digest Association, Inc.
Pleasantville, NY / Montreal

ISBN 978-1-60652-970-6

Address any comments about *Mind Stretchers, Moss Edition* to:

The Reader's Digest Association, Inc.
Editor in Chief, Books
Reader's Digest Road
Pleasantville, NY 10570-7000

To order copies of this or other editions of the *Mind Stretchers* book series, call 1-800-846-2100.

Visit our online store at **rdstore.com**

For many more fun games and puzzles, visit www.rd.com/games.

Printed in the United States of America

1 3 5 7 9 10 8 6 4 2

US 4967/L-18

Contents

Dear Puzzler,

Many people think that a steady decline in one's mental faculties is a normal, natural result of the aging process. What do you think? Speaking for myself, I strongly disagree. Though I'm of baby-boomer age, I sincerely believe that I'm a better thinker now than I've ever been—both logically and creatively. Virtually every day I find myself in real-life situations where "brain power" comes to my aid. Truth be told, I actually keep a sharp eye out for such situations, and I'd like to share with you one of my most gratifying thinking experiences of the recent past.

Last year, my wife and I spent ten days on a cruise ship. Among the ship's many amenities was a laundry service. Our stateroom was provided with a rather small canvas laundry bag, and an accompanying price list: $1.75 to wash a handkerchief, $5.00 for a pair of pants, etc. But one line on the list really caught my attention: "Special rate: All you can fit in this bag for $20." That sounded like a challenge to me!

So, how much laundry *could* I fit in this bag? Clearly, treating the bag like a clothes hamper and just "tossing it in" wasn't the optimal way. Remembering a TV commercial I had seen for a plastic-bag clothes storage system that vacuums the air out to save space, I decided that rolling up each article of clothing tightly would squeeze the air out and minimize the space it would take up in the bag. Using this technique, I was able to fit nearly 50 pieces of clothing into that bag! The fact that the canvas fabric of the bag had some "give" to it helped a lot!

Sure, we saved some cash this way. But it was the creative thinking and successful "memory-tapping" that made it most satisfying. To preserve the moment, my wife took a photo of me proudly holding the overstuffed laundry bag.

Of course, a good memory and creative thinking will be very helpful in successfully solving the puzzles in this *Mind Stretchers* volume. But I hope that you'll also find many occasions to apply your puzzling skills to everyday life, as I do.

Your comments on any aspect of *Mind Stretchers* are most welcome. You can reach me by regular mail at the address below, or by e-mail at mindstretchers@readersdigest.com.

Best wishes for happy and satisfying solving!

Stanley Newman
Mind Stretchers Puzzle Editor
c/o Reader's Digest Association
1 Reader's Digest Rd.
Pleasantville, NY 10570-7000

(Please enclose a self-addressed stamped envelope if you'd like a reply.)

Foreword

Meet the Puzzles!

Mind Stretchers is filled with a delightful mix of classic and new puzzle types. To help you get started, here are instructions, tips, and examples for each.

WORD GAMES

Crossword Puzzles

Edited by Stanley Newman

Crosswords are arguably America's most popular puzzles. As presented in this book, the one- and two-star puzzles test your ability to solve straightforward clues to everyday words. "More-star" puzzles have a somewhat broader vocabulary, but most of the added challenge in these comes from less obvious and trickier clues. These days, you'll be glad to know, uninteresting obscurities such as "Genus of fruit flies" and "Famed seventeenth-century soprano" don't appear in crosswords anymore.

Our 60 crosswords were authored by more than a dozen different puzzle makers, all nationally known for their skill and creativity.

Clueless Crosswords

by George Bredehorn

A unique crossword variation invented by George, these 7-by-7 grids primarily test your vocabulary and reasoning skills. There is one simple task: Complete the crossword with common uncapitalized seven-letter words, based entirely on the letters already filled in for you.

EXAMPLE

M			K			G
	■		■	G	■	
			C			
T	■	K	■		■	
				N		
K	■	H	■		■	
			P	S		D

SOLUTION

M	A	R	K	I	N	G
I	■	I	■	G	■	O
S	U	C	C	U	M	B
T	■	K	■	A	■	B
A	R	S	E	N	A	L
K	■	H	■	A	■	E
E	L	A	P	S	E	D

Hints: *Focusing on the last letter of a word, when given, often helps. For example, a last letter of G often suggests that IN are the previous two letters. When the solutions aren't coming quickly, focus on the shared spaces that are blank—you can often figure out whether it has to be a vowel or a consonant, helping you solve both words that cross it.*

Split Decisions

by George Bredehorn

Crossword puzzle lovers also enjoy this variation. Once again, no clues are provided except within the diagram. Each answer consists of two words whose spellings are the same, except for two consecutive letters. For each pair of words, the two sets of different letters are already filled in for you. All answers are common words; no phrases or hyphenated or capitalized words are used. Certain missing words may have more than one possible solution, but there is only one solution for each word that will correctly link up with all the other words.

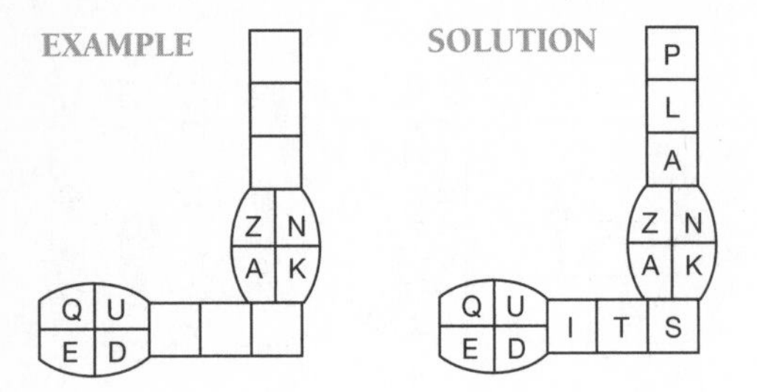

Hints: *Start with the shorter (three- and four-letter) words, because there will be fewer possibilities that spell words. In each puzzle, there will always be a few such word pairs that have only one solution. You may have to search a little to find them, since they may be anywhere in the grid, but it's always a good idea to fill in the answers to these first.*

Triad Split Decisions

by George Bredehorn

This puzzle is solved the same way as Split Decisions, except you are given three letters for each word instead of two.

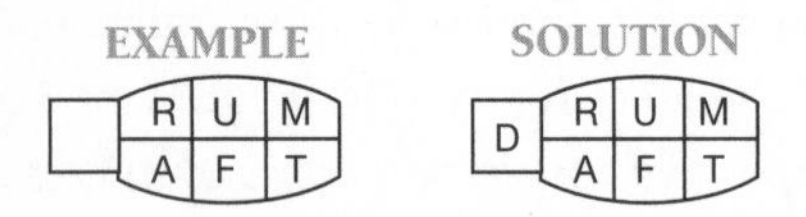

Word Searches

Kids love 'em, and so do grownups, making word searches perhaps the most widely appealing puzzle type. In a word search, the challenge is to find hidden words within a grid of letters. In the typical puzzle, words can be found in vertical columns, horizontal rows, or along diagonals, with the letters of the words running either forward or backward. Usually, a list of words to search for is given to you. But to make word searches harder, puzzle writers sometimes just point you in the right direction, such as telling you to find 25 foods. Other twists include allowing words to take right turns, or leaving letters out of the grid.

Hints: *One of the most reliable and efficient searching methods is to scan each row from top to bottom for the first letter of the word. So if you are looking for "violin" you would look for the letter "v." When you find one, look at all the letters that surround it for the second letter of the word (in this case, "i"). Each time you find a correct two-letter combination (in this case, "vi"), you then scan either for the correct three-letter combination ("vio") or the whole word.*

ANSWERS!

Answers to all the puzzles are found beginning on page 233, and are organized by the page number on which the puzzle appears.

NUMBER GAMES

Sudoku

by Conceptis Ltd.

Sudoku puzzles have become massively popular in the past few years, thanks to their simplicity and test of pure reasoning. The basic Sudoku puzzle is a 9-by-9 square grid, split into 9 square regions, each containing 9 cells. Each puzzle starts off with roughly 20 to 35 of the squares filled in with the numbers 1 to 9. There is just one rule: Fill in the rest of the squares

EXAMPLE

8	4						7	1
3			7	1	8			9
		5	9		3	6		
	9	7	8		1	2	3	
	6						9	
	3	1	2		9	7	6	
		4	3		2	9		
1			5	9	4			6
9	8						5	3

SOLUTION

8	4	9	6	2	5	3	7	1
3	2	6	7	1	8	5	4	9
7	1	5	9	4	3	6	8	2
5	9	7	8	6	1	2	3	4
2	6	8	4	3	7	1	9	5
4	3	1	2	5	9	7	6	8
6	5	4	3	8	2	9	1	7
1	7	3	5	9	4	8	2	6
9	8	2	1	7	6	4	5	3

with the numbers 1 to 9 so that no number appears twice in any row, column, or region.

Hints: *Use the numbers provided to rule out where else the same number can appear. For example, if there is a 1 in a cell, a 1 cannot appear in the same row, column, or region. By scanning all the cells that the various 1 values rule out, you often can find where the remaining 1 values must go.*

Hyper-Sudoku

by Peter Ritmeester

Peter is the inventor of this unique Sudoku variation. In addition to the numbers 1 to 9 appearing in each row and column, Hyper-Sudoku also has four 3-by-3 regions to work with, indicated by gray shading.

EXAMPLE

1	4	5	9			7		
		7	5	8	4	1		
3				7	2		5	
5	9		4	2	7			
	6		8					7
	7	4				2	9	5
	1						8	
	5		2			6		
6			7			5		

SOLUTION

1	4	5	9	3	6	7	2	8
9	2	7	5	8	4	1	3	6
3	8	6	1	7	2	9	5	4
5	9	3	4	2	7	8	6	1
2	6	1	8	5	9	3	4	7
8	7	4	6	1	3	2	9	5
7	1	9	3	6	5	4	8	2
4	5	8	2	9	1	6	7	3
6	3	2	7	4	8	5	1	9

LOGIC PUZZLES

Find the Ships

by Conceptis Ltd.

If you love playing the board game Battleship, you'll enjoy this pencil-and-paper variation! In each puzzle, a group of ships of varying sizes is provided on the right. Your job: Properly place the ships in the grid. A handful of ship "parts" are put on the board to get you started. The placement rules:

1. Ships must be oriented horizontally or vertically. No diagonals!

2. A ship can't go in a square with wavy lines; that indicates water.

3. The numbers on the left and bottom of the grid tell you how many squares in that row or column contain part of ships.

4. No two ships can touch each other, even diagonally.

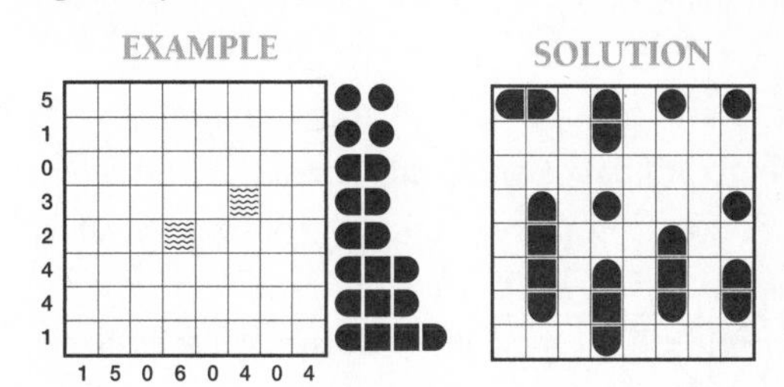

Hints: *The solving process involves both finding those squares where a ship must go and eliminating those squares where a ship cannot go. The numbers provided should give you a head start with the latter, the number 0 clearly implying that every square in that row or column can be eliminated. If you know that a square will be occupied by a ship, but don't yet know what kind of ship, mark that square, then cross out all the squares that are diagonal to it—all of these must contain water.*

ABC

by Peter Ritmeester

This innovative new puzzle challenges your logic much in the way a Sudoku puzzle does. Each row and column in an ABC puzzle contains exactly one A, one B, and one C, plus one blank (or two, in harder puzzles). Your task is to figure out where the three letters go in each row. The clues outside the puzzle frame tell you the first letter encountered when moving in the direction of an arrow.

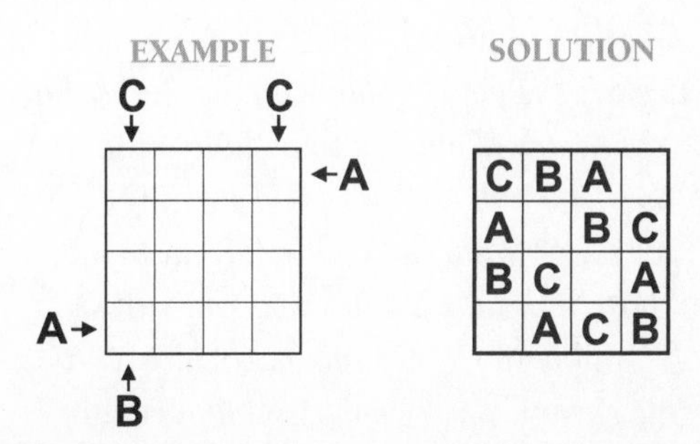

***Hints:** If a clue says a letter is first in a row or column, don't assume that it must go in the first square. It could go in either of the first two squares (or first three, in the harder puzzles). A good way to start is to look for where column and row clues intersect (for example, when two clues look like they are pointing at the same square). These intersecting clues often give you the most information about where the first letter of a row or column must go. At times, it's also possible to figure out where a certain letter goes by eliminating every other square as a possibility for that letter in a particular row or column.*

Fences

by Conceptis Ltd.

Lovers of mazes will enjoy these challenges. Connect the dots with vertical or horizontal lines, so that a single loop is formed with no crossings or branches. Each number indicates how many lines surround it; squares with no number may be surrounded by any number of lines.

EXAMPLE

SOLUTION

***Hints:** Don't try to solve the puzzle by making one continuous line—instead, fill in the links (that is, spaces between two dots) you are certain about, and then figure out how to connect those links. To start the puzzle, mark off any links that can't be connected. That would include all four links around each 0. Another good starting step is to look for any 3 values next or adjacent to a 0; solving those links is easy. In time, you will see that rules and patterns emerge, particularly in the puzzle corners, and when two numbers are adjacent to each other.*

Number-Out

by Conceptis Ltd.

This innovative new puzzle challenges your logic in much the same way a Sudoku puzzle does. Your task is to shade squares so that no number appears in any row or column more than once. Shaded squares may not touch each other horizontally or vertically, and all unshaded squares must form a single continuous area.

EXAMPLE

5	3	1	4	3
4	5	3	4	2
2	1	2	3	4
1	3	2	1	4
3	4	2	5	4

SOLUTION

5	3	1	4	3
4	5	3	4	2
2	1	2	3	4
1	3	2	1	4
3	4	2	5	4

***Hints:** First look for all the numbers that are unduplicated in their row and column. Those squares will never be shaded, so we suggest that you circle them as a reminder to yourself. When there are three of the same number consecutively in a row or column, the one in the middle must always be unshaded, so you can shade the other two. Also, any square that is between a pair of the same numbers must always be unshaded. Once a square is shaded, you know that the squares adjacent to it, both horizontally and vertically, must be unshaded.*

Star Search

by Peter Ritmeester

Another fun game in the same style of Minesweeper. Your task: find the stars that are hidden among the blank squares. The numbered squares indicate how many stars are hidden in squares adjacent to them (including diagonally). There is never more than one star in any square.

EXAMPLE

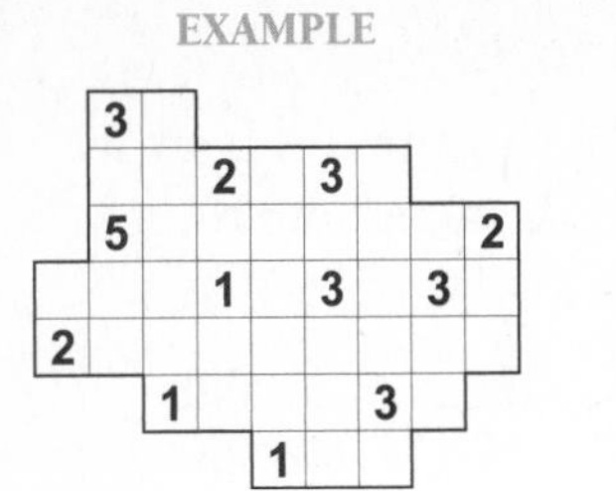

SOLUTION

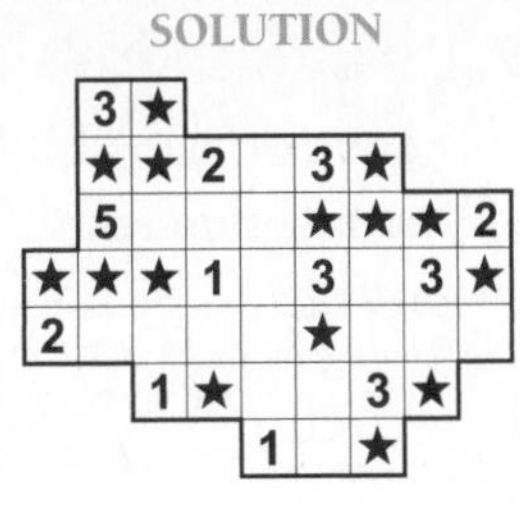

Hint: *If, for example, a 3 is surrounded by four empty squares, but two of those squares are adjacent to the same square with a 1, the other two empty squares around the 3 must contain stars.*

123

by Peter Ritmeester

Each grid in this puzzle has pieces that look like dominoes. You must fill in the blank squares so that each "domino" contains one each of the numbers 1, 2, and 3, according to these two rules:

EXAMPLE

				1	
	3				
3				2	
	2				
		1		1	

SOLUTION

2	1	2	3	1	3
3	2	3	1	2	1
1	3	1	2	3	2
3	1	2	3	2	1
1	2	3	1	3	2
2	3	1	2	1	3

1. No two adjacent squares, horizontally or vertically, can have the same number.

2. Each completed row and column of the diagram will have an equal number of 1s, 2s, and 3s.

Hints: *Look first for any blank square that is adjacent to two different numbers. By rule 1 above, the "missing" number of 1-2-3 must go in that blank square. Rule 2 becomes important to use later in the solving process. For example, knowing that a 9-by-9 diagram must have three 1s, three 2s, and three 3s in each row and column allows you to use the process of elimination to deduce what blank squares in nearly filled rows and columns must be.*

VISUAL PUZZLES

Throughout *Mind Stretchers* you will find unique mazes, visual conundrums, and other colorful challenges, each developed by maze master Dave Phillips. Each comes under a new name and has unique instructions. Our best advice? Patience and perseverance. Your eyes will need time to unravel the visual secrets.

In addition, you will also discover these visual puzzles:

Line Drawings

by George Bredehorn

George loves to create never-before-seen puzzle types, and here is another unique Bredehorn game. Each Line Drawing puzzle is different in its design, but the task is the same: Figure out where to place the prescribed number of lines to partition the space in the instructed way.

Hint: *Use a pencil and a straightedge as you work. Some lines come very close to the items within the region, so being straight and accurate with your line-drawing is crucial.*

One-Way Streets

by Peter Ritmeester

Another fun variation on the maze. The diagram represents a pattern of streets. A and B are parking spaces, and the black squares are stores. Find a route that starts at A, passes through all the stores exactly once, and ends at B. (Harder puzzles use P's to indicate parking spaces instead of A's and B's, and don't tell you the starting and ending places.) Arrows indicate one-way traffic for that block only. No

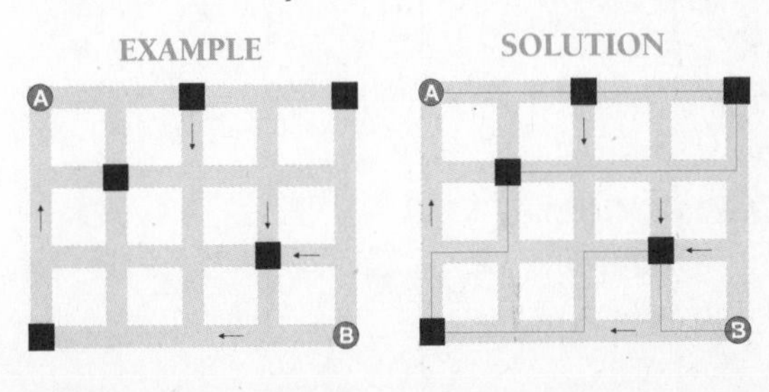

block or intersection may be entered more than once.

Hints: *The particular arrangement of stores and arrows will always limit the possibilities for the first store passed through from the starting point A and the last store passed through before reaching ending point B. So try to work both from the start and the end of the route. Also, the placement of an arrow on a block doesn't necessarily mean that your route will pass through that block. You can also use arrows to eliminate blocks where your path will not go.*

BRAIN TEASERS

To round out the more involved puzzles are more than 150 short brain teasers, most written by our puzzle editor, Stanley Newman. Stan is famous in the puzzle world for his inventive brain games. An example of how to solve each puzzle appears in the puzzle's first occurrence (the page number is noted below). You'll find the following types scattered throughout the pages.

** Invented by and cowritten with George Bredehorn*

*** By George Bredehorn*

But wait...there's more!

At the top of many of the pages in this book are additional brain teasers, organized into three categories:

- QUICK!: These tests challenge your ability to instantly calculate numbers or recall well-known facts.
- DO YOU KNOW ...: These more demanding questions probe the depth of your knowledge of facts and trivia.
- HAVE YOU ... and DO YOU ...: These reminders reveal the many things you can do each day to benefit your brain.

For the record, we have deliberately left out answers to the QUICK! and DO YOU KNOW ... features. Our hope is that if you don't know an answer, you'll be intrigued enough to open a book or search the Internet for it!

Meet the Authors

STANLEY NEWMAN (puzzle editor and author) is crossword editor for *Newsday,* the major newspaper of Long Island, New York. He is the author/editor of over 125 books, including the autobiography and instructional manual *Cruciverbalism* and the best-selling *Million Word Crossword Dictionary.* Winner of the First U.S. Open Crossword Championship in 1982, he holds the world's record for the fastest completion of a *New York Times* crossword—2 minutes, 14 seconds. Stan operates the website www.StanXwords.com and also conducts an annual Crossword University skill-building program on a luxury-liner cruise.

GEORGE BREDEHORN is a retired elementary school teacher from Wantagh, New York. His variety word games have appeared in the *New York Times* and many puzzle magazines. Every week for the past 20 years, he and his wife, Dorothy, have hosted a group of Long Island puzzlers who play some of the 80-plus games that George has invented.

CONCEPTIS (www.conceptispuzzles.com) is a leading supplier of logic puzzles to printed, electronic, and other gaming media all over the world. On average, ten million Conceptis puzzles are printed in newspapers, magazines and books each day, while millions more are played online and on mobile phones each month.

DAVE PHILLIPS has designed puzzles for books, magazines, newspapers, PC games, and advertising for more than 30 years. In addition, Dave is a renowned creator of walk-through mazes. Each year his corn-maze designs challenge visitors with miles of paths woven into works of art. Dave is also codeveloper of eBrainyGames.com, a website that features puzzles and games for sale.

PETER RITMEESTER is chief executive officer of PZZL.com, which produces many varieties of puzzles for newspapers and websites worldwide. Peter is also general secretary of the World Puzzle Federation. The federation organizes the annual World Puzzle Championship, which includes difficult versions of many of the types of logic puzzles that Peter has created for *Mind Stretchers.*

Master Class: **Beyond Crosswords**

Meet George "Mr. Puzzle" Bredehorn

Your humble puzzle editor's first "big step" into the crossword business took place in late March, 1988, when my first crossword appeared in the Sunday magazine section of the Long Island, New York, newspaper *Newsday*. Since my puzzle was replacing a syndicated crossword that had appeared in the paper for many years, the *Newsday* editors and I were expecting a torrent of reader backlash over the change.

So you can imagine what might have been running through my mind when the phone rang the very next day, and the caller spoke these words: "Are you the Newman who had the crossword in *Newsday* yesterday?"

After my tentative response of "Yes," the caller continued, "I'm a member of a group of puzzlers who get together every Tuesday night to play word games, and we'd like to invite you to stop by tomorrow evening at 7 p.m."

Since this was happening in a Long Island town that was just a short distance from my home, I agreed to drive on over. But after hanging up the phone, I began to have second thoughts. As I relate in my book *Cruciverbalism*, I was "half-imagining a horror-film plot featuring a newly hired puzzle editor lured to his death by solvers enraged over their favorite newspaper puzzle's being handed to an interloper."

Fortunately for me, my wild imaginings turned out to be just that. The address to which I was invited turned out to be the home of George Bredehorn and his wife, Dorothy. For the past several years, George, a retired elementary school teacher of gifted children, had been hosting a weekly gathering of his friends for an evening of word-based board games—games I had never seen or heard of before, because, as I quickly discovered, George had invented them, *and built them*, all himself! (Two of George's dozens of original games, Grid Luck and My Word, can be seen in the accompanying photo.)

Now relieved that the invitation was based upon only the kindest of intentions, I phoned my wife to let her know that all was okay, and that I'd be home in a few hours. (I had given her the exact address of where I was going, just in case.) And, for more than 20 years, "Tuesday Word-Game night" at George and Dorothy's has been a weekly ritual for me.

Though I was the first professional puzzler in the group, others soon followed, including crossword constructors Richard Silvestri and Randolph Ross. The fellow who invited me to the group, Fred Piscop, had been a student in one of George's classes many years before. Fred was doing computer work for a defense contractor back in 1988, but he later became a professional puzzle author and editor himself. And, I'm pleased to say, I had a little something to do with George applying his formidable creative skills to pencil-and-paper games for grownups.

Today, George's puzzles appear regularly in *The New York Times* and puzzle magazines, and he has published several puzzle collections in book form as well. Not surprisingly, when I was asked to assemble a varied collection of puzzles for *Mind Stretchers*, George was the first person I asked to participate.

Now, it's my pleasure to share with you this recent conversation I had with George about how he creates his puzzles and games, which I hope you will find as fascinating as I did.

Coincidentally, George's "Mr. Puzzle" nickname was bestowed on him by *Newsday* in 1972, when he was the cover story for their Sunday magazine—16 years before my byline first appeared in that same magazine.

Stan Newman: Do you remember when you created your first games?

George Bredehorn: Growing up in Queens, New York, I started creating games to play with my friends when I was around ten years old. I was always good at making up "rules" for activities, and the games I invented helped me cement relationships with the neighborhood kids. One of the earliest games I remember dreaming up was a variation on the popular (though frowned upon by most parents) kids' gambling game of the time called "pitching pennies," where you tried to toss pennies as close to a wall as possible. Since I lived in a not-very-affluent neighborhood, most kids didn't have a lot of pennies available. So, proving that necessity really is the mother of invention, I created a variation of the game that used pebbles instead of pennies.

SN: Over the years, I've gotten to know many puzzle constructors, but you're the only one I've ever met with real "constructing" skills—that is, the ability to build the physical games you invent. How did you get so good at it?

GB: My father had a basement workshop, and he taught me at a very young age the basic techniques like sawing wood and hammering nails. I received more formal training at Brooklyn Technical High School, which placed an emphasis on manual and engineering skills.

SN: Obviously, your teaching career is what got you started creating puzzles in an organized way. Did you always want to be a teacher?

GB: Not at all. I would never have become a teacher if I hadn't been drafted into the army in the closing days of World War II. Because I've never had very good eyesight, I wasn't a very good candidate for the armed services. But for no good reason, a recruiting officer decided to stamp "ACCEPTED" instead of "REJECTED" on my application. I ended up serving in the Army Air Forces (the predecessor of the U.S.

Air Force) as a control-tower technician. So, thanks to the G.I. Bill, I was eligible for a free college education when I got out of the Army.

SN: When and how did puzzles and games become part of your teaching program for gifted children?

GB: It all started in the early '50s, soon after I began my teaching career, when I was required to give an hour-long math test every Friday. I discovered that some kids would need the full hour to complete the test, while others would get it done in as little as 20 minutes. Not wanting the quicker students to be bored in the interim, I began putting math puzzles on the blackboard for them to do. That soon evolved into a weekly sheet of math and word games that I would hand to students if they completed a test early. As a result of those game sheets, my students began to look forward to Friday mornings rather than dreading them.

The Creative Process

SN: Do you recall how you came to create any of your classroom games?

GB: Whether they were board games or pencil-and-paper games, they were always intended to teach specific facts and concepts in an entertaining way. One game that my kids really seemed to like was Gram Cracker, which I invented to help teach new vocabulary words. For the game, I built a spinner and a multi-flap device that allowed one letter of the word to be revealed at a time. The class was divided into two teams, with the object being for one team to guess a hidden word before the other team. Each round started with my announcing how many letters were in the word and what the word meant. Then, a member of each team would alternate spinning the spinner, which would determine what letter of the word would be revealed.

SN: How do your ideas for puzzles and games come to you these days?

GB: I try to develop a new idea every day, sitting in the easy chair in my den. These ideas all start with the "germ," some quirky little notion that occurs to me. I next try to elaborate upon it, to create a larger concept that would make a good game. Then I put together some samples of the game, and test it out with the members of the Tuesday night group, who have been a great "laboratory" for my games—helping a lot in refining my ideas, adjusting the rules, etc.

SN: Having appeared in so many venues, your Split Decisions puzzle is the one that people are most likely to be familiar with. How did you come to invent it?

GB: I created the first one about 20 years ago. I happened to be thinking one day about pairs of words that are spelled the same except for two consecutive letters, such as MAGICAL and LOGICAL. There are only two common words that fit the pattern of __ __ G I C A L, so I thought it might be fun to think of those two words from that pattern, where knowing the meaning of the words wouldn't be necessary.

Seeing how that worked, I thought it might be more interesting to have these incomplete pairs of words in a grid pattern, giving solvers the "different pairs" of letters and leaving blank the letters that were the same. The intersecting-word pattern would give people two attempts to get some of the letters in each word.

I tried to make a few that way, but they didn't look very attractive. So, next I added standard crossword symmetry (with the pattern looking the same if turned upside down), and that had what I thought was the "right look." By the way, Will Shortz came up with the name "Split Decisions" for the puzzle, when he first published it in *Games* magazine.

Three or four years later, I created my first

Triad Split Decisions (with pairs of words that differed by three consecutive letters), just by thinking about ways I could vary the original game.

SN: Did any of the games you created as a teacher evolve into grownup games?

GB: Quite a few of them are based on ideas I first used in my classes. One example is the Three of a Kind puzzles in *Mind Stretchers*, which hide three related words in a sentence. That started out as a series of sentences, each of which had just one hidden word, but the words would all be from the same category, such as articles of clothing. Clueless Crosswords dates from my teaching days as well. Starting out with a completed crossword diagram, I wondered how many letters you could remove and still be able to "re-complete" it without any clues.

SN: Your Line Drawings puzzles are a relatively new invention. I clearly remember how impressed I was with the idea, which was unlike any other puzzle I'd ever seen, when you showed your first creations to me a few years ago. How did you think of that one?

GB: As you know, many word games require entering letters into a square pattern of lines on a piece of paper. The inspiration just popped into my head one day to try to "reverse" that—could a puzzle be made where you started out with individual letters on a page and had to figure out where to draw the lines? The partitioning of the square into regions, working with the letters within each region, just seemed

Are You as Smart as a Fourth Grader?

Try these brainteasers originally created by George for his fourth-grade classes. (Answers are upside-down at the bottom of the page.)

1. What is the only four-letter word in the English language which, when printed in capital letters, reads the same upside down?

2. Fill in the blanks with two different words that are pronounced the same:

   Look how neatly the hotel __________ __________ the bed.

3. Rearrange the letters in a four-letter word that means "a type of fish," to form a new word meaning "family member."

4. The same three letters (in the same order) are missing from each of these words. What are the words?

   P _ _ _ SH   T _ _ _ NG   RE _ _ _ ON   _ _ _ TE

5. The five-letter word NINJA has the fourth letter J. What other common five-letter word (for something made with strings) also has the fourth letter J?

ANSWERS: 1. NOON 2. maid, made 3. TUNA, AUNT 4. PUNISH, TUNING, REUNION, UNITE 5. BANJO

to “flow” from that. Then, it was just a natural extension for me to try things other than letters, such as numbers and shapes.

Postscript: George vs. Computers

Surprisingly, though his wife, Dorothy, spends part of each day on her personal computer, George has never owned his own computer. I’ve always wondered about that, and this interview gave me the opportunity to finally ask him about it.

GB: It’s not that I don’t like computers or that I’m afraid of them. When computers first arrived in Long Island classrooms in the 1970s, I was appointed the “computer expert” in my school, and I would conduct assemblies demonstrating computer capabilities for students and teachers.

When personal computers began to catch on in the 1980s, I never wanted one for myself, only because I never learned to type very quickly or very well. At the typewriter, I would use what I called the “Biblical System”: “seek and ye shall find.” I’m certainly not technology-averse, since I do use handheld electronic word-finders to create many of my games.

—Stanley Newman

★ Poor Posture by Gail Grabowski

ACROSS

1 Curvy letters
6 Not guilty, for one
10 Identical
14 Bracelet attachment
15 "Shall we?" reply
16 Old-time oath
17 Use one's intuition
19 Words of denial
20 Be in debt
21 Mediocre
22 Elevation of a mountain
24 Slangy refusal
25 Jules Verne captain
26 Pavement fixer
29 British-beverage serving piece
32 Spills the beans
33 Home for hens
34 Vending-machine opening
36 Alan of *M*A*S*H*
37 Raggedy doll
38 Miner's bonanza
39 Drought ender
40 Drags along
41 Sahara mounds
42 Party organizer
44 Sahara animals
45 Prepare to be photographed
46 Angelic instrument
47 Isn't selfish
50 Apple center
51 New bride's title, often
54 Radiant quality
55 Small porch at an entry door
58 Got taller
59 Competent
60 West Florida city
61 List-ending abbr.
62 Neat
63 Beginning stage

DOWN

1 Canyon sound
2 Playwright George Bernard
3 Rescue
4 Before, in poems
5 Breaks into pieces
6 Luxurious
7 Carson's replacement
8 And so on: Abbr.
9 Fireplace pile
10 Upcoming grad's lack of motivation
11 Highly excited
12 High-school subject
13 Prepare for publication
18 Frequent TV episode length
23 CPR specialist
24 City's widespread development
25 Sign gases
26 Skier's lift
27 Islam's Almighty
28 Dashboard accessory
29 Salad-bar implements
30 By oneself
31 Alpine song
33 Bring about
35 Thomas Hardy heroine
40 Healthy food phrase
41 Has the nerve
43 Part of a sock
44 Golf-course rental
46 Hive product
47 Wise person
48 Injured
49 General region
50 Chilly
51 Pops' partners
52 Catch, as calves
53 Petty quarrel
56 Baseball stat.
57 Sunbather's goal

★ Track Meet

Which track was laid down in the middle, having the same number of tracks below it as above it?

CENTURY MARKS

Select one number in each of the four columns so that the total adds up to exactly 100.

Example: $\frac{6}{(8)} + \frac{(15)}{73} + \frac{(40)}{61} + \frac{29}{(37)} = 100$

17	+	13	+	29	+	48	= 100
19		37		23		17	

★ About Time

Find these time-related words that are hidden in the diagram, either across, down, or diagonally.

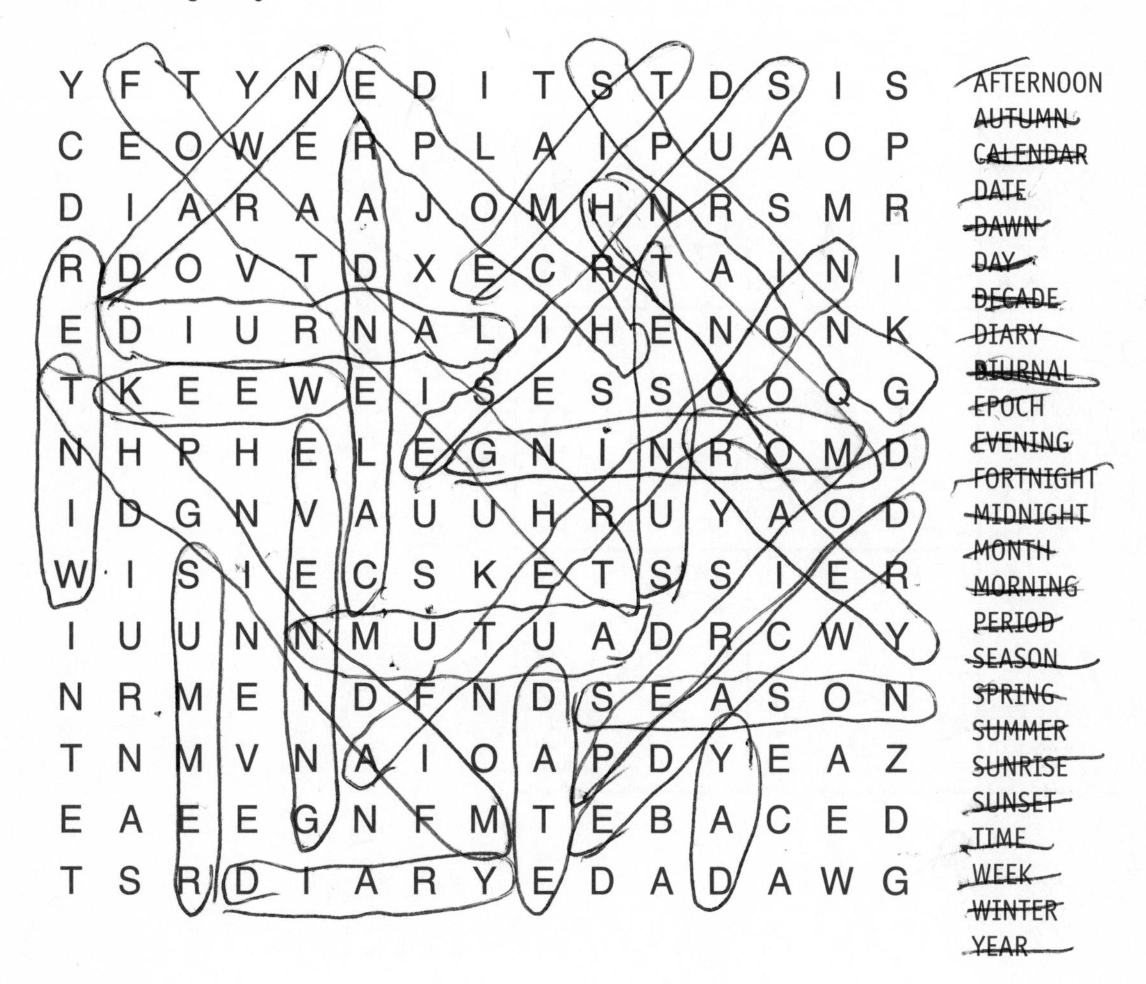

INITIAL REACTION

Identify the well-known proverb from the first letters in each of its words.
Example: L.B.Y.L. Answer: Look Before You Leap

H. R. I. ______________________________

★ Sudoku

Fill in the blank boxes so that every row, column, and 3x3 box contains all of the numbers 1 to 9.

6			8	5	2			4
	9						5	
1		5				7		6
8			9		1			7
7								9
5			6		4			2
3		4				2		1
	7						8	
9			1	2	7			3

MIXAGRAMS

Each line contains a five-letter word and a four-letter word that have been mixed together (the order of the letters in each word has not been changed). Unmix the two words on each line and write them in the spaces provided. When you're done, find a two-part answer to the clue by reading down the letter columns in the answers. Example: D A R I U N V E T = DRIVE + AUNT

CLUE: Lip

D E B E R B Y T S = _ _ _ _ _ + _ _ _ _

B A R E W A D A Y = _ _ _ _ _ + _ _ _ _

S H A P I C L O Y = _ _ _ _ _ + _ _ _ _

A C O W A K K E E = _ _ _ _ _ + _ _ _ _

★ Italian Dinners by Sally R. Stein

ACROSS

1 "Stars and Stripes Forever" composer
6 Ireland alias
10 Prefix for social
14 Decide to participate
15 Western alliance: Abbr.
16 Surprise attack
17 Stop
18 Per __ (daily)
19 South Seas spot
20 Italian poultry entrée
23 Accomplished
24 Mon. follower
25 Cookware coating
29 Husband or wife
31 __ Vegas
34 Employee's last words
35 Plentiful
36 Held on to
37 Italian seafood entrée
40 Toward the dawn
41 At any time
42 Soldier's reply
43 Cunning
44 Floor-washing implements
45 Tiny
46 Unwitting victim
47 Encouraging touch
48 Italian meat entrée
56 Wheel bar
57 Authentic
58 Maui greeting
60 Potato, informally
61 Send reeling
62 Misplaces
63 Male turkeys
64 Went fast
65 Looks to be

DOWN

1 The S in ASPCA: Abbr.
2 Petroleum cartel
3 Nevada neighbor
4 Argentine's emphatic assent
5 Short, amusing story
6 Stopped
7 Picnic spoiler
8 Supermarket-line unit
9 "Never mind"
10 Get out of bed
11 Cape Canaveral org.
12 Cash register
13 Brainstorm
21 Uncle or cousin
22 Regret
25 Uses a stopwatch on
26 The same, mathematically
27 Very particular
28 Roster
29 Silent performers
30 Worship from __
31 Minimum amount
32 Spring month
33 Long look
35 Letters on an invitation
36 Shoelace securer
38 Wildcats with spots
39 Monogram parts
44 Tourist's reference
45 Fall behind
46 Vehicles on snow
47 Accumulated, with "up"
48 Enormous
49 Trade show, for short
50 Grad
51 Gather, as grain
52 Labyrinth
53 Lotion additive
54 Have a __ for news
55 Throat-clearing sound
59 Wild equine

★ Fences

Connect the dots with vertical or horizontal lines, so that a single loop is formed with no crossings or branches. Each number indicates how many lines surround it; squares with no number may be surrounded by any number of lines.

				1	0	2	
2		1	1	1	2		2
2							3
	1	2					2
2					0	3	
2							1
2		2	2	1	2		3
	2	0	2				

WRONG IS RIGHT

Which of these four words is misspelled?

A) catalist B) mysterious

C) existence D) philatelist

★★ Line Drawing

Draw three straight lines, each from the top of the square to the bottom, so that the square is divided into six pieces of the same size and shape.

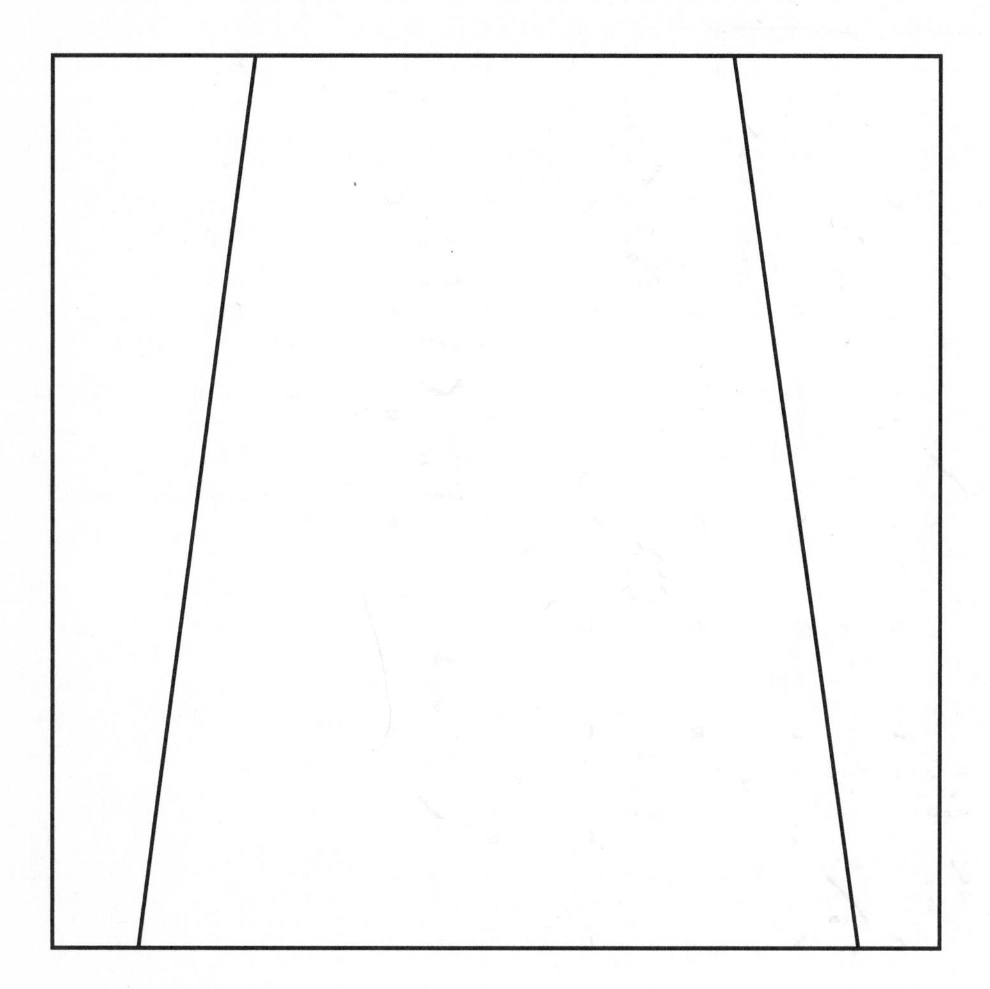

THREE OF A KIND

Find the three hidden words in the sentence that go together in some way.
Example: Chefs were <u>bus</u>ily slicing <u>car</u>rots and <u>cab</u>bage (Answer: bus, car, cab).

He took a pleasure trip to Aspen if I needed him to.

★ All in the Games

Find these Summer Olympics events and related terms that are hidden in the diagram, either across, down, or diagonally.

ARCHERY
ATHLETICS
BADMINTON
BIATHLON
BRONZE
CHEERS
CROWD
DIVING
GOLD
HEATS
HURDLES
MEDALS
MENS' EVENTS
OLYMPICS
PERSONAL BEST
PODIUM
RULES
SAILING
SCORES
SILVER
SPORTS
SPRINT
STADIUM
SWIMMING
TABLE TENNIS
TRAINING
VILLAGE
WARM UP
WEIGHTLIFTING
WORLD RECORD

WHO'S WHAT WHERE?

The correct term for a resident of Abilene, Texas, is:

A) Abilener B) Abilenite

C) Abilenian D) Abileno

★ Outdo Yourself by Gail Grabowski

ACROSS

1 Group of experts
6 Summon
10 Post-workout complaint
14 Exact copy
15 Slender woodwind
16 Fly like an eagle
17 Special-occasion clothing
19 24-karat
20 Deer relative
21 Reduce one's altitude
23 Erode
25 Mannerly man
26 Energy
29 "You wish!"
32 Have a meal
35 Barrel of laughs
37 Store event
38 Late
40 Rude starer
42 Morning moisture
43 Abs exercise
44 "Rise and __!"
45 Guitarist Clapton
47 Burrowing mammal
48 And so on: Abbr.
49 Business associate
52 Quart parts: Abbr.
53 Water pitcher
55 Down in the dumps
57 Make illegal
60 Dishonest ones
63 Consumer
64 Ticket for unlimited attendance
67 Uncluttered
68 Roof projection
69 High-society group
70 Solemn vow
71 Whole lot
72 Heavy, as fog

DOWN

1 Workstation machines, for short
2 Grad
3 Something prohibited
4 Fund, as a scholarship
5 Rented
6 Corn holder
7 Under the covers
8 Finish last
9 Impatient one's urging
10 Colorado resort
11 Kitchen surface
12 Difficult
13 Before, in verse
18 Twelve-month periods
22 Pennies
24 Library patron
26 Nonpoetic writing
27 Figure __ (skating maneuver)
28 Officer's regular route
30 Watchful
31 Kitten's sound
33 Grownup
34 Uses a keyboard
36 Coffee-break time, often
39 Prepare to shoot
41 Force back
46 Stringed instrument
50 Gets up
51 Destroyed
54 Value
56 Syrup source
57 On an ocean liner
58 Close tightly
59 Possess
61 Parade spoiler
62 Retired planes: Abbr.
63 One, in Mexico
65 Attach a button
66 Get a look at

★ Number-Out

Shade squares so that no number appears in any row or column more than once. Shaded squares may not touch each other horizontally or vertically, and all unshaded squares must form a single continuous area.

4	2	5	4	1
2	5	1	4	5
1	4	2	4	3
1	3	4	5	3
1	1	1	3	4

THINK ALIKE

Unscramble the letters in the phrase GEE OVAL to form two words with the same or similar meanings. Example: The letters in BEST RATING can be rearranged to spell START and BEGIN.

____________________ ____________________

★ Go With the Flow

Enter the maze at the bottom, pass through all the yellow circles exactly once, then exit. You must go with the flow, making no sharp turns, and you may use paths more than once.

SMALL CHANGE

Change one letter in each of these two words, to form a common two-word phrase.
Example: PANTRY CHEW Answer: PASTRY CHEF

GEM SHOT

____

★ Like a River by Sally R. Stein

ACROSS

1 Sheets of sea ice
6 Scorch
10 Break in friendly relations
14 National bird
15 Own
16 Norway's capital
17 Webcam broadcasts
20 Appear to be
21 Finishes
22 Flows slowly
23 Opinion piece
25 Winter ailment
26 "Marching in" group of song
29 Coconut-custard holders
33 Augment
34 Fitness centers
36 Mauna __ (Hawaiian volcano)
37 Adapts sensibly
41 Historical period
42 Ill-mannered men
43 Not restrictive
44 Carbonated water
47 At an incline
48 Get __ of (throw out)
49 Hand-drying cloth
51 Short putt
54 Author Morrison
55 Sources of silver
59 Stay up-to-date about
62 Sandwich cookie
63 Leaning Tower city
64 Overact
65 Was a retailer in
66 __ as a cucumber
67 Distributed, with "out"

DOWN

1 __ up (admit the truth)
2 Past the deadline
3 Mean person
4 Copper and carbon
5 Caribbean, for one
6 Beijing's land
7 Conveniently located
8 Typical amounts: Abbr.
9 Accelerate, as an engine
10 Arrived on horseback
11 "That's clear"
12 Unsuccessful performance
13 Easy throw
18 Disorderly place
19 Castaway's locale
24 Stash away
25 Marlin or mackerel
26 Wise folks
27 Like a lot
28 Just right
29 Butter portions
30 Distribute
31 Rope slipknot
32 Made a cut in lumber
34 Headliner
35 Professor's deg.
38 Like tea in a tumbler
39 Peace Nobelist Wiesel
40 "Walk this way ..."
45 Camera stand
46 Metal in pennies
47 Exact match
49 Sculpted figure
50 Shaquille of basketball
51 Boxing results: Abbr.
52 Prefix for space
53 Banana covering
54 Threesome
56 Something very funny
57 Diminutive ending
58 Backyard structure
60 Checkout-counter scan: Abbr.
61 President pro __

★ One-Way Streets

The diagram represents a pattern of streets. A and B are parking spaces, and the black squares are stores. Find the route that starts at A, passes through all stores exactly once, and ends at B. Arrows indicate one-way traffic for that block only. No block or intersection may be entered more than once.

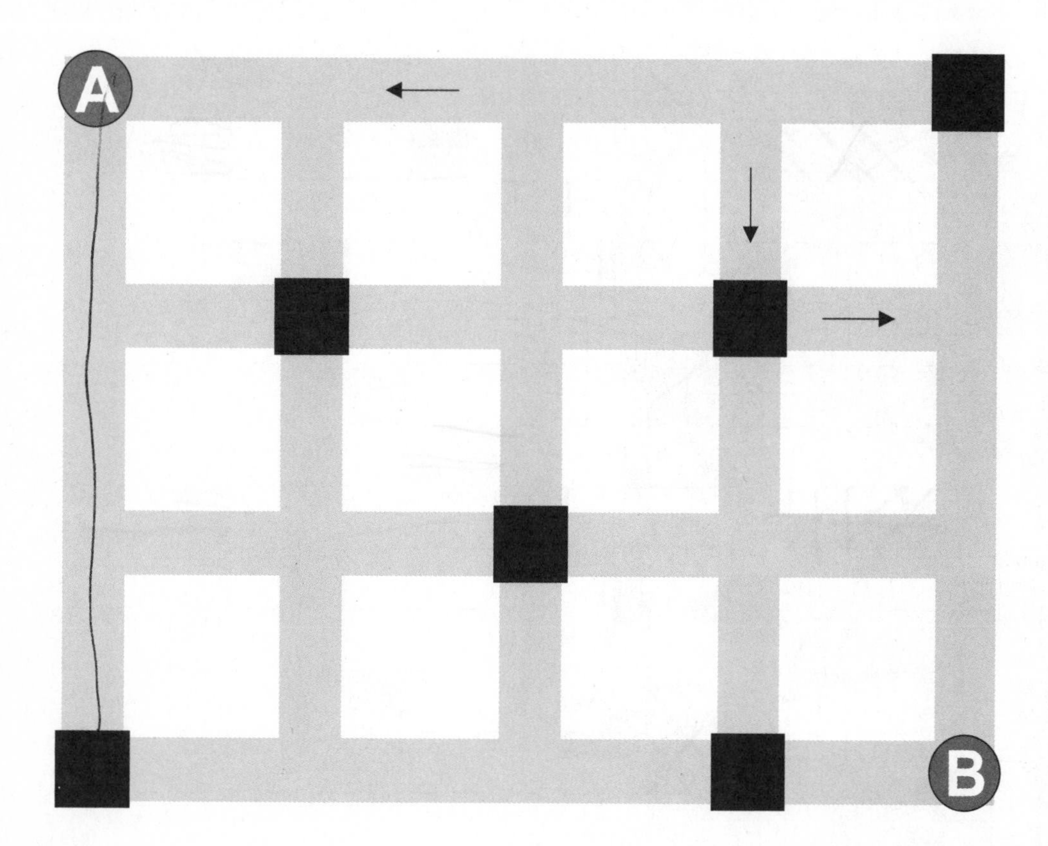

SOUND THINKING

There is only one common uncapitalized word whose consonant sounds are M, S, L, and N, in that order. What is it?

____

★★ Split Decisions

In this clueless crossword puzzle, each answer consists of two words whose spellings are the same, except for the consecutive letters given. All answers are common words; no phrases or hyphenated or capitalized words are used. Some of the clues may have more than one solution, but there is only one word pair that will correctly link up with all the other word pairs.

TRANSDELETION

Delete one letter from the word YANKED and rearrange the rest, to get a nation of the world.

____

★ Star Search

Find the stars that are hidden in some of the blank squares. The numbered squares indicate how many stars are hidden in the squares adjacent to them (including diagonally). There is never more than one star in any square.

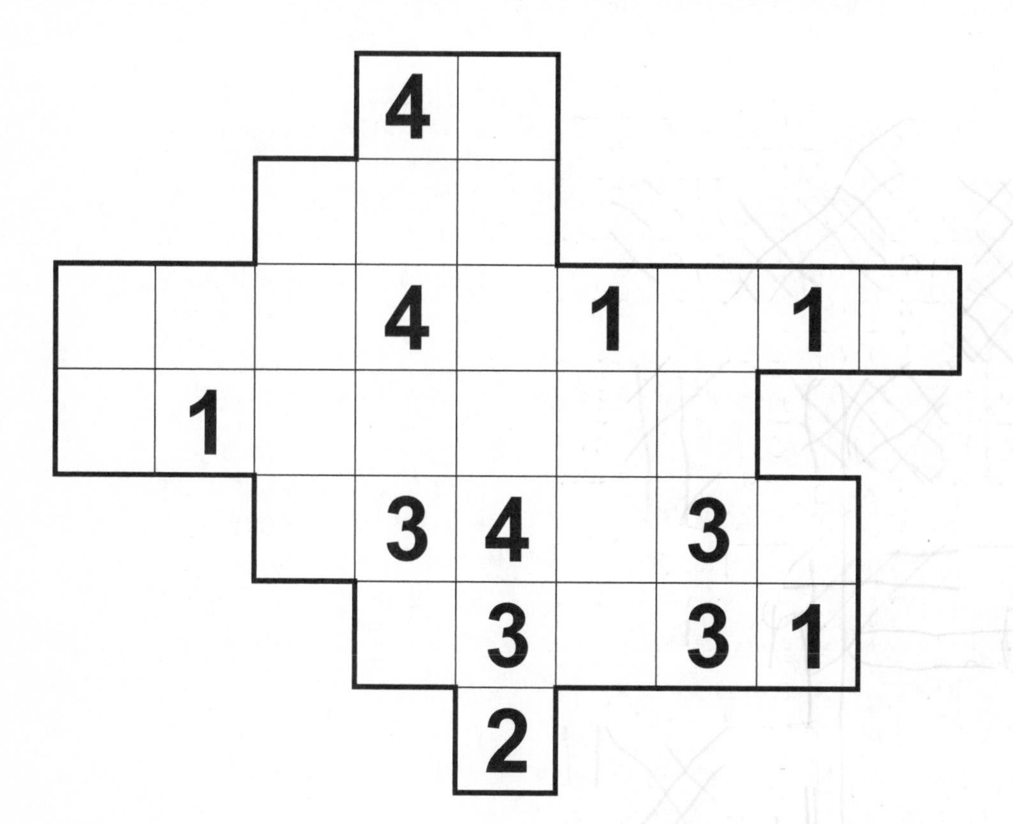

CHOICE WORDS

Form three six-letter words from the same category, by selecting one letter from each column three times. Each letter will be used exactly once.

Example: B A B C O T / J O E U A R / O C G L A T — Answer: BOBCAT, JAGUAR, OCELOT

A	A	R	L	I	S
D	A	S	E	A	N
L	U	L	T	D	O

_ _ _ _ _ _

_ _ _ _ _ _

_ _ _ _ _ _

★ "Many" Words

Find this potpourri of words (all containing the letters M, A, N, and Y) that are hidden in the diagram, either across, down, or diagonally. There's one additional eight-letter answer in the category, not listed below, that's also hidden in the diagram—a word meaning "by hand." What's that word?

MACHINERY
MAGNANIMITY
MAGNIFY
MAHOGANY
MAINLY
MAINSTAY
MALEVOLENTLY
MANDATORY
MANFULLY
MANIFESTLY
MANLY
MARGINALLY
MARRYING
MATERNITY
MATRIMONY
MAYONNAISE
MEANLY
MELANCHOLY
MENDACITY
MENTALITY
MERCENARY
MINIMALLY
MISCELLANY
MISSIONARY
MISTAKENLY
MONASTERY
MONETARY
MONEYMAKER
MONOGAMY
MONOSYLLABLE
MULLIGATAWNY
MYNAH

IN OTHER WORDS

There is only one common uncapitalized word that contains the consecutive letters PEV. What is it?

____

★ Easy as Nails by Gail Grabowski

ACROSS

1 Curved part of the foot
5 Grade-school basics
9 Greta of films
14 Tra __
15 Hawaiian party
16 In progress
17 Whitish gemstone
18 Piece of paper to fill out
19 Not sharp, as a pencil
20 Civil War fan, for one
23 Prefix meaning "recent"
24 Stick (to)
25 Beseech
27 Decorate anew
29 Of value
32 Toast topping
35 From the sun
38 Tot's three-wheeler
39 Sci-fi vehicles
41 Before, in poems
42 Toast topping
43 Stately home
45 Hidden stockpile
48 Curvy letter
49 Like better
51 Twosomes
53 New Haven Ivy Leaguer
55 Removes whiskers
59 Chest muscle, for short
61 Curry favor by flattery
64 Dole out
66 Secret message
67 Run-of-the-mill
68 Country singer Patsy
69 Ready for customers
70 "There ought to be __!"
71 Recorded
72 Look after
73 Utters

DOWN

1 15 Across greeting
2 Speedy
3 Look bad together, fashionwise
4 Horse's headgear
5 Type of creamy pasta sauce
6 Waterway marker
7 Dietary component, for short
8 Restate concisely
9 Conversational gathering
10 CIO partner
11 Office trash basket, slangily
12 Skeleton part
13 *Beetle Bailey* bulldog
21 Mine deposits
22 Winter ailment
26 Prefix for dynamic
28 Bullring shouts
30 15 Across instruments, for short
31 Most August babies
32 Use a parachute
33 At a distance
34 Men's wallet alternative
36 Mural or sculpture
37 Sit down with a book
40 Couch
44 Told, as a story
46 Hang, as a chandelier
47 Syllables from Santa
50 Pull apart
52 Spicy dips
54 Orlando-area attraction
56 Cello kin
57 English-class assignment
58 Nightclub performances
59 Treaty
60 Singer Fitzgerald
62 Easy stride
63 Biblical paradise
65 Early afternoon hour

★ Hyper-Sudoku

Fill in the blank boxes so that every row, column, 3x3 box, *and* each of the four 3x3 gray regions contains all of the numbers 1 to 9.

1				9			3	
	8		7		6	1		
7	3		4		8		2	6
9			1	8		3		5
				2	9	4		
	4			5	7		9	1
	7					5		
		2			1		4	
6					5	7	1	

MIXAGRAMS

Each line contains a five-letter word and a four-letter word that have been mixed together (the order of the letters in each word has not been changed). Unmix the two words on each line and write them in the spaces provided. When you're done, find a two-part answer to the clue by reading down the letter columns in the answers.

CLUE: One way to throw

S E T A R C O P H = _ _ _ _ _ + _ _ _ _

G A G R A L V A Y = _ _ _ _ _ + _ _ _ _

A P E N O T E R N = _ _ _ _ _ + _ _ _ _

B U R S A R O I D = _ _ _ _ _ + _ _ _ _

★★ Catfisher

Which numbered picture is the true reflection of Catfisher and his boat?

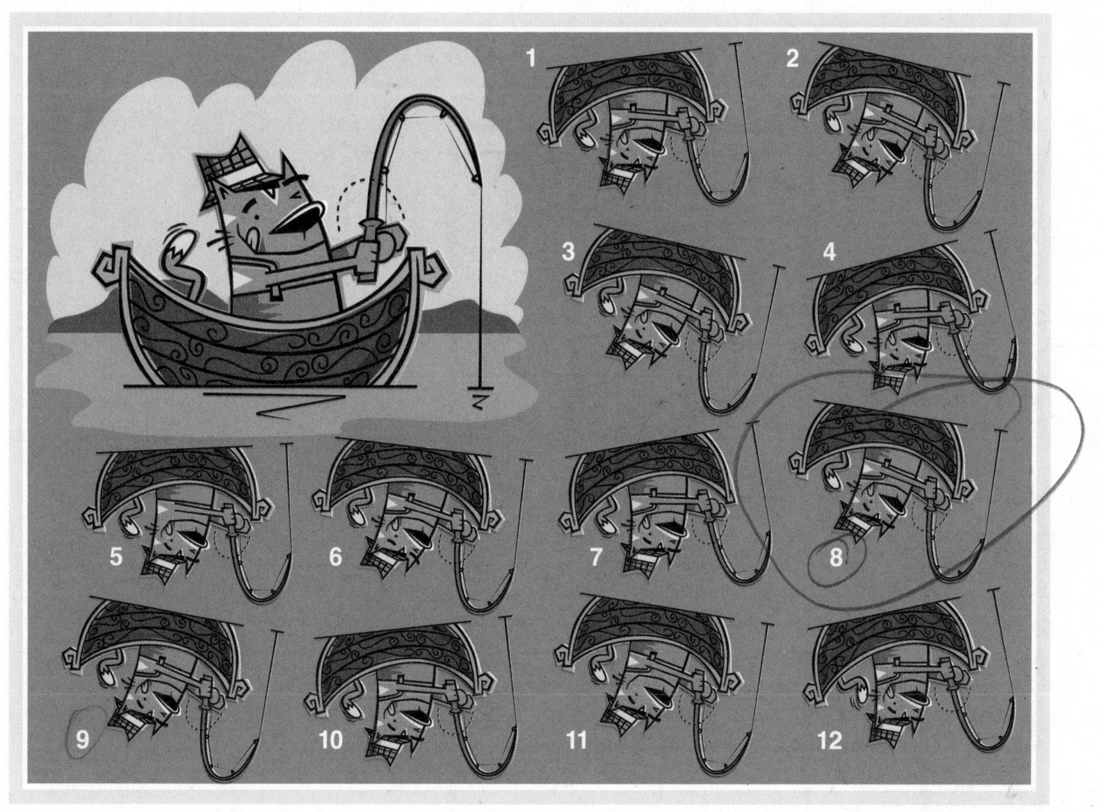

BETWEENER

What three-letter word belongs between the word at left and the word at right, so that the first and second word, and the second and third word, each form a common compound word?

HAND __ __ __ PIPE

★ 123

Fill in the diagram so that each rectangular piece has one each of the numbers 1, 2, and 3, under these rules: 1) No two adjacent squares, horizontally or vertically, can have the same number. 2) Each completed row and column of the diagram will have an equal number of 1s, 2s, and 3s.

	1				2
			3		
1				1	
	3			2	
1					

SUDOKU SUM

Fill in the missing numbers from 1 to 9, so that the sum of each row and column is as indicated.

EXAMPLE

	12	14	19
6			3
17	6		
22		8	

ANSWER

	12	14	19
6	1	2	3
17	6	4	7
22	5	8	9

	22	6	17
14		3	
12	6		
19			8

★ Beach Bringalongs by Sally R. Stein

1	2	3	4	■	5	6	7	8	■	9	10	11	12	13
14				■	15				■	16				
17				■	18				■	19				
20				21					22	■	23			
■	■	■	24				■	■	25	26				
27	28	29				■	30	31				■	■	■
32				■	■	33					■	34	35	36
37				38	39						40			
41			■	42					■	■	43			
■	■	■	44					■	45	46				
47	48	49				■	■	50				■	■	■
51				■	52	53	54					55	56	57
58				59	■	60				■	61			
62					■	63				■	64			
65					■	66				■	67			

ACROSS

1 Criticism, slangily
5 Short swims
9 Toned down
14 The __ Ranger (Tonto's pal)
15 Best-selling cookie
16 Cinema employee
17 Internet auction locale
18 Benchmark
19 Milk producer
20 Party pooper
23 French cheese
24 Meal for a horse
25 Construction worker
27 Get away
30 Martini add-in
32 Shakespearean king
33 Make amends
34 Large body of water
37 Hawaii's former name
41 Point opposite WSW
42 TV-commercial writers
43 "Ah, me!" sound
44 Long-distance runner
45 Small beard
47 4 Down "strike-out" button
50 Imperfection
51 Iraq neighbor
52 Ship's communications room
58 Part of 41 Across
60 *Tonight Show* host
61 Woodwind instrument
62 Poe's first name
63 Polite term of address
64 Like a wet noodle
65 Fishing-line holders
66 Comrade
67 Coup d'__

DOWN

1 Went by air
2 Part of an ear
3 Medical-sch. class
4 Typist's target
5 Support a charity
6 Fairway golf clubs
7 Job benefit, for short
8 A portion of
9 Wet ground
10 In working order
11 Baseball base
12 Spooky
13 Laundry appliance
21 In the __ of luxury
22 "Identical" pair
26 Daredevil Knievel
27 Otherwise
28 Actor Connery
29 Walking stick
30 "None of the above" category
31 Cut of pork
33 Apex
34 Ornery mood
35 Sharp part of a razor blade
36 Arthur of tennis
38 Be patient
39 Lazybones
40 All things considered
44 __ giant (genius)
45 Pessimistic
46 W. Hemisphere alliance
47 Informal eatery
48 Destroy slowly
49 Egg size
50 Most important class exam
53 __ mater
54 Start a card hand
55 Just slightly
56 Deep sleep
57 Held onto
59 Many mins.

★ ABC

Enter the letters A, B, and C into the diagram so that each row and column has exactly one A, one B, and one C. The letters outside the diagram indicate the first letter encountered, moving in the direction of the arrow. Keep in mind that after all the letters have been filled in, there will be one blank box in each row and column.

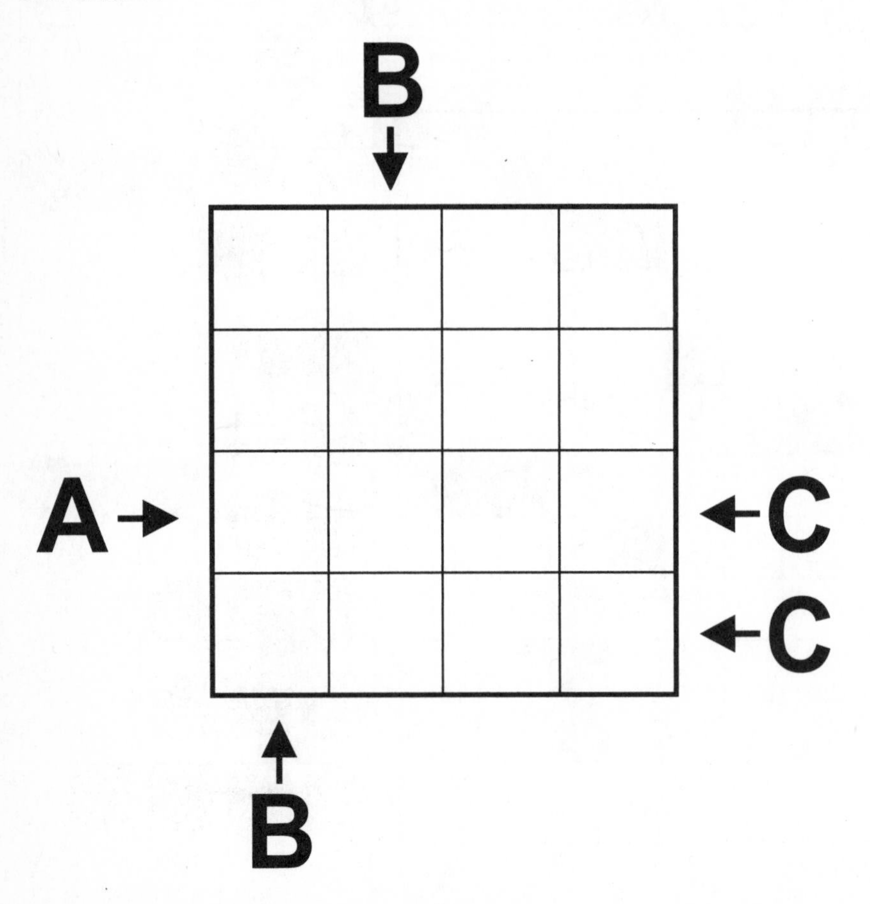

CLUELESS CROSSWORD

Complete the crossword with common uncapitalized seven-letter words, based entirely on the letters already filled in for you.

C	A	B				S
				S		T
W		L				
B		G				L
					M	I
		G	M	E		

★ Find the Ships

Determine the position of the 10 ships listed to the right of the diagram. The ships may be oriented either horizontally or vertically. A square with wavy lines indicates water and will not contain a ship. The numbers at the edge of the diagram indicate how many squares in that row or column contain parts of ships. When all 10 ships are correctly placed in the diagram, no two of them will touch each other, not even diagonally.

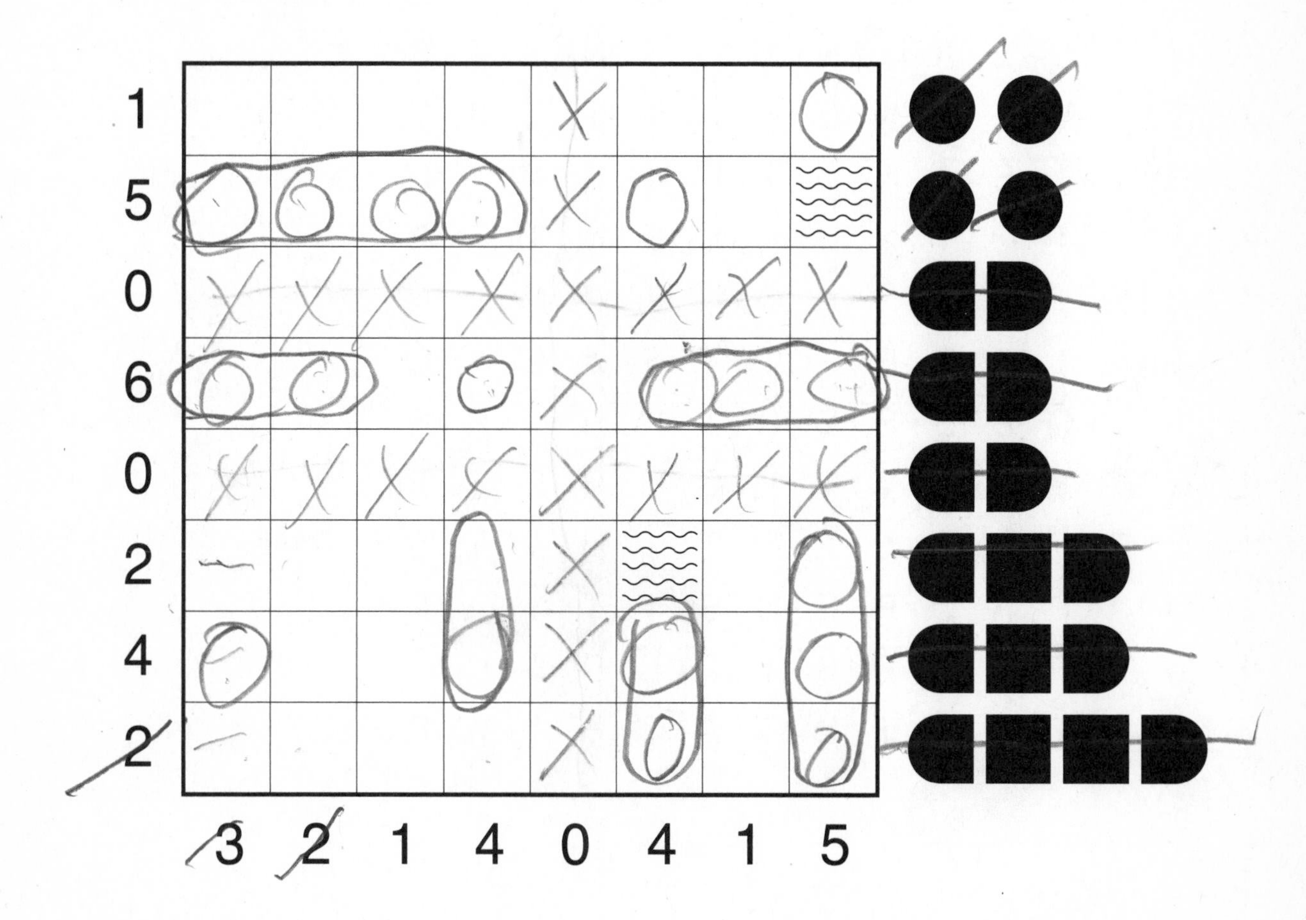

TWO-BY-FOUR

The eight letters in the word FALCONRY can be rearranged to form a pair of common four-letter words in only one way. Can you find the two words?

_ _ _ _ _ _ _ _

★ Leaning

Find these various meanings of "leaning" that are hidden in the diagram, either across, down, or diagonally.

```
T I E S D E N G S B O H A B N
E A N V L B C N N R E P K O S
N T G C E A I N I I T N I Z S
D T Y V L T N E E I T T L J E
E R T I S I N T T R I S X Y N
N A I I O T N U I S E N I T E
C C L T A N D A O N I F N L N
Y T A T I E E P T T G A E L O
B I I Q B B S B S I H B M R R
E O T Y T I V I L C O R P B P
N N R P D S L A N T I N A I S
H U A P R O P E N S I T Y A R
B W P F L O P S I D E D I C I
G N I T L I T B I A O B I A B
```

APTITUDE
ATTRACTION
BENT
BIAS
DISPOSITION
INCLINATION
LISTING
LOPSIDED
ORIENTATION
PARTIALITY
PENCHANT
PREFERENCE
PROCLIVITY
PRONENESS
PROPENSITY
SLANTING
TENDENCY
TILTING

INITIAL REACTION

Identify the well-known proverb from the first letters in each of its words.

F. W. M. M. ____________________

★ Around the House by Gail Grabowski

ACROSS

1 Shove
5 March 17 honoree, for short
10 Football throw
14 China's continent
15 Spaghetti topping
16 Singer Fitzgerald
17 Cats and dogs
18 Get really mad
20 Soul singer Franklin
22 Took to court
23 Lamb's mom
24 Wish earnestly
26 Potpie veggies
28 Pesky insects, informally
32 Taxi device
36 Bread unit
37 Family rooms
39 Kitchen appliance
40 British nobleman
41 Dairy animal
42 Years and years
43 "Rocket Man" singer __ John
45 Donald Duck or Pluto
47 Is unable to
48 Western resort lake
49 Puts up a fuss
51 Wealthy
54 507, to Caesar
55 Sound from a 23 Across
58 Get taller
60 Join the army
64 Outlandish
67 Doing nothing
68 Raisin __ (type of cereal)
69 Balance-sheet item
70 Gas in bright signs
71 Arrange in numerical order
72 Peter Rabbit's sibling
73 Talks a lot

DOWN

1 Largest of the Three Bears
2 Computer operator
3 Location
4 Is standing and speaking, at a meeting
5 Like some curvy roads
6 Mai __ (cocktail)
7 Places in position
8 Misbehave
9 Giggling sound
10 For each
11 Skin-lotion ingredient
12 Far from rapid
13 Strongbox relative
19 Dutch cheeses
21 Like some peppers
25 Build, as a building
27 Place an upper limit on
28 Icy precipitation
29 Australian animal
30 The third planet
31 Nosy one
33 Ancient Roman robes
34 Important occurrence
35 Takes a breather
38 Fighting blade
44 Horse sound
46 New or strange thing
50 Sardine container
52 Dairy product
53 "In what way?"
55 Dylan and Hope
56 Frizzy hairdo
57 At a distance
59 Stinging insect
61 Creative thought
62 Messy type
63 Change for a $20 bill
65 Explosive initials
66 __ *Misérables*

★ Koala Maze

Enter the maze where indicated at bottom, pass through all the stars exactly once, then exit at top left. You may not retrace your path.

SMALL CHANGE

Change one letter in each of these two words, to form a common two-word phrase.

COLT RACE

____

★ Fences

Connect the dots with vertical or horizontal lines, so that a single loop is formed with no crossings or branches. Each number indicates how many lines surround it; squares with no number may be surrounded by any number of lines.

1		1	1	3	1		
		3				3	0
		0				2	1
		3					
					3		
2	0				1		
3	3				2		
		2	3	2	1		2

WRONG IS RIGHT

Which of these four words is misspelled?

A) glottis
B) glossery
C) glockenspiel
D) glowworm

★ Dinner Date

Try to find these "night out" terms that are hidden in the diagram either across, down, or diagonally, and you'll find that one of them has left the premises and isn't there. What's the missing answer? (Individual words of all multiple-word answers are hidden separately.)

BAR
BILL
BISTRO
BLACKBOARD
CAFÉ
CHEF
COFFEE
CUTLERY
DESSERT
DINING OUT
EATERY
ITALIAN
KITCHEN
MAIN COURSE
MEAL
MENU
MINTS
PASTA
PIZZA
PLATE
RESERVATION
RESTAURANT
SERVICE
SIDE SALAD
STARTER
STEAKHOUSE
TABLE
TOAST
TIP
WAITER
WINE

WHO'S WHAT WHERE?

The correct term for a resident of Tangier, Morocco, is:

A) Tangerine B) Tangierite

C) Tangerian D) Tangieri

★ Hello, Hello, Hello by Sally R. Stein

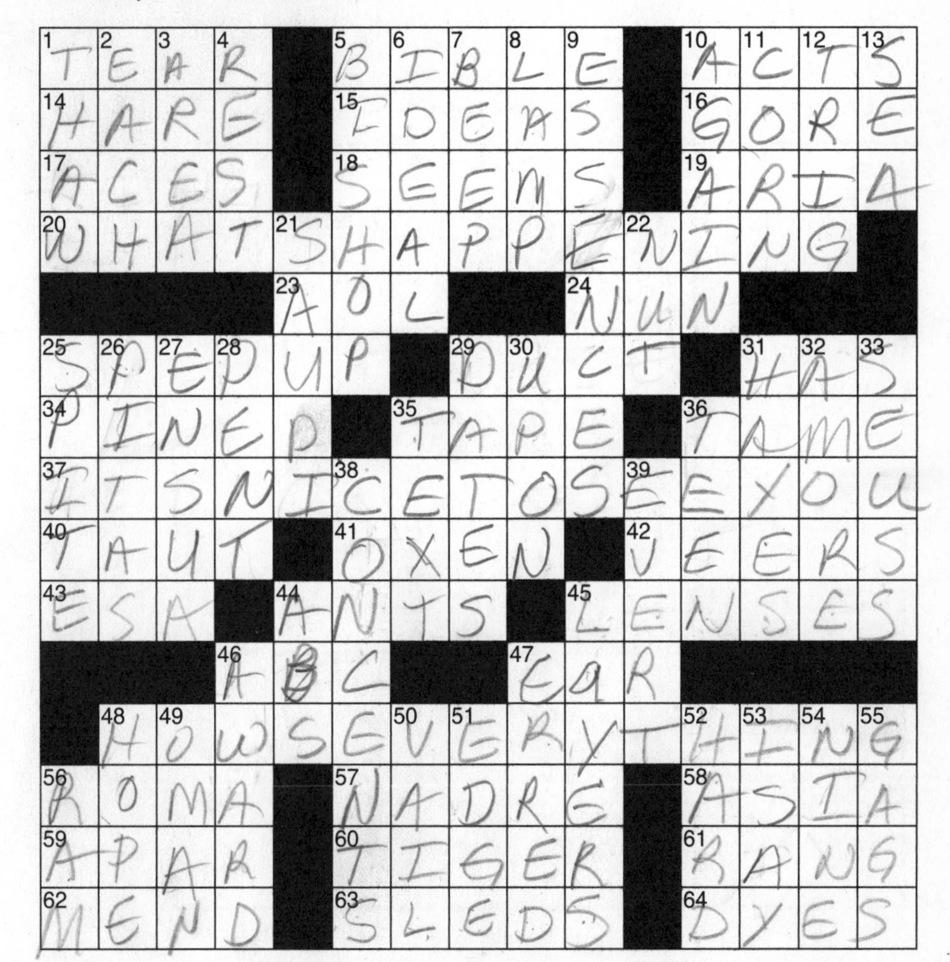

ACROSS

1 Shed a __ (cry)
5 Holy book
10 Comics' performances
14 Rabbit relative
15 Notions
16 Clinton's veep
17 High cards
18 Appears to be
19 Operatic solo
20 Phrase of greeting
23 E-mail service, for short
24 Convent dweller
25 Accelerated
29 Air passage
31 Owns
34 Yearned
35 Package sealer
36 Like petting-zoo animals
37 Phrase of greeting
40 Tightly stretched
41 Bovine beasts of burden
42 Changes direction
43 Nationality suffix
44 Industrious insects
45 Parts of eyeglasses
46 2 on a telephone
47 11 Down portion
48 Phrase of greeting
56 Italy's capital, to natives
57 Chaplain
58 Mount Everest's continent
59 Imitative person
60 Fierce fighter
61 Pushed, as a doorbell
62 Fix, as a shirt
63 Winter vehicles
64 Fabric colorings

DOWN

1 Begin to melt
2 Apiece
3 Carpet-store calculation
4 Take a break
5 Diagonal-moving chess piece
6 Just perfect
7 Pager sound
8 Genie's home
9 Basic natures
10 One more time
11 Iowa crop
12 High-school math
13 Caribbean, for one
21 __ Arabia (Mideast nation)
22 Pecan or cashew
25 Malice
26 Breads with pockets
27 Come next
28 Fender damage
29 Calendar numbers
30 Once __ a time
31 President Rutherford B.
32 Love, in 56 Across
33 Cat in the Hat creator
35 Schoolbook
36 Person who's not quite 20
38 Notions
39 Chris of tennis
44 Belly muscles
45 Coats of paint
46 Medal or trophy
47 Made a mistake
48 Partner of Faith and Charity
49 Sign of the future
50 Colorado ski resort
51 Advantage
52 Tough to solve
53 Londoner's exclamation
54 Supreme Court complement
55 One-liners
56 Lamb's father

★ Sudoku

Fill in the blank boxes so that every row, column, and 3x3 box contains all of the numbers 1 to 9.

9			7					1
		4		9	2	6		
	7	2	6			3	9	
	1			4		5		6
	2						1	
5		3		6			4	
	9	8			7	1	3	
		7	1	5		2		
2					6			9

MIXAGRAMS

Each line contains a five-letter word and a four-letter word that have been mixed together (the order of the letters in each word has not been changed). Unmix the two words on each line and write them in the spaces provided. When you're done, find a two-part answer to the clue by reading down the letter columns in the answers.

CLUE: Ferdinand was one

O P A N D I C O R = _ _ _ _ _ + _ _ _ _

A C U R I M E N T = _ _ _ _ _ + _ _ _ _

S A C K T O R I D = _ _ _ _ _ + _ _ _ _

S E W C H I N E T = _ _ _ _ _ + _ _ _ _

★ 123

Fill in the diagram so that each rectangular piece has one each of the numbers 1, 2, and 3, under these rules: 1) No two adjacent squares, horizontally or vertically, can have the same number. 2) Each completed row and column of the diagram will have an equal number of 1s, 2s, and 3s.

			2		
					2
		2			
	3			**3**	
2					

ADDITION SWITCH

Switch the positions of two of the digits in the incorrect sum at right, to get a correct sum.
Example: 955+264 = 411. Switch the second 1 in 411 with the 9 in 955 to get: 155+264 = 419

```
  143
+ 218
-----
  405
```

★ A Little Light by Gail Grabowski

1	2	3	4	5	■	6	7	8	9	■	10	11	12	13
14					■	15				■	16			
17					18					■	19			
20			■	21				■	22	23				
■	■	■	24				■	25				■	■	■
26	27	28				■	29					30	31	■
32					■	33				■	34			35
36				■	■	37			■	■	38			
39				■	40				■	41				
■	42			43				■	44					
■	■	■	45				■	46				■	■	■
47	48	49				■	50				■	51	52	53
54				■	55	56					57			
58				■	59				■	60				
61				■	62				■	63				

ACROSS

1 Glowing coal
6 Computer junk mail
10 Stinging remark
14 Auto-club suggestion
15 Make a duplicate
16 Spiny houseplant
17 "I Can't Stop Loving You" singer
19 Doily material
20 Urban roads: Abbr.
21 Israeli airline
22 Word of appreciation
24 Item on an end table
25 Connery or Penn
26 First appearances
29 Fruit with a pit
32 Baldwin and Guinness
33 Pottery material
34 British nobleman
36 Necktie fabric
37 Ignited
38 French cheese
39 Sacred
40 Sock parts
41 Looks for
42 Experimental trial
44 Digging tools
45 Frog relative
46 Limerick, for one
47 Find out about
50 Carton sealer
51 Feel poorly
54 High point
55 '83 film featuring "What a Feeling"
58 Mets' ballpark until 2009
59 Charged particles
60 Use, as a dining room table
61 Toot the horn
62 Salad slice, for short
63 Thick-skinned beast

DOWN

1 Makes a mistake
2 Castle protection
3 Purchases
4 And so on: Abbr.
5 Prepares, as leftovers
6 Paper fragment
7 Opinion collection
8 King Kong, for example
9 Agatha Christie offering
10 Gymnastics rail
11 Actor Alda
12 Boulder
13 Spelling competitions
18 Charitable gifts
23 "Bali __"
24 Run of good fortune
25 Petty quarrels
26 Move rapidly
27 Author T.S.
28 Gal at a ball
29 Sci-fi character
30 Rowed
31 Tot's three-wheeler
33 Puffy sky sight
35 Not as much
40 Rush-hour woe
41 One risking a ticket
43 In addition
44 Second-year student, for short
46 Out of style
47 Corned-beef concoction
48 Sound in a cave
49 Congregation's response
50 Armored vehicle
51 Prefix for freeze
52 Computer image
53 Carson successor
56 Baseball great Gehrig
57 Sound of satisfaction

★ One-Way Streets

The diagram represents a pattern of streets. A and B are parking spaces, and the black squares are stores. Find the route that starts at A, passes through all stores exactly once, and ends at B. Arrows indicate one-way traffic for that block only. No block or intersection may be entered more than once.

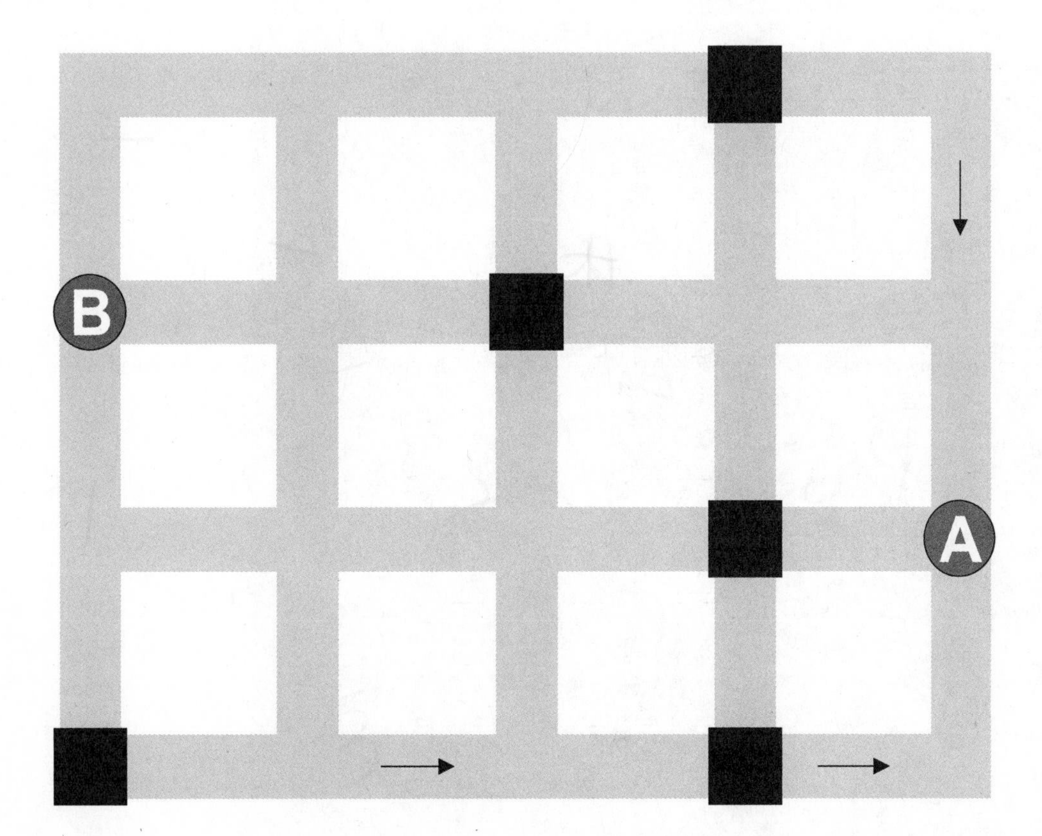

SOUND THINKING

There are two common uncapitalized word whose consonant sounds are N, K, L, and D, in that order. One of them is UNCLAD. What's the other one?

____

★ Missing Links

Find the three hexagons that are linked together, but linked to no others on the page.

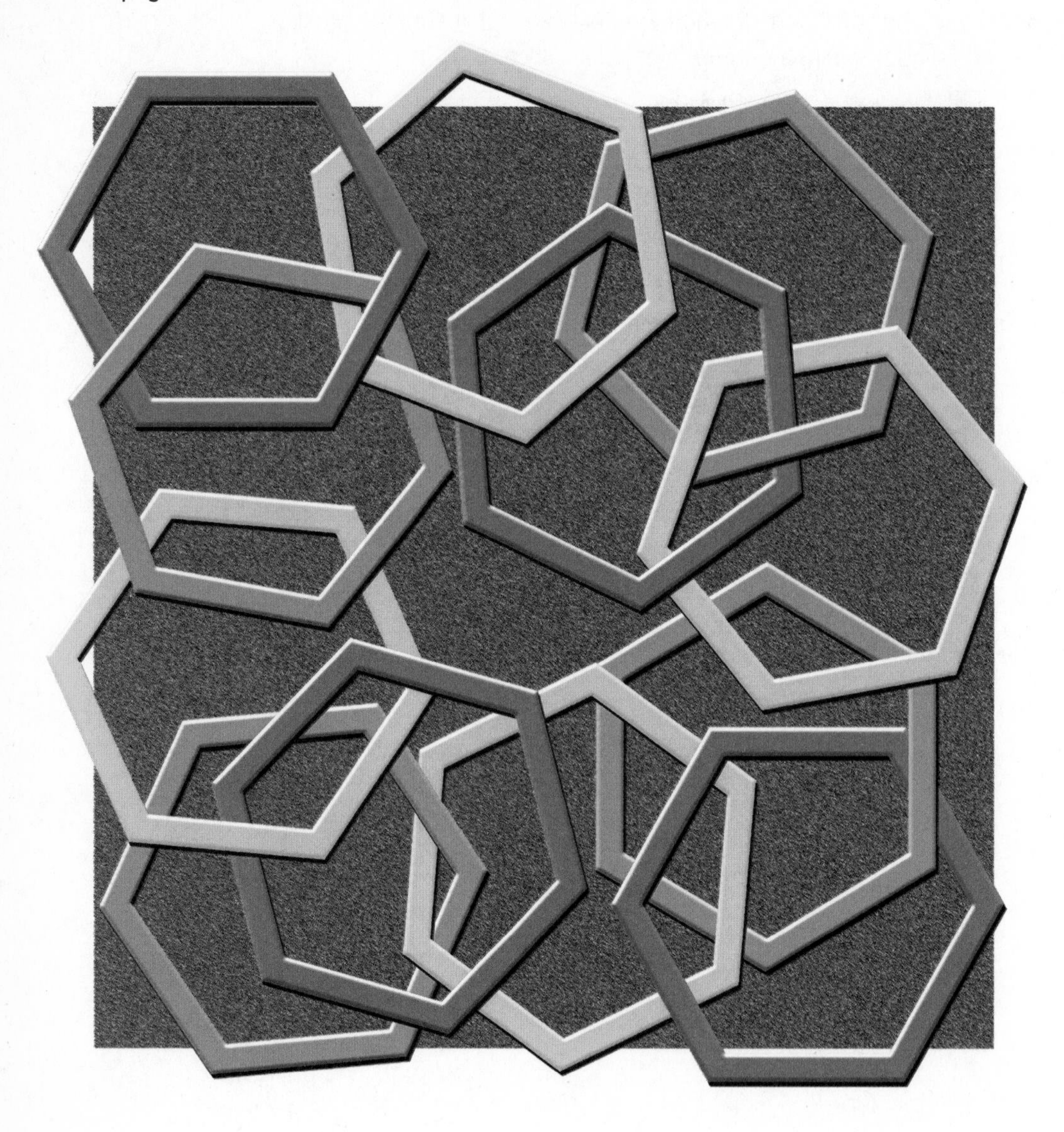

SAY IT AGAIN

What three-letter word can be either a type of animal or a verb meaning "follow"?

_ _ _

★ Star Search

Find the stars that are hidden in some of the blank squares. The numbered squares indicate how many stars are hidden in the squares adjacent to them (including diagonally). There is never more than one star in any square.

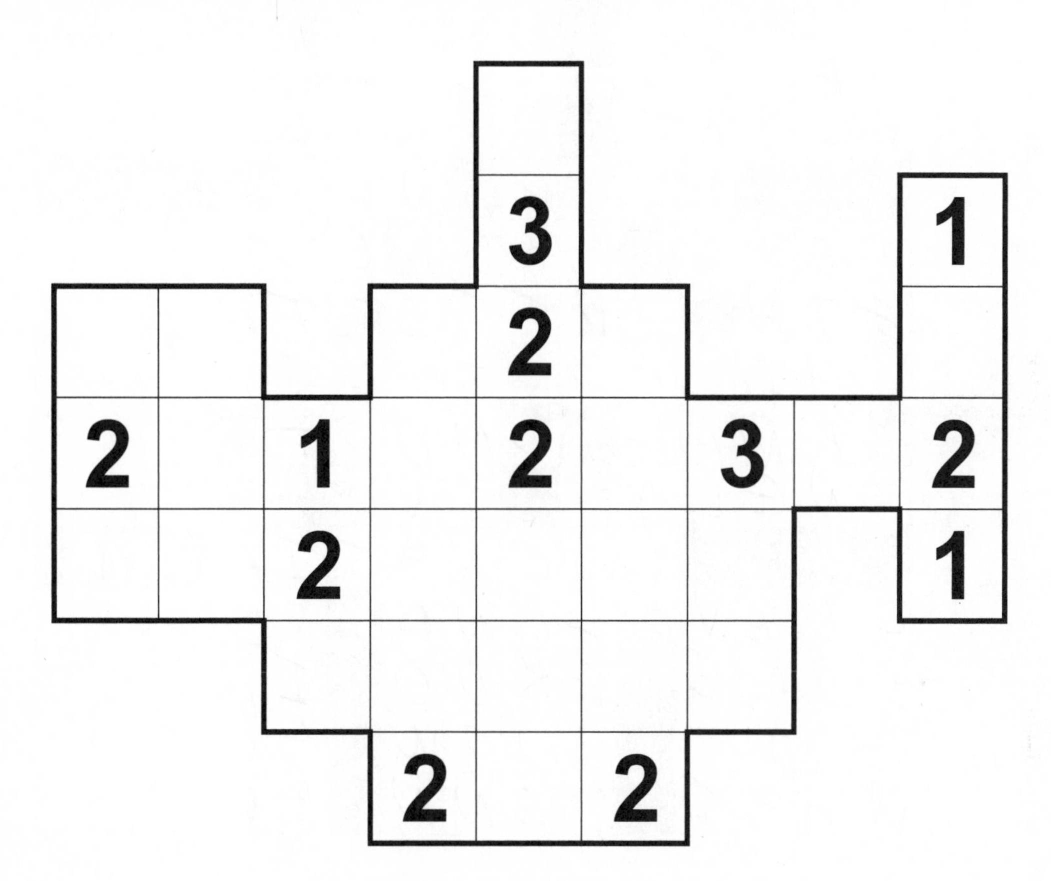

CHOICE WORDS

Form three six-letter words from the same category, by selecting one letter from each column three times. Each letter will be used exactly once.

C	N	M	I	E	L	_ _ _ _ _ _
I	E	M	A	S	D	_ _ _ _ _ _
D	O	S	P	N	T	_ _ _ _ _ _

★ Cee the USA by Sally R. Stein

ACROSS

1 Junkyard metal
6 Snips, as hair
10 Enthusiasm
14 Fraternity headquarters
15 Cincinnati's state
16 Trade show, for short
17 Desert stopover
18 Phrase of denial
19 Something very funny
20 Fabric fold
21 Largest North Carolina city
23 Brief letter
25 Prefix meaning "new"
26 Sharks' habitats
29 Day fractions: Abbr.
31 Beverly Hills home
36 Water w. of Portugal
37 On-the-green golf strokes
39 Informal farewells
40 Third-largest US city
43 Suez or Panama
44 Nose, slangily
45 Compass pt.
46 Running-track unit
48 Small even number
49 Parakeets and poodles
50 Tic-__-toe
52 Agitate
54 City near Akron
59 Hunter's weapon
63 Entice
64 Slangy suffix
65 Spouse's relative
66 With no warranty
67 Skiing surface
68 Part of a play
69 Sharpen, as an appetite
70 Chattanooga's state: Abbr.
71 Magic spells

DOWN

1 Boutique, for one
2 Fossil fuel
3 Pretext
4 Cambodians and Sri Lankans
5 Green pasta sauce
6 Orchestral works
7 "Yikes!"
8 Giant of industry
9 Evening party
10 48 Across less than 48 Across
11 Cinema sign
12 Dry cleaner's challenge
13 Carryall bag
22 Went wild
24 Hoodlum
26 Vanzetti co-defendant
27 Colonial patriot __ Allen
28 Drop __ to (write)
30 Tour of duty
32 Catch some rays
33 Make up (for)
34 Besmirch
35 19th letters
37 Sense of taste
38 Applies the brake
41 Coolidge nickname
42 Stolen property
47 Least ruddy
49 Son of a queen
51 Chili con __
53 From Killarney
54 Lobster weapon
55 Luxurious
56 A Great Lake
57 Three-piece suit part
58 Midday
60 Show off, as one's muscles
61 Narrow street
62 Lambs' mamas

★ Paper Chase

Find these paper-related words that are hidden in the diagram, either across, down, or diagonally.

```
G H P W G E S S A M D E E D R
S A P S N W N L E T T C R C A
R S R E I D L I C E N S E A R
S S E R P I I X Z P N R T E O
J E S P P S B O A A T R T G P
E O K A A S E G C I G S E U U
E R U N R E E I F E O A L A E
E E A R W R D I R P R L M L M
H P I U N T C T N E M U C O D
S O S O Y A R Y N D C I Q S Y
N R E J T T L E E E T O H M A
E T H E S I S E P R W E R J S
W L T Z A O Y A A A E F H D S
S V T D D N P P P T P L U P E
```

ARTICLE
CERTIFICATE
DAILY
DEED
DISSERTATION
DOCUMENT
ESSAY
JOURNAL
LETTER
LICENSE
MAGAZINE
NEWS
PAGE
PAPER
POSTER
PRESS
PULP
RAG
REAM
RECORD
REPORT
SHEET
THESIS
WRAPPING

IN OTHER WORDS

There is only one common uncapitalized word that contains the consecutive letters GEV. What is it?

____

BRAIN BREATHER
HOME SECURITY: PUTTING PROWLERS OUT OF BUSINESS

Check out this advice from the experts—including some from burglars themselves! Some of these tips may surprise you but they'll definitely help you avoid being surprised by the bad guys.

Adopt a pooch If it's practical, adopt a *big* pooch—a dog is one of the best burglar deterrents around. Good watchdogs include Doberman pinschers, huskies, Great Danes, German shepherds, and retrievers. If having a dog isn't possible, you might get a tape recording of a barking dog to play once in a while (and have it running on your answering machine's message!).

Consider this often-overlooked alarm protection If you have a home alarm system, opt for the "phone line cut" service, which can detect whether an intruder has cut your phone line. It automatically sends the police to your house, even though you're not able to call them yourself.

Watch the foliage Overgrown shrubbery and high hedges around your home's perimeter provide as much privacy for burglars as they do for you. Trim foliage often so it can't camouflage a burglar's activities from the view of neighbors and passersby. Think twice before installing a tall fence or planting a tall hedge.

Enlist your neighbor's help You'll hear a thousand different ideas on the best hiding place for your spare key, but you'll seldom hear the correct one: "Nowhere." Instead of hiding your key, exchange keys with your neighbor. This also establishes mutual trust between you and your neighbor—an important security strategy in and of itself. Whenever you're away, have your neighbor gather mail, watch for strangers, and even park in your driveway sometimes, to simulate occupancy. Make sure to offer to reciprocate.

What burglars don't want you to know about break-ins:

- They prefer to break in during the day. While most people fret about night prowlers, competent burglars look for open windows during daylight, when most folks are out of the house.
- As noted above, they hate barking dogs. And, whether you actually have a dog or not, don't forget to display a prominent, menacing "Beware of Dog" sign.
- They'll come right up to your door and knock. If there's no answer, they can look for a hidden key or an open window—or just kick in your front door, if you don't use a strong deadbolt lock.
- They don't care if your income is modest. Don't think you're safe because you're not swimming in jewelry or valuable art. Burglars usually look for quick cash, not the big score. They're most interested in small, easy-to-grab and easy-to-sell items, such as laptops, watches, and small electronic devices.

★★ Line Drawing

Draw four straight lines, each from one edge of the square to another edge, so that the letters in each of the five regions spell a four-letter word.

A Z
C Z
U
A
C Z
Z F
I F
J
I
F H
E Z
Z Z

THREE OF A KIND

Find the three hidden words in the sentence that go together in some way.

Now I see—the message came from a cruise ship.

★ ABC

Enter the letters A, B, and C into the diagram so that each row and column has exactly one A, one B, and one C. The letters outside the diagram indicate the first letter encountered, moving in the direction of the arrow. Keep in mind that after all the letters have been filled in, there will be one blank box in each row and column.

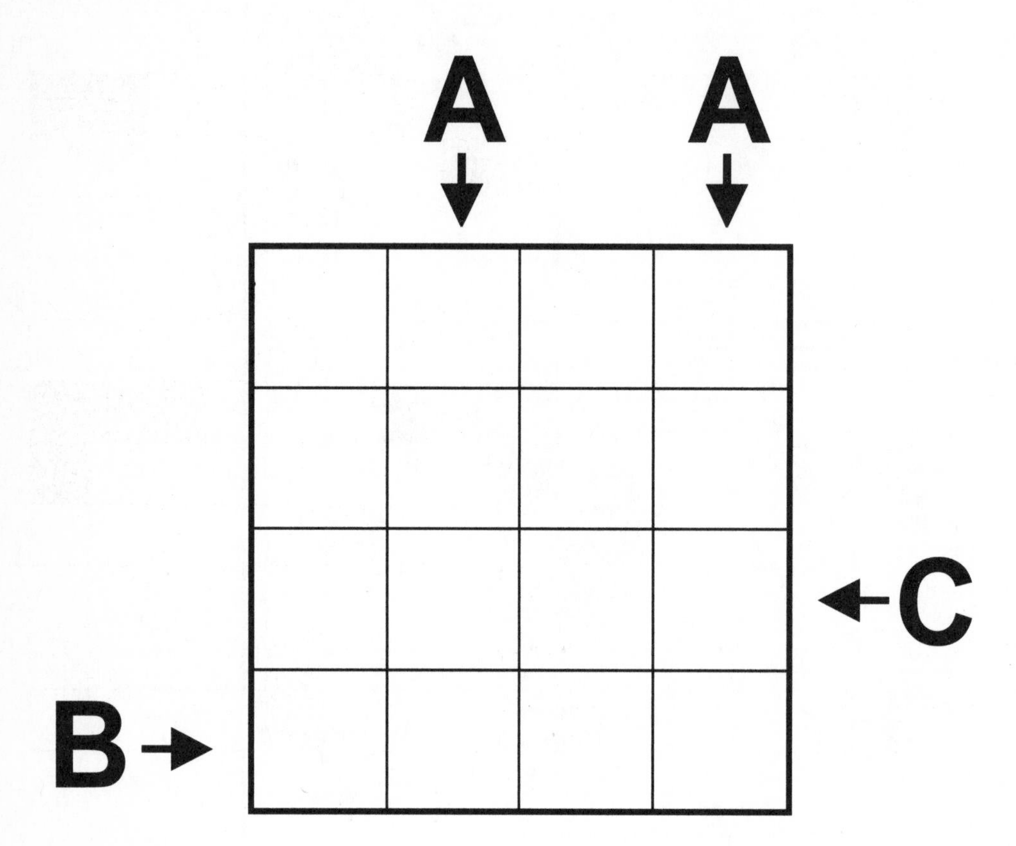

NATIONAL TREASURE

Besides WAIT, what's the other common four-letter word that can be formed from the letters in KUWAITI?

_ _ _ _

★ Restaurant Work by Gail Grabowski

ACROSS

1 Something extra
5 Yardstick unit
9 Nickels and dimes
14 Expel, as from power
15 Song for one person
16 Upper-arm muscle
17 Students' vehicle
19 Entrap
20 Stadium levels
21 General Grant's foe
22 Be aware of
23 Feared greatly
25 Guitarist Atkins
27 Deli loaf
28 Turnpike or street
31 One in charge
34 Bandleaders' sticks
37 Logger's tool
38 Conceit
39 "Baloney!"
40 Under the weather
41 Cartoon bark
42 Low-scoring tie
43 Dance move
44 Keyboarded again
46 Zilch
48 Gardener's purchase
49 Walks a beat
53 Poems of praise
55 Shirt-sleeve filler
56 Molecule parts
58 Handbag
60 Author of medical fiction
62 Blacksmith's block
63 Trucker with a transmitter
64 Italian wine region
65 Impolite looks
66 Roll-call response
67 Wind-instrument insert

DOWN

1 Fence stake
2 Clearheaded
3 Theater employee
4 They stockpile stuff
5 Oahu or Maui: Abbr.
6 Aristocratic
7 Tipped off, with "in"
8 Fire-hydrant attachment
9 *CSI* network
10 Grunted, as a pig
11 Remark of impatience
12 Infamous Roman emperor
13 Eject, as lava
18 National anthem start
24 Like a fish fillet
25 Permission
26 Breakfast side dish
28 Speckle-coated horse
29 Wheel connector
30 Shrill bark
31 Grizzly, for one
32 Fairy-tale monster
33 Machine-dispensed ice cream
35 Like fine wine
36 A pair of
39 Wish earnestly
43 Toy on grooved tracks
45 Corporal's affirmative
47 Tehran's country
49 Investigate
50 Traffic-light color
51 Off the leash
52 Struck forcefully
53 Milky gem
54 Sand hill
55 Part of the foot
57 Lose control on ice
59 Overhead trains
61 Make angry

★★ Five by Five

Group the 25 numbers in the grid into five sets of five, with each set having all of the numbers 1 through 5. The numbers in each set must all be connected to each other by a common horizontal or vertical side.

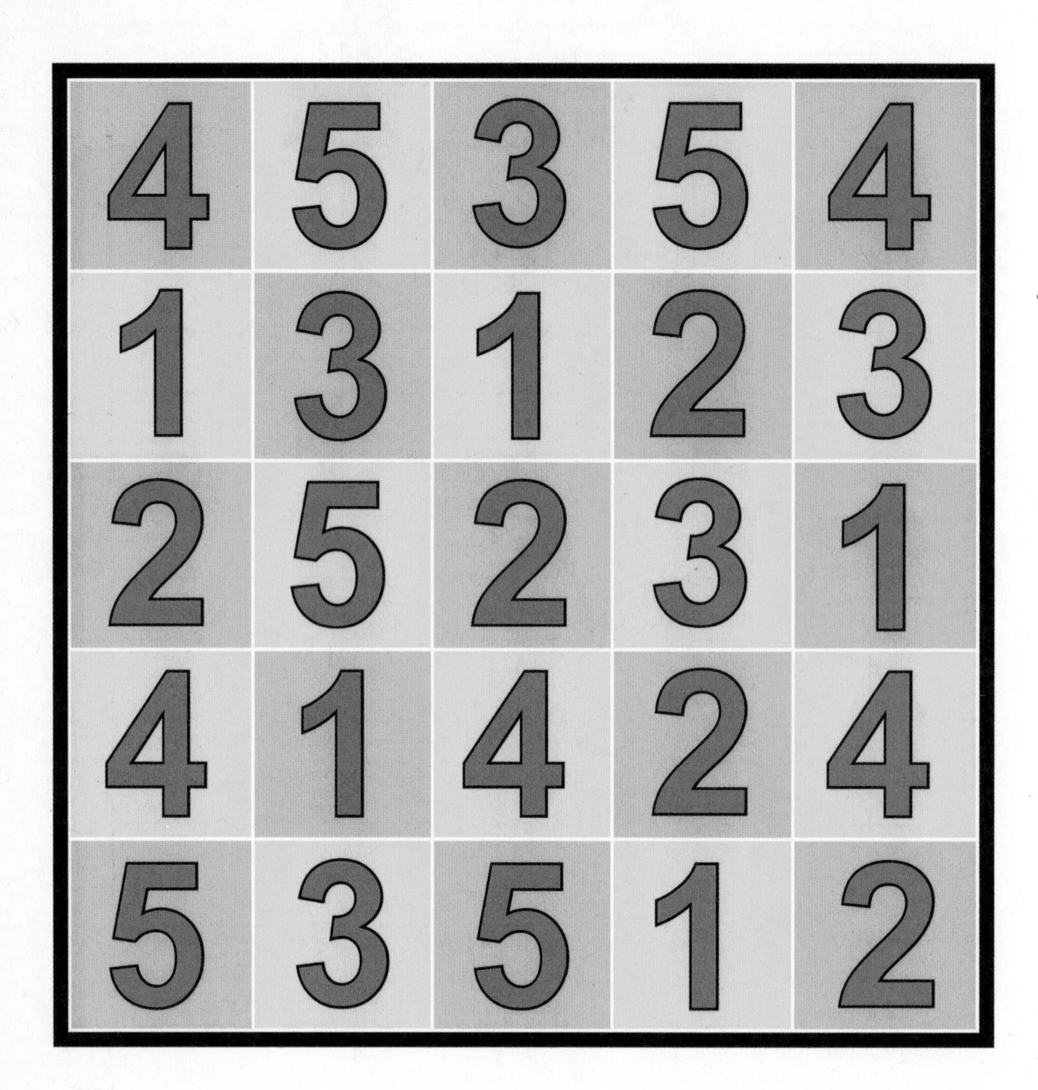

BETWEENER

What three-letter word belongs between the word at left and the word at right, so that the first and second word, and the second and third word, each form a common compound word?

SHOT _ _ _ POWDER

★ "Dry" to Remember

Find these "dry" words that are hidden in the diagram, either across, down, or diagonally. There's one additional six-letter answer not listed below that's also hidden in the diagram—a place known for being rather dry. What's that word?

```
P P A R C H E D W I N
B R F W I Z E N E D E
L A O S D U S T R A R
A Z A S L T A C T C R
X N A S A C O O U E A
D I W L C I W R U R B
A O R I K E C Q R B B
T R S A L L M A R I J
R E I R U I P L L C D
D I W D S R E L A T S
Y O R S T E R I L T M
T R M A E T I N B E S
V R D T R S D U S T Y
E T A R D Y H E D B G
L A C K L U S T R A T
S A R C A S T I C R L
W I T H E R E B E R D
D W S T T O E S R E Y
R I D H A S E D K U W
S Z U I R D A A W I R
C E S R O I B N T O Y
D N T S P L V H E T P
A E D T A O E E S S M
D R H N V R W R L A N
D N S C E B I D R H I
B I A D R H A T D A A
R R N L T O I K H R R
U O Y N B N C A E A D
T B O R I N G S A N K
```

ACERBIC
ARID
BAKED
BARREN
BLAND
BORING
BRUT
DEHYDRATE
DESERT
DESICCATE
DRAIN
DRY
DUSTY
EVAPORATE
LACKLUSTER
MARTINI
PARCHED
POWDER
PROSAICAL
SAND
SARCASTIC
SCORCHED
SEC
SHRIVEL
STALE
STERILE
THIRSTY
TORRID
TOWEL
WITHERED
WIZENED

INITIAL REACTION

Identify the well-known proverb from the first letters in each of its words.

I. T. O. T. K. O. ______________________

★ Find the Ships

Determine the position of the 10 ships listed to the right of the diagram. The ships may be oriented either horizontally or vertically. A square with wavy lines indicates water and will not contain a ship. The numbers at the edge of the diagram indicate how many squares in that row or column contain parts of ships. When all 10 ships are correctly placed in the diagram, no two of them will touch each other, not even diagonally.

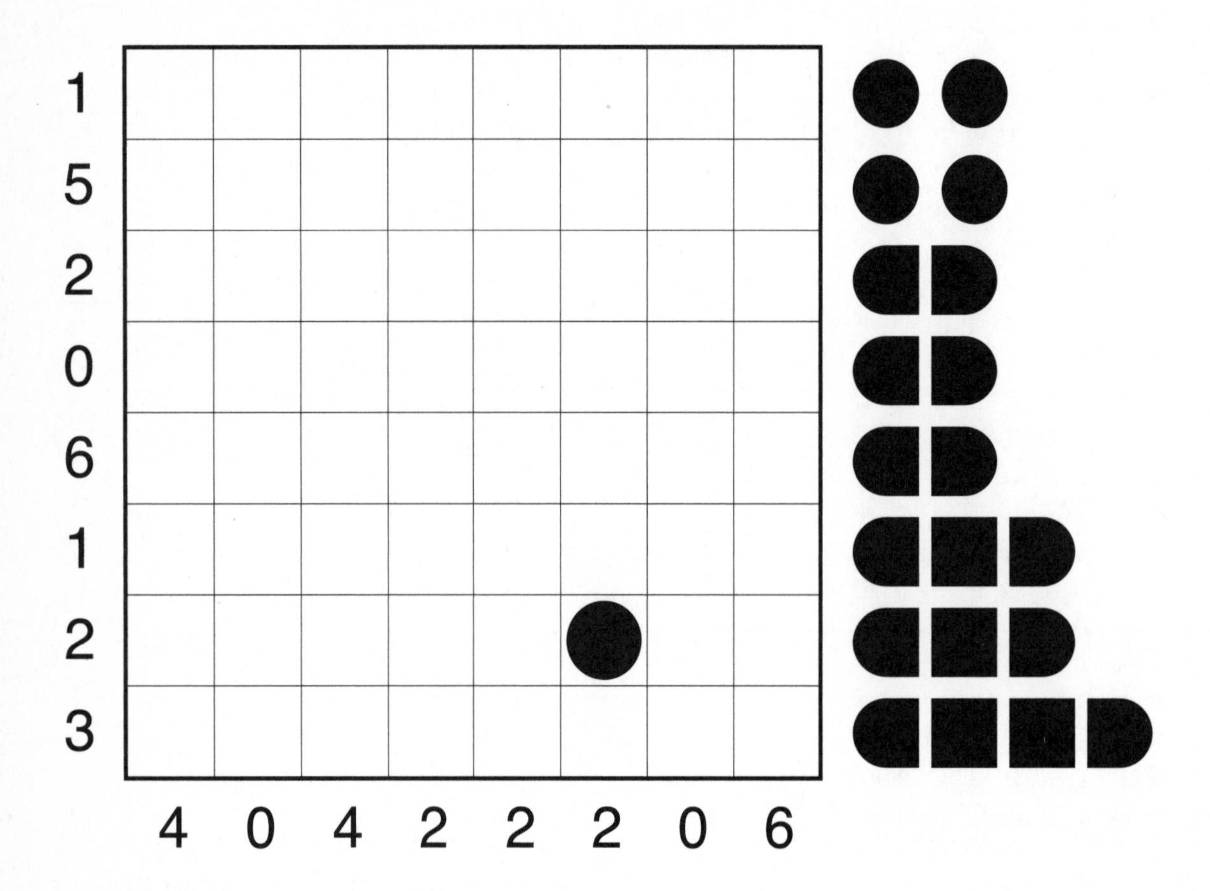

TWO-BY-FOUR

The eight letters in the word GRUMPILY can be rearranged to form a pair of common four-letter words in only one way. Can you find the two words?

_ _ _ _   _ _ _ _

★★ Sudoku

Fill in the blank boxes so that every row, column, and 3x3 box contains all of the numbers 1 to 9.

			4	5	1			
	3	8					7	
		4		3		1	9	
2			9		4			6
3		6		8		5		4
8			5		3			7
	8	9		2		7		
	5					3	4	
			8	4	5			

MIXAGRAMS

Each line contains a five-letter word and a four-letter word that have been mixed together (the order of the letters in each word has not been changed). Unmix the two words on each line and write them in the spaces provided. When you're done, find a two-part answer to the clue by reading down the letter columns in the answers.

CLUE: Barbecue locale

E T H E R O R B Y = _ _ _ _ _ + _ _ _ _

P A S O N D A D A = _ _ _ _ _ + _ _ _ _

F R A P I N C E R = _ _ _ _ _ + _ _ _ _

H O B O R O D O K = _ _ _ _ _ + _ _ _ _

★ What's the Skinny? by Sally R. Stein

ACROSS

1 Incites
6 Female singing range
10 British fellow
14 Just hangs around
15 Kingly address
16 Walesa of Poland
17 Tilt right, at sea
20 Helper: Abbr.
21 Ball-__ hammer
22 Tahiti and Sicily
23 Business-envelope letters
25 Secret writing
27 Spicy beef/beans dish
30 Those folks
32 Took a photo of
36 Atmosphere
37 Tiny amount
39 Each
41 Took a big risk
44 Term of office
45 Old furnace fuel
46 Source of natural light
47 Ireland, informally
48 Throat-clearing sound
50 Contest mail-in
52 Singer Guthrie
54 Helper
56 Regretful feeling
59 Sinking-ship deserters
61 Apex
65 Gets one's hair cut, perhaps
68 Iridescent mineral
69 Insignificant
70 Journalistic angle
71 Exited
72 Money players
73 Church songs

DOWN

1 __ monster (southwestern lizard)
2 Some Keats poems
3 "That's too bad!"
4 Teeth-related
5 Retired fast plane: Abbr.
6 Approve
7 Lo-cal
8 Hypnotic state
9 "__ the fields we go ..."
10 Approaches one's objective
11 Become well
12 Land measure
13 Profs.' degrees
18 Make a choice
19 Auction action
24 Track-meet official
26 Nebraska city
27 Social stratum
28 Walker in the woods
29 Armenian neighbor
31 Therefore
33 Robbery, slangily
34 Come to pass
35 Very small
38 Flawless
40 Made a stack
42 Fish + cheese sandwich
43 Ketchup ingredients
49 Pie eater of rhyme
51 In a tidy way
53 Second notes of the scale
55 Neighbor of Leb.
56 Garbage boat
57 Be optimistic
58 To __ (unanimously)
60 Spherical hairdo
62 Study hard
63 St. Paul's state
64 CPR experts
66 Mischievous kid
67 Barbecue residue

★ Fences

Connect the dots with vertical or horizontal lines, so that a single loop is formed with no crossings or branches. Each number indicates how many lines surround it; squares with no number may be surrounded by any number of lines.

1	0				2	3	
3			3		2		3
1	3		3				3
2				3		2	2
2		0		0			2
	3	3				3	3

WRONG IS RIGHT

Which of these four words is misspelled?

A) analyze B) pasturize

C) satirize D) accessorize

★★ Triad Split Decisions

In this clueless crossword puzzle, each answer consists of two words whose spellings are the same, except for the consecutive letters given. All answers are common words; no phrases or hyphenated or capitalized words are used. Some of the clues may have more than one solution, but there is only one word pair that will correctly link up with all the other word pairs.

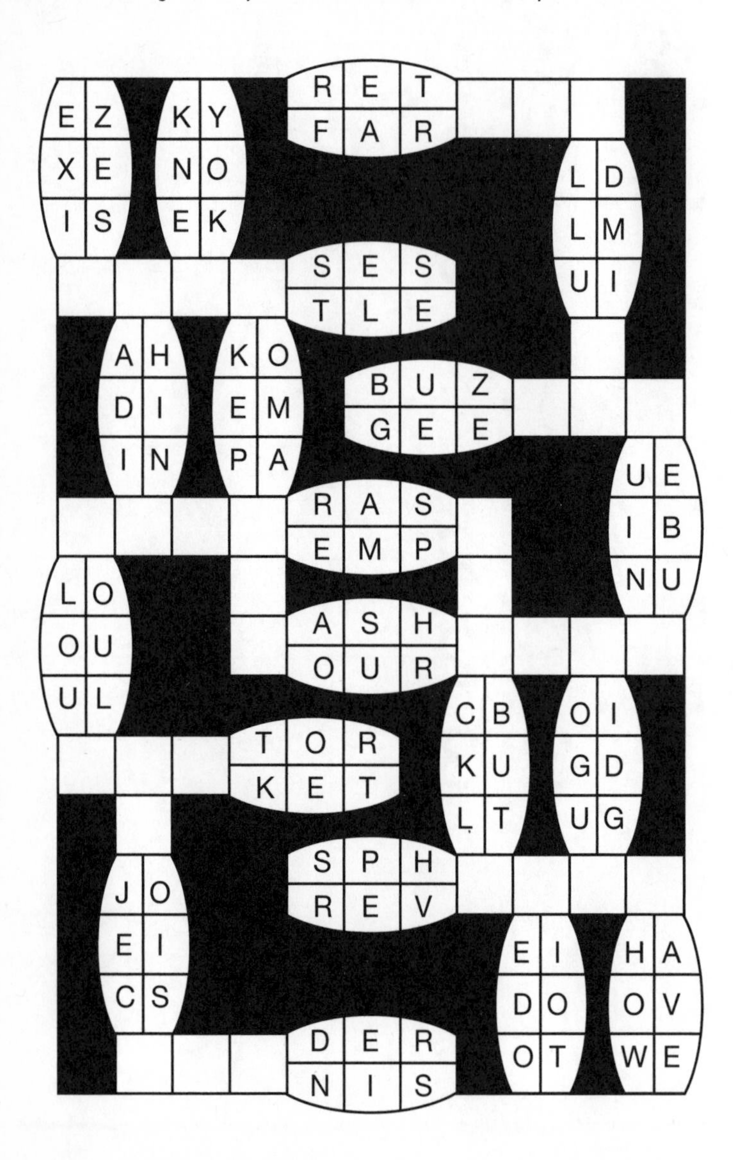

TRANSDELETION

Delete one letter from the word LOCALE and rearrange the rest, to get something musical.

____

★ 123

Fill in the diagram so that each rectangular piece has one each of the numbers 1, 2, and 3, under these rules: 1) No two adjacent squares, horizontally or vertically, can have the same number. 2) Each completed row and column of the diagram will have an equal number of 1s, 2s, and 3s.

		1			
			2		
3					
	1			3	

SUDOKU SUM

Fill in the missing numbers from 1 to 9, so that the sum of each row and column is as indicated.

	23	8	14
16		1	
12	6		
17			5

★ Summer Wear by Gail Grabowski

ACROSS

1 Shorten, as slacks
6 Eager
10 Planet beyond Earth
14 Poke fun at
15 Traditional knowledge
16 Toast topping
17 Covers on end-table items
19 Turn sharply
20 African snake
21 To-do list entry
22 Eave hanger in winter
24 Looked steadily
26 Up __ (cornered)
28 Aroma
30 Hearing and sight
33 Wash-up need
36 Uncluttered
38 Little Pigs complement
40 Game-show host
42 Christmas tree
43 Shoe bottoms
44 Church donation
45 Russian river
47 Wine-list choices
48 Jeweled crowns
50 Treaty
52 Poem parts
54 Earn $200, in Monopoly
58 Tries, as food
61 Annoying one
63 Hot drink
64 "That's clear"
65 Golfer's pegs
68 Close by
69 City in Oklahoma
70 Get out of bed
71 Scottish caps
72 Depend (on)
73 Window parts

DOWN

1 Book of maps
2 Minimal amount
3 West Florida city
4 Sixth sense: Abbr.
5 Took a breather
6 "Too bad!"
7 Russian liquor
8 Anger
9 Long for
10 Brief films before the feature
11 Actor Baldwin
12 Fishing-line holder
13 Angry
18 Was wearing
23 Pennies
25 Cord headgear for horses
27 Women's shoe fastener
29 Say no to
31 Author __ Stanley Gardner
32 Bird food
33 Stage background
34 Leave out
35 First part of a play
37 Tire filler
39 Mountain curve
41 Spine-tingling
46 Expire, as a membership
49 Respond
51 Short snooze
53 Go bad
55 Pub mug
56 Formation fliers
57 Fertile desert areas
58 Add some color to
59 On the ocean
60 Stitched line
62 Whirlpool
66 Dollar bill
67 Singing syllable

★ Number-Out

Shade squares so that no number appears in any row or column more than once. Shaded squares may not touch each other horizontally or vertically, and all unshaded squares must form a single continuous area.

4	2	5	3	2
3	2	1	3	4
1	2	4	2	5
4	4	4	1	5
5	1	2	4	5

THINK ALIKE

Unscramble the letters in the phrase GATE BREW to form two words with the same or similar meanings.

________________ ________________

★ No Three in a Row

Enter the maze at upper left, pass through all the squares exactly once, then exit, all without retracing your path. You may not pass through three squares of the same color consecutively.

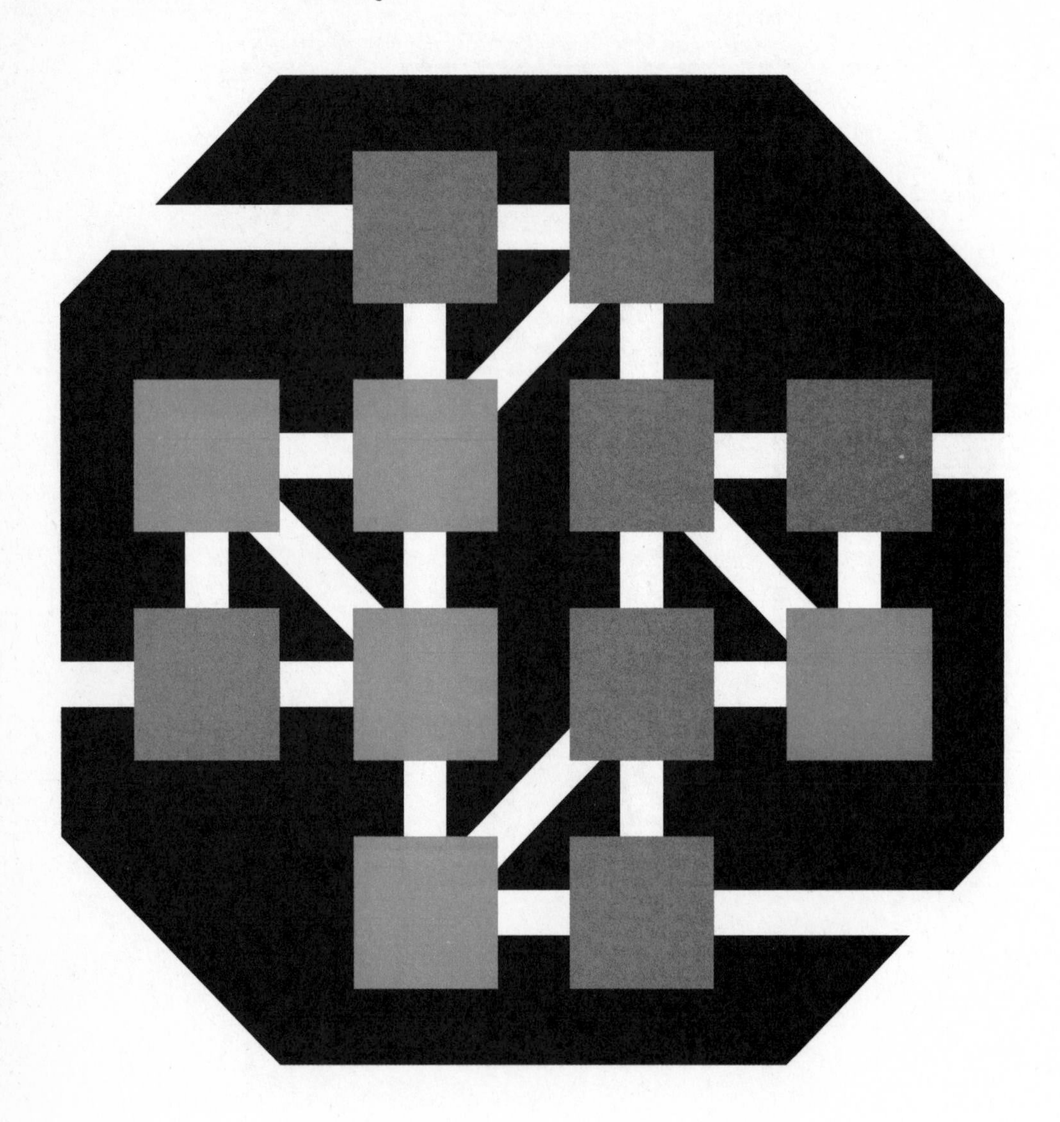

SAY IT AGAIN

What three-letter verb can mean either "strike" or "arrive in"?

— — —

★ "Hot" Stuff

Find these words related to heat and cooking that are hidden in the diagram, either across, down, or diagonally.

```
G F N I T S A O T L N W O X G
R T E T S A O T C E L W O R B
I Y R T L U S O V E Z I I A A
D I B S I T T O R R I Q R W B
D H G S W E S I Z Z L I N G E
L G N I R E M M I S T U N U K
E A I G R I L Y F O A I C R S
D I T W Z N L T A B L E O E A
N L S G A G O S E I B V V T U
I Z A F N R T K O R W R E S T
K Z O N R I K B A H I O T A E
O I R I N Y T B W O O N K O E
O S D G G H I S J T P H G T I
C O O K I N G N A H W A R M N
S I M M E R I M G B G R I L E
```

BARBECUE
BASTING
BOILING
COOKING
FRYING
GRIDDLE
GRILL
HOT
KEBAB
OVEN
ROASTING
SAUTÉING
SIMMERING
SIZZLING
SULTRY
SWELTERING
TOASTER
TOASTING
TORRID
WARM
WOK

WHO'S WHAT WHERE?

The correct term for a resident of Moose Jaw, Saskatchewan, is:

A) Moosie

B) Jawer

C) Moose Javian

D) Moosite

★ Hardware Store by Sally R. Stein

ACROSS

1 Synagogue scroll
6 Find a sum
9 Cobra or python
14 Abrasive material
15 Life story, for short
16 Like Swiss cheese
17 Civil-rights org.
18 Lend an __ (listen)
19 Make amends
20 Something in a ltr.
21 High-school aide
24 Books' names
26 Droop
27 Opening speech
30 President Jefferson
35 Popular lunch hour
38 Knock-on-door sounds
40 Got up from one's chair
41 Certain stationery manufacturer
44 Courtroom employee
45 Spruce or sycamore
46 *Moby-Dick* captain
47 Sculptor's subjects
49 Make adjustments
51 Compete in a slalom
53 Fond hopes
57 Disneyland character
63 Chop (off), as a branch
64 In unison
65 Commercials, e.g.
66 Type of tooth
68 Director Woody
69 "Golly!"
70 Privileged group
71 Allotted, with "out"
72 Tee preceder
73 Tightly packed

DOWN

1 Doctrine
2 Certain Middle Easterner
3 Show surprise, perhaps
4 Curved line
5 Punctuation in "patty-cake"
6 Brother of Cain
7 Dashboard feature
8 Campus residence halls
9 China's largest city
10 Phrase of denial
11 Very much
12 Casino game
13 One who stares
22 Houston baseballer
23 Feedbag morsel
25 Pillowcases and sheets
28 Fully attentive
29 Musical drama
31 Highly adorned
32 Butterfly relative
33 In between ports
34 Belgrade resident
35 Robin's home
36 Not fooled by
37 Above
39 Moved quickly
42 Unresolved detail
43 Peruses
48 "Wild blue yonder"
50 Doc-to-be's program
52 Public-relations concern
54 Very tired
55 Castle protectors
56 Shopper's splurging trip
57 What cowboys call women
58 Castaway's home
59 Young stallion
60 __-jerk reaction
61 Some Keats poems
62 Gets value from
67 Bullfight cheer

★★ One-Way Streets

The diagram represents a pattern of streets. A and B are parking spaces, and the black squares are stores. Find a route that starts at A, passes through all stores exactly once, and ends at B. Arrows indicate one-way traffic for that block only. No block or intersection may be entered more than once.

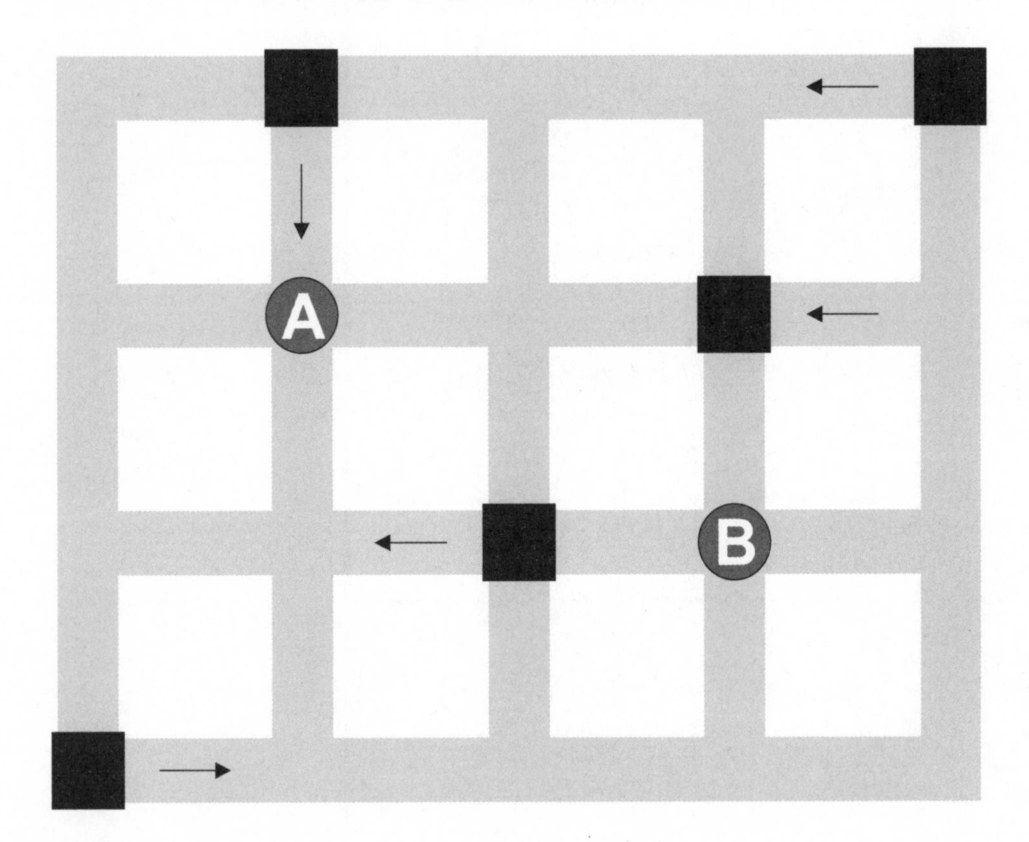

SOUND THINKING

There are two common uncapitalized word whose consonant sounds are P, L, R, and T, in that order. One of them is POLARITY. What's the other one?

____

★ Hyper-Sudoku

Fill in the blank boxes so that every row, column, 3x3 box, *and* each of the four 3x3 gray regions contains all of the numbers 1 to 9.

7	4		3				9	
	8	6	2		9	5		4
5						3	2	
	3	4	5		1	6		
8					6			2
	6				2			
6		3		2				
	2	7	4		3	9	6	
4							3	1

CENTURY MARKS

Select one number in each of the four columns so that the total adds up to exactly 100.

42	+	9	+	51	+	21	=	100
19		41		36		28		

★ Star Search

Find the stars that are hidden in some of the blank squares. The numbered squares indicate how many stars are hidden in the squares adjacent to them (including diagonally). There is never more than one star in any square.

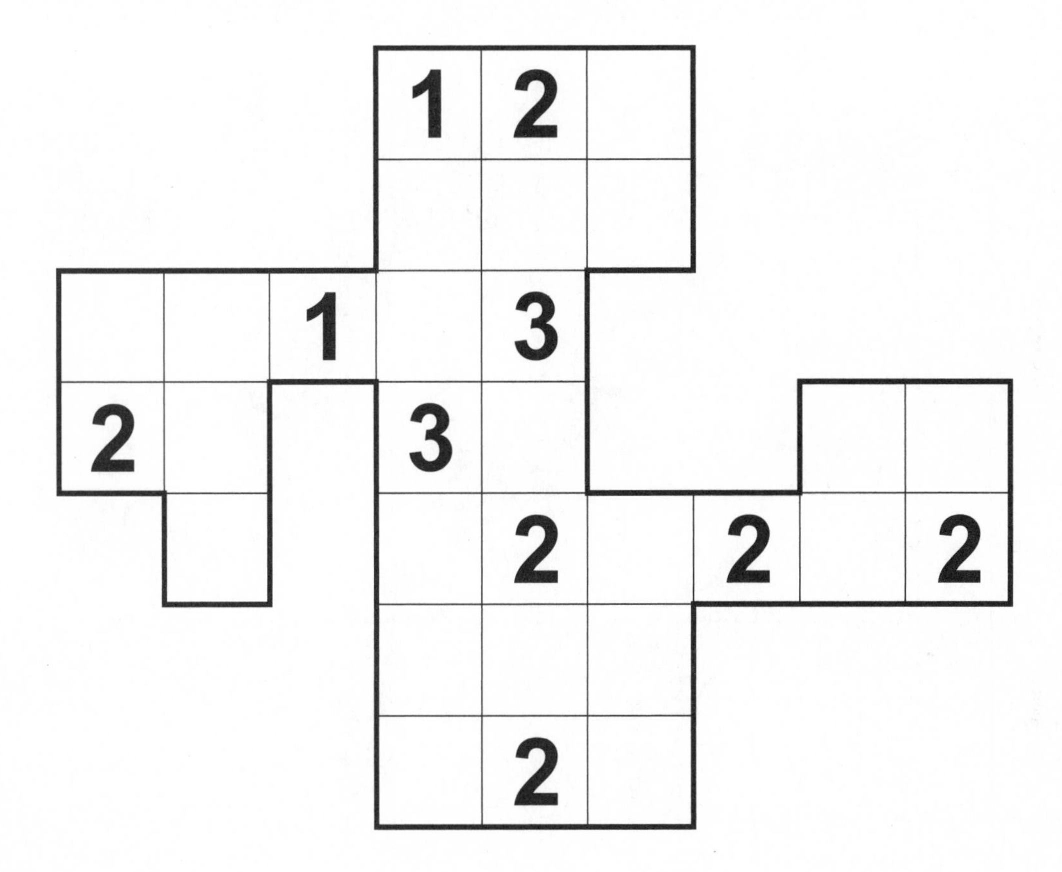

CHOICE WORDS

Form three six-letter words from the same category, by selecting one letter from each column three times. Each letter will be used exactly once.

R	A	N	T	A	E	_ _ _ _ _ _
M	E	R	G	O	R	_ _ _ _ _ _
C	O	A	R	E	N	_ _ _ _ _ _

★ Gossipy by Gail Grabowski

1	2	3	4	5	■	6	7	8	9	■	10	11	12	13
14					■	15				■	16			
17					18					■	19			
20						■	21			22	■	23		
■	■	■	24			25	■	26			27			■
28	29	30					■	■	31				■	■
32			■	■	33		34	35	■	36			37	38
39			40	■	41				42	■	43			
44				45	■	46				■	■	47		
■	■	48			49	■	■	50		51	52			
■	53					54	■	55				■	■	■
56			■	57			58	■	59			60	61	62
63			64	■	65			66						
67				■	68				■	69				
70				■	71				■	72				

ACROSS

1 Pickled vegetables, for short
6 Fishhook attachment
10 Deception
14 In flames
15 Furthermore
16 Kitchen-flooring piece
17 Serious speech
19 Wineglass feature
20 Igloo dweller
21 Sunflower edible
23 Tennis instructor
24 Hammer's target
26 Be short with
28 Purplish red
31 Move to and fro
32 __ Baba
33 Brings to a halt
36 Gentle push
39 Great review
41 Smells awful
43 Easter bloom
44 Scornful smile
46 Scissors sound
47 Regret
48 Speak unclearly
50 Blew, as a volcano
53 Helium and neon
55 Have an evening meal
56 Spider's creation
57 "So long!" in London
59 Connects with
63 Unpleasant responsibility
65 Spy's countersign, perhaps
67 Flow slowly
68 Aware of
69 Spine-tingling
70 Flabbergast
71 Like a snoop
72 Flows slowly

DOWN

1 Sidewalk eatery
2 Sci-fi sightings: Abbr.
3 Actor __ Douglas
4 Expensive fur
5 Sailor
6 Flying mammal
7 Word of regret
8 Small spots of land
9 __ of appreciation (symbolic gifts)
10 Urban roads: Abbr.
11 Strike it rich
12 Watchful
13 Office note
18 Hang around
22 Sunrise
25 Bowling alleys
27 McCartney of the Beatles
28 Planet beyond Earth
29 Alda of *M*A*S*H*
30 Calls to chat
34 Cozy room
35 Went down Aspen's slopes
37 Modeler's adhesive
38 Looked at
40 Snakelike swimmers
42 Pixie
45 Metal corrosion
49 Motive
51 Brings together
52 Something small
53 Columbus' Italian home
54 Shorthand taker
56 Carpentry raw material
58 Circus routines
60 Feeling achy
61 Lose one's footing
62 Poems of praise
64 Get a look at
66 Cowboy actor Rogers

★ ABC

Enter the letters A, B, and C into the diagram so that each row and column has exactly one A, one B, and one C. The letters outside the diagram indicate the first letter encountered, moving in the direction of the arrow. Keep in mind that after all the letters have been filled in, there will be one blank box in each row and column.

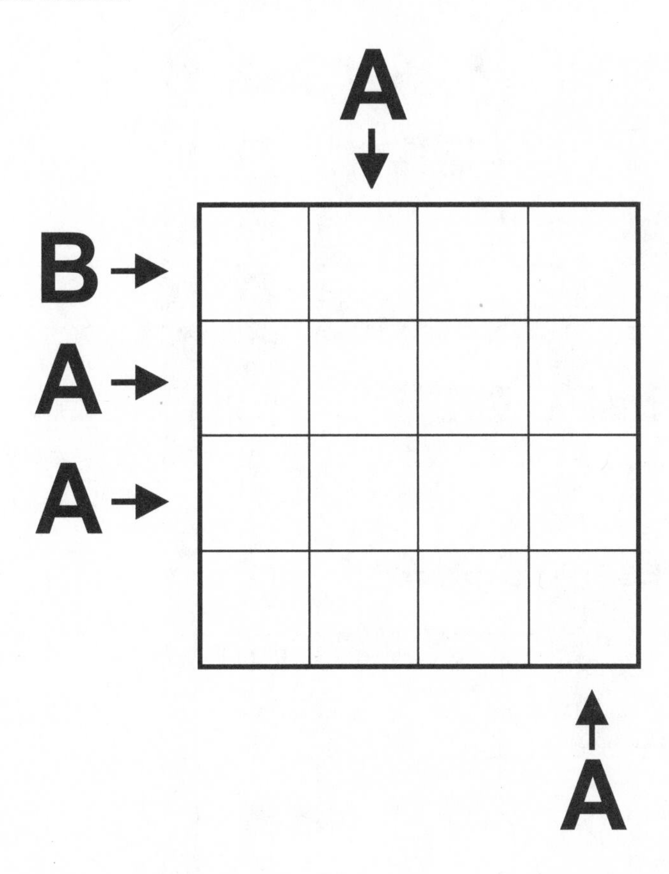

CLUELESS CROSSWORD

Complete the crossword with common uncapitalized seven-letter words, based entirely on the letters already filled in for you.

Z					H	S
	■		■		■	
		P		R		
	■		■	S	■	C
	X				Z	
U	■		■		■	
S		L				E

★★ Square Route

Enter the maze, pass through all the yellow squares exactly once, then exit, all without retracing your path.

BETWEENER

What three-letter word belongs between the word at left and the word at right, so that the first and second word, and the second and third word, each form a common compound word?

LOCK _ _ _ BREAKER

★★ Sudoku

Fill in the blank boxes so that every row, column, and 3x3 box contains all of the numbers 1 to 9.

		4	3	7	9	2		
			1		5			
3								6
1	5						3	8
4								2
7	8						5	1
2								4
			6		1			
		6	9	8	2	1		

MIXAGRAMS

Each line contains a five-letter word and a four-letter word that have been mixed together (the order of the letters in each word has not been changed). Unmix the two words on each line and write them in the spaces provided. When you're done, find a two-part answer to the clue by reading down the letter columns in the answers.

CLUE: Track event

J O S H A B L E S = _ _ _ _ _ + _ _ _ _

R U N T I G O I D = _ _ _ _ _ + _ _ _ _

M A G I C L E O W = _ _ _ _ _ + _ _ _ _

P U S H N E L L Y = _ _ _ _ _ + _ _ _ _

★ Dog Day by Sally R. Stein

1	2	3	4	■	5	6	7	8	■	9	10	11	12	13
14				■	15				■	16				
17				■	18				■	19				
20				21					22					
■	■	■	■	23			■	■	24			■	■	■
25	26	27	28			■	29	30			■	31	32	33
34					■	35				■	36			
37					38					39				
40				■	41				■	42				
43			■	44				■	45					
■	■	■	46			■	■	47			■	■	■	■
48	49	50				51	52				53	54	55	56
57					■	58				■	59			
60					■	61				■	62			
63					■	64				■	65			

ACROSS

1 Person in charge
5 Mountains of Switzerland
9 Marsh bird
14 Do newspaper work
15 Make angry
16 Sleeper's noise
17 Acting part
18 Brag about
19 Professional joke teller
20 Sound of hunger
23 Wild equine
24 Metallic rock
25 Release, as from confinement
29 Schoolbook
31 Make a tear in
34 Surrounded by
35 Sandwich shop
36 Fizzy drink
37 Native American boats
40 Otherwise
41 Up in __ (angry)
42 Three Musketeers creator
43 Summer zodiac sign
44 Quantities: Abbr.
45 Sock's diamond pattern
46 Poetic sphere
47 Opposite of post-
48 They came with a man's suit, once
57 Feud participant, for one
58 __-Seltzer
59 Plumbing problem
60 Violet or sound preceder
61 Person in attendance
62 Long skirt
63 Be too smug
64 Menial medieval worker
65 Desertlike

DOWN

1 Floating mass of ice
2 Limburger cheese feature
3 Farm's storage structure
4 Beef + potatoes dish
5 Illustrator, for example
6 Jungle roarers
7 Drain stopper
8 Hardens, as cement
9 Chaperone
10 Folklore creature
11 Italy's capital, to residents
12 Explorer __ the Red
13 Engineering school, for short
21 React to a 19 Across
22 Poisonous
25 Paper on a soup can
26 Author Zola
27 Sculpted figure
28 First word of a fairy tale
29 Details of a contract
30 Some lodge members
31 Spacious
32 Just perfect
33 No longer in fashion
35 Pub missile
36 Comfortable and cozy
38 Disney deer
39 Mag's space seller
44 Ark's landing spot
45 Dog's remarks
46 Gig for a soprano
47 Card game seen on TV
48 Hoodlum
49 Room separator
50 *Beetle Bailey* dog
51 Dustcloths
52 Plumlike fruit
53 __ mater
54 Close by
55 Vehicle with a meter
56 Lose traction

★★ Line Drawing

Draw the smallest number of lines possible, each from one edge of the square to another edge, so that at least one line passes through each of the 12 dots.

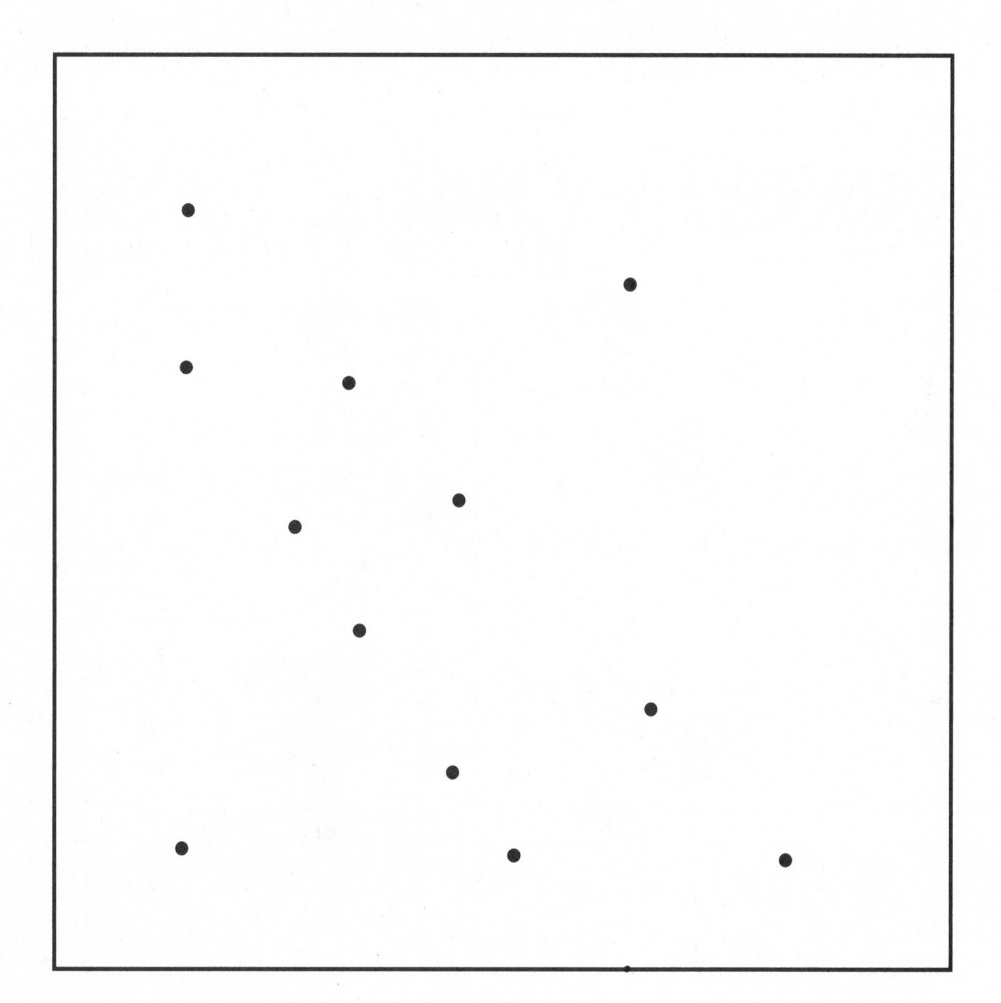

THREE OF A KIND

Find the three hidden words in the sentence that go together in some way.

Last August, a nightingale flew in my window.

★★ Find the Ships

Determine the position of the 10 ships listed to the right of the diagram. The ships may be oriented either horizontally or vertically. A square with wavy lines indicates water and will not contain a ship. The numbers at the edge of the diagram indicate how many squares in that row or column contain parts of ships. When all 10 ships are correctly placed in the diagram, no two of them will touch each other, not even diagonally.

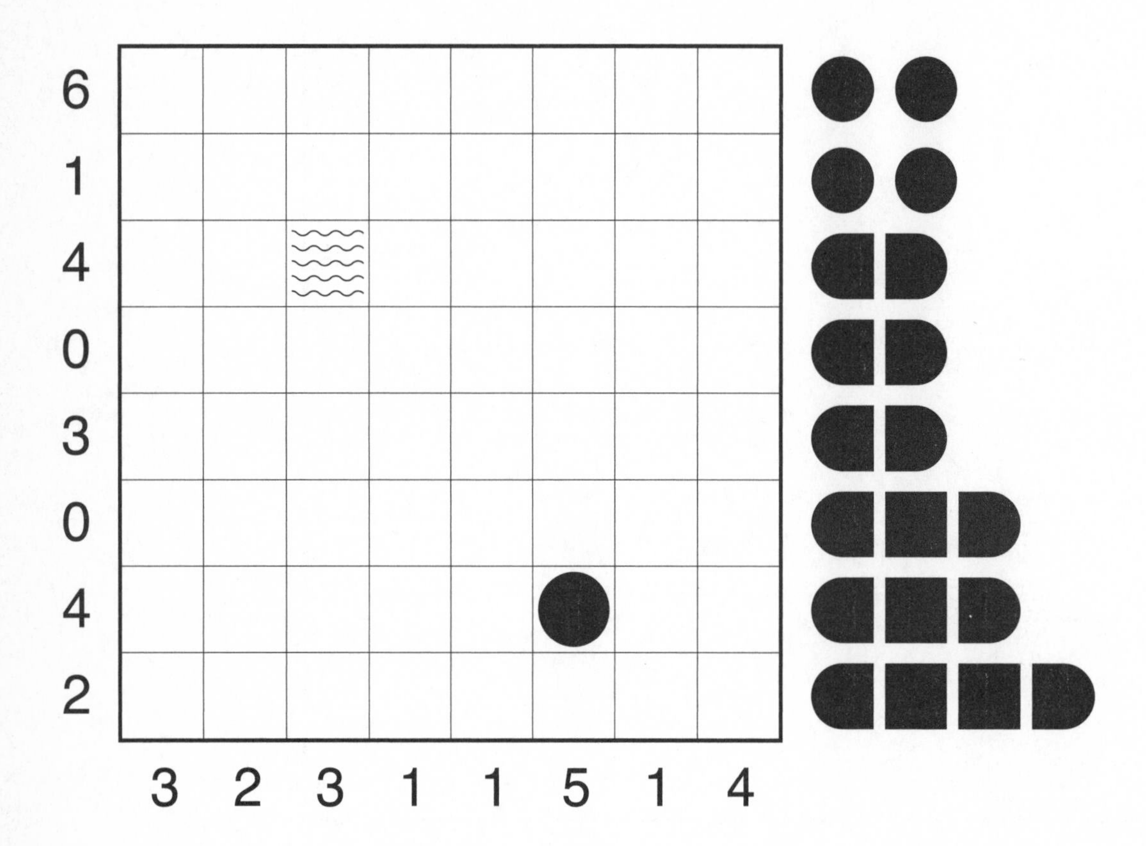

TWO-BY-FOUR

The eight letters in the word HICCUPED can be rearranged to form a pair of common four-letter words in two different ways. Can you find both pairs of words?

_ _ _ _ _ _ _ _

_ _ _ _ _ _ _ _

★★ Fences

Connect the dots with vertical or horizontal lines, so that a single loop is formed with no crossings or branches. Each number indicates how many lines surround it; squares with no number may be surrounded by any number of lines.

				1		3	
2	1	1		2	3		
1						0	3
		1	3				
				0	2		
2	3						3
		1	3		3	0	3
	3		3				

ADDITION SWITCH

Switch the positions of two of the digits in the incorrect sum at right, to get a correct sum.

$$\begin{array}{r} 256 \\ +\,373 \\ \hline 932 \end{array}$$

★ Swim Meet by Gail Grabowski

1	2	3	4	■	5	6	7	8	9	■	10	11	12	13
14				■	15					■	16			
17				■	18					■	19			
20				21					■	22				
■	■	■	23				■	24					■	■
25	26	27				■	■	28					29	30
31					■	32	33				■	34		
35			■	■	36					■	■	37		
38			■	39					■	40	41			
42			43				■	■	44					
■	■	45				■	46	47				■	■	■
48	49				■	50						51	52	53
54				■	55					■	56			
57				■	58					■	59			
60				■	61					■	62			

ACROSS

1 Sharp taste
5 Witch-trial locale
10 Urban pollution
14 Moisturizer ingredient
15 Auto-tire pattern
16 War honoree
17 Grocery shopper's aid
18 Gather up
19 Sign of things to come
20 Typist's action
22 Not tight
23 Fret
24 Moose relative
25 Airline's prime concern
28 Granted permission
31 Make a speech
32 Necklace components
34 Place to apply gloss
35 Lower, as headlights
36 Turnpike charges
37 Commotion
38 "Just __ thought!"
39 Breakfast bread
40 Solitary one
42 Compromise one's integrity
44 Leave stranded
45 Calendar span
46 Diamond unit
48 Paid to play poker
50 Mankind
54 Wild animal's home
55 Absorb, as gravy
56 Misfortunes
57 Silent performer
58 Self-assurance
59 Applaud
60 Snow vehicle
61 Did some arithmetic
62 Song of praise

DOWN

1 Have a chat
2 "That's __!" ("Not true!")
3 Apt to snoop
4 Takes a walk in the rain
5 Like a bright night
6 Knight's suit
7 Faulty, as a faucet
8 Make simpler
9 Prescription writers: Abbr.
10 Chased away
11 Nostalgic "location"
12 Mine deposits
13 No longer around
21 Large bag
22 Hawaiian garlands
24 June honorees
25 Bottled soft drinks
26 Get out of bed
27 When parents and kids are together
28 Pretzel topper
29 Comforter filling
30 Volleyball or soccer
32 Canoe, for one
33 Overhead trains
36 Guided vacation
39 Frog relative
40 Low in fat
41 Large flightless bird
43 Looked impolitely
44 Hung in folds, as banners
46 Valentine's Day archer
47 Entertain
48 Charitable donation
49 Carpenter's fastener
50 Parka part
51 Comrade
52 Chowder ingredient
53 TV sports channel
55 Fitness center

★★ Mental Exercise

From the comments below, match each person with his or her exercise equipment.

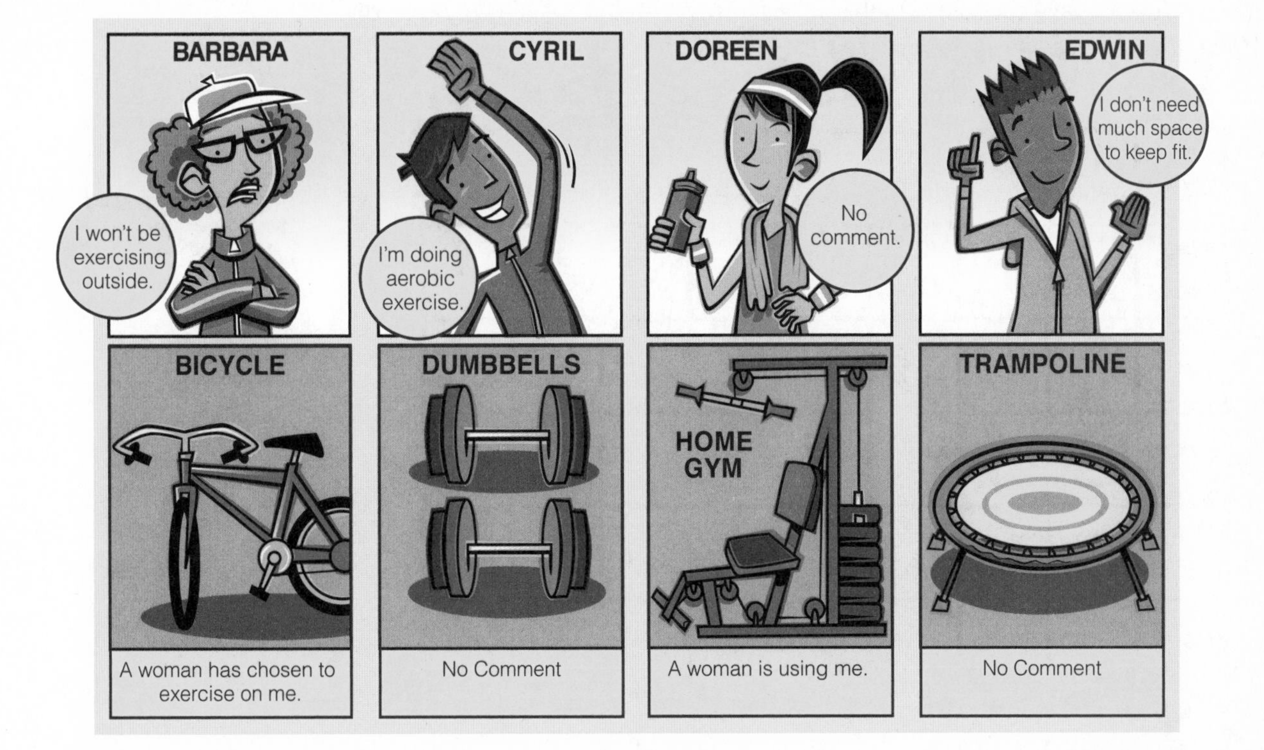

SMALL CHANGE

Change one letter in each of these two words, to form a common two-word phrase.

SOFA SOOT

____

★★ 123

Fill in the diagram so that each rectangular piece has one each of the numbers 1, 2, and 3, under these rules: 1) No two adjacent squares, horizontally or vertically, can have the same number. 2) Each completed row and column of the diagram will have an equal number of 1s, 2s, and 3s.

					3			
2							1	
			3					
	3			2				
								1
2						2		
	2							
			2				1	

WRONG IS RIGHT

Which of these four words is misspelled?

A) venison B) jettison

C) bison D) liason

★ Number-Out

Shade squares so that no number appears in any row or column more than once. Shaded squares may not touch each other horizontally or vertically, and all unshaded squares must form a single continuous area.

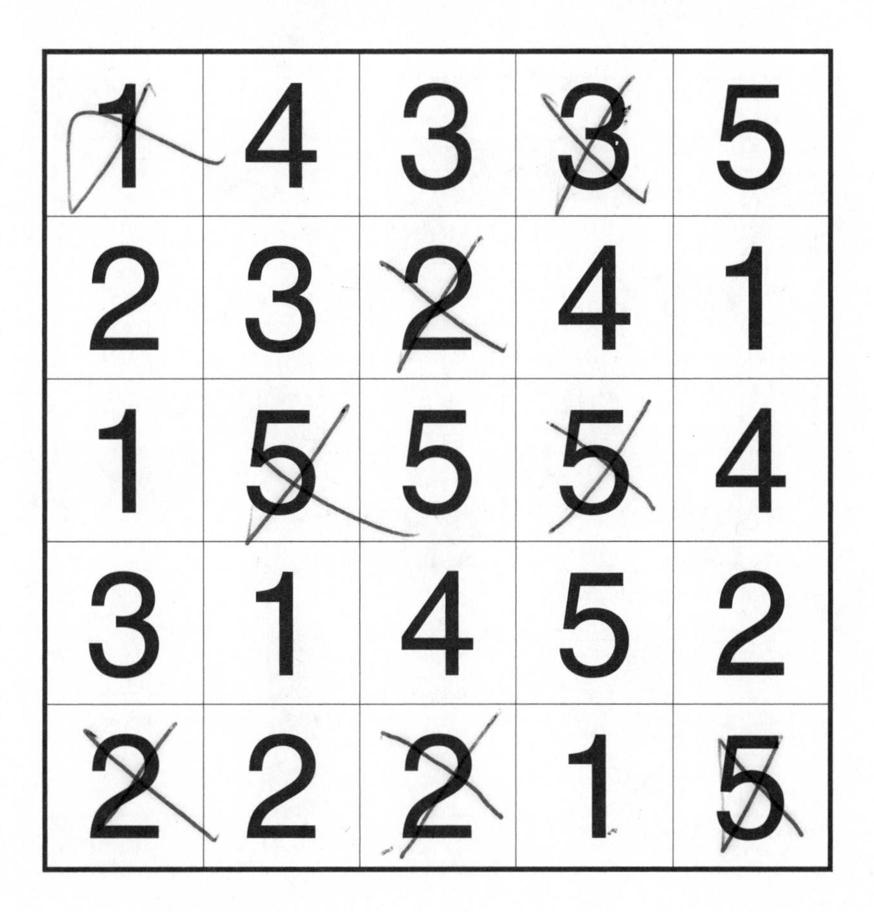

1	4	3	3	5
2	3	2	4	1
1	5	5	5	4
3	1	4	5	2
2	2	2	1	5

THINK ALIKE

Unscramble the letters in the phrase SUMO KELP to form two words with the same or similar meanings.

________________ ________________

★ Newsworthy by Shirley Soloway

1	2	3	4	■	5	6	7	8	9	■	10	11	12	13
14				■	15					■	16			
17				■	18					■	19			
20				21						22			■	■
23					■	■	■	24			■	25	26	27
■	■	■	28		29	30	31	■	32		33			
34	35	36	■	■	37			38	■	39				
40			41	42					43					
44					■	45				■	■	46		
47					48	■	49			50	51	■	■	■
52			■	53		54	■	■	■	55		56	57	58
■	■	59	60				61	62	63					
64	65			■	66					■	67			
68				■	69					■	70			
71				■	72					■	73			

ACROSS

1 At the __ time (simultaneously)
5 Generous one
10 Additionally
14 Overhead transportation
15 __ acids (protein building blocks)
16 "Now see here!"
17 Very mean one
18 Gales, for example
19 Clumsy one's remark
20 Newspaper features
23 Enter, as data
24 Twosome
25 Poetic "before"
28 Is ahead
32 Early round, briefly
34 Gateway Arch city: Abbr.
37 Bank offering
39 Courtroom worker
40 Newspaper feature
44 Very strange
45 Bistro handout
46 Lawyer's charge
47 Well-behaved kids
49 After-bath wraps
52 Sandwich bread
53 __ Angeles
55 Din
59 Newspaper features
64 Man-made place to swim
66 Uplift
67 Vessels for frying
68 Martial art
69 __ days (long ago)
70 Otherwise
71 Hang around
72 Dandelions, for example
73 Hairdresser's bottles

DOWN

1 Have in inventory
2 Bicker
3 Tie the knot
4 Onetime Food Network chef
5 Daybreak
6 Leave out
7 Highest digit
8 How new videos are released
9 Revolted
10 Frequently
11 Binder with rings
12 Soak (up)
13 Approvals
21 180 degrees from WSW
22 Like the Vikings
26 Dishwasher cycle
27 Overact
29 Pub beverage
30 Student's quarters
31 Less chancy
33 List-shortening abbr.
34 Give testimony
35 Wee
36 Fast-food order
38 Something forbidden
41 Secure, as shoelaces
42 Conversation starter
43 Massage
48 Feeling of regret
50 Concluding part
51 Lathered
54 No longer fresh
56 Florence's country
57 Taste or smell
58 Double-curve letters
60 Ruse
61 On the __ (separately)
62 Pre-owned
63 Homes for hogs
64 Nightclothes, for short
65 Unconscious

★★ Tasmanian Devil Maze

Enter the maze where indicated at bottom left, pass through all the stars exactly once, then exit at bottom right. You may not retrace your path.

SAY IT AGAIN

What three-letter noun can be either a mode of transportation or a dark color?

— — —

★★ Split Decisions

In this clueless crossword puzzle, each answer consists of two words whose spellings are the same, except for the consecutive letters given. All answers are common words; no phrases or hyphenated or capitalized words are used. Some of the clues may have more than one solution, but there is only one word pair that will correctly link up with all the other word pairs.

TRANSDELETION

Delete one letter from the word GROANER and rearrange the rest, to get something edible.

____

★ Hyper-Sudoku

Fill in the blank boxes so that every row, column, 3x3 box, *and* each of the four 3x3 gray regions contains all of the numbers 1 to 9.

	3		8				9	5
			1		9	2		
			7					
	5	3		9	1			8
4	7		2		3	5		
	8	6					2	
8					7			
9		7	3	6			5	
	6			1	2	8	7	

MIXAGRAMS

Each line contains a five-letter word and a four-letter word that have been mixed together (the order of the letters in each word has not been changed). Unmix the two words on each line and write them in the spaces provided. When you're done, find a two-part answer to the clue by reading down the letter columns in the answers.

CLUE: Track tie

W R A T H E E D Y = _ _ _ _ _ + _ _ _ _

P O R S E S L E Y = _ _ _ _ _ + _ _ _ _

V I T A L S T E A = _ _ _ _ _ + _ _ _ _

V A S T L O P I D = _ _ _ _ _ + _ _ _ _

★ Evaluations by Gail Grabowski

ACROSS

1 Chew, squirrel-style
5 More than enough
10 At a distance
14 Apiece
15 From the backwoods
16 Heap
17 Italian wine region
18 Computer-mouse sound
19 Nudge
20 Baseball-game ticket stub
22 Outdoes
23 Teen music, to some adults
24 Babysitter's challenge
25 Clothing
28 Salon stylist's goo
31 Discharged, as a cannon
32 Piece of dinnerware
34 *Norma* __
35 Surprise attack
36 Couples
37 Computer input
38 "Are you a man __ mouse?"
39 Oregon's capital
40 A triangle has three of them
41 Soup cracker
43 Quite calm
44 Fast planes
45 Religious doctrine
47 Dried plum
49 Like some mortgages
53 Boys
54 Chop into tiny pieces
55 Vocal
56 Strongly recommend
57 Rile up
58 Swiss peaks
59 Crystal-ball user
60 Banana coverings
61 Amount of medicine

DOWN

1 Toothed machine part
2 Cape Canaveral org.
3 First part of a play
4 Neighed
5 Bunker of *All in the Family*
6 Stubborn beasts
7 Cost
8 Don't have
9 Fraternal-order member
10 Come into sight
11 Class following kindergarten
12 Tremendously
13 Wine-list choices
21 Strong rope
22 French cheese
24 Flying mammals
25 Frizzy hairdos
26 Jeweled crown
27 Courtroom official
28 Do damage to
29 All gone, as food
30 Rental agreement
32 Lacking color
33 Be untruthful
36 Baking containers
37 Unpaved street
39 Location
40 Gardener's purchase
42 More uptight
43 Scornful smiles
45 Trace of color
46 Do well (at)
47 Furthermore
48 Steak preference
49 "Okay!"
50 Folk singer Guthrie
51 Bugler's evening call
52 "Anything __?"
54 Traveler's guide

★ Picture Perfect

Try to find these shutterbug terms that are hidden in the diagram either across, down, or diagonally, and you'll find that one of them has become camera-shy and isn't there. What's the missing answer? (Individual words of all multiple-word answers are hidden separately; ignore the lowercase words.)

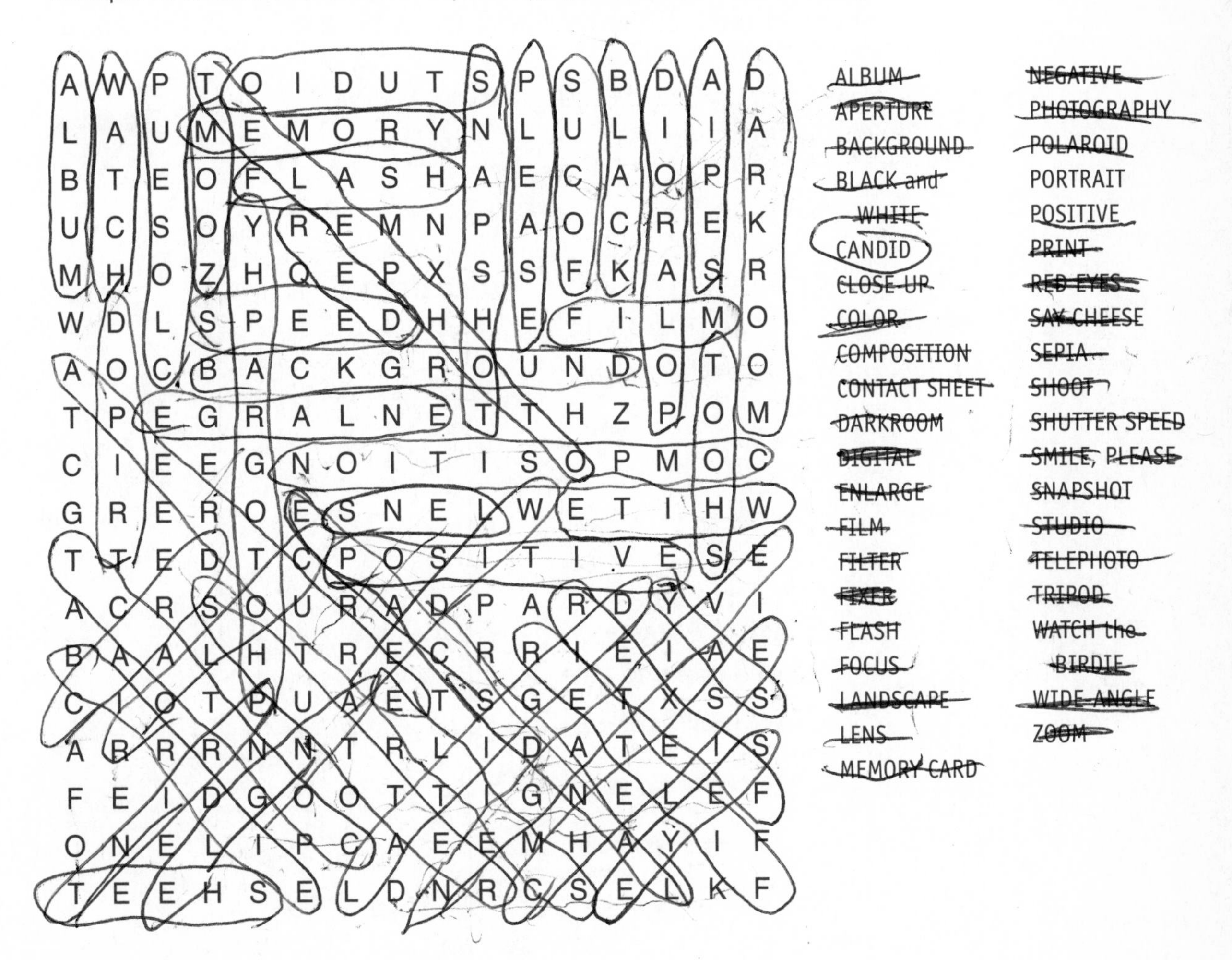

IN OTHER WORDS

There is only one common uncapitalized word that contains the consecutive letters RLF. What is it?

____

BRAIN BREATHER

IT'S GREAT TO BE ALIVE

Human life is so awesome, some people choose to deal with it by making jokes about it. Here are a few good ones.

All modern men are descended from a worm-like creature, but it shows more on some people.

—WILL CUPPY

Brain: An apparatus with which we think we think.

—AMBROSE BIERCE

One thing about baldness: It's neat.

—DON HEROLD

I get mail; therefore I am.

—SCOTT ADAMS

Why isn't there a special name for the tops of your feet?

—LILY TOMLIN

The goal of all inanimate objects is to resist man and ultimately defeat him.

—RUSSELL BAKER

I recently had my annual physical examination, which I get once every seven years, and when the nurse weighed me, I was shocked to discover how much stronger the Earth's gravitational pull has become since 1990.

—DAVE BARRY

Man is the only animal that can remain on friendly terms with the victims he intends to eat until he eats them.

—SAMUEL BUTLER

★★ One-Way Streets

The diagram represents a pattern of streets. P's are parking spaces, and the black squares are stores. Find the route that starts at a parking space, passes through all stores exactly once, and ends at the other parking space. Arrows indicate one-way traffic for that block only. No block or intersection may be entered more than once.

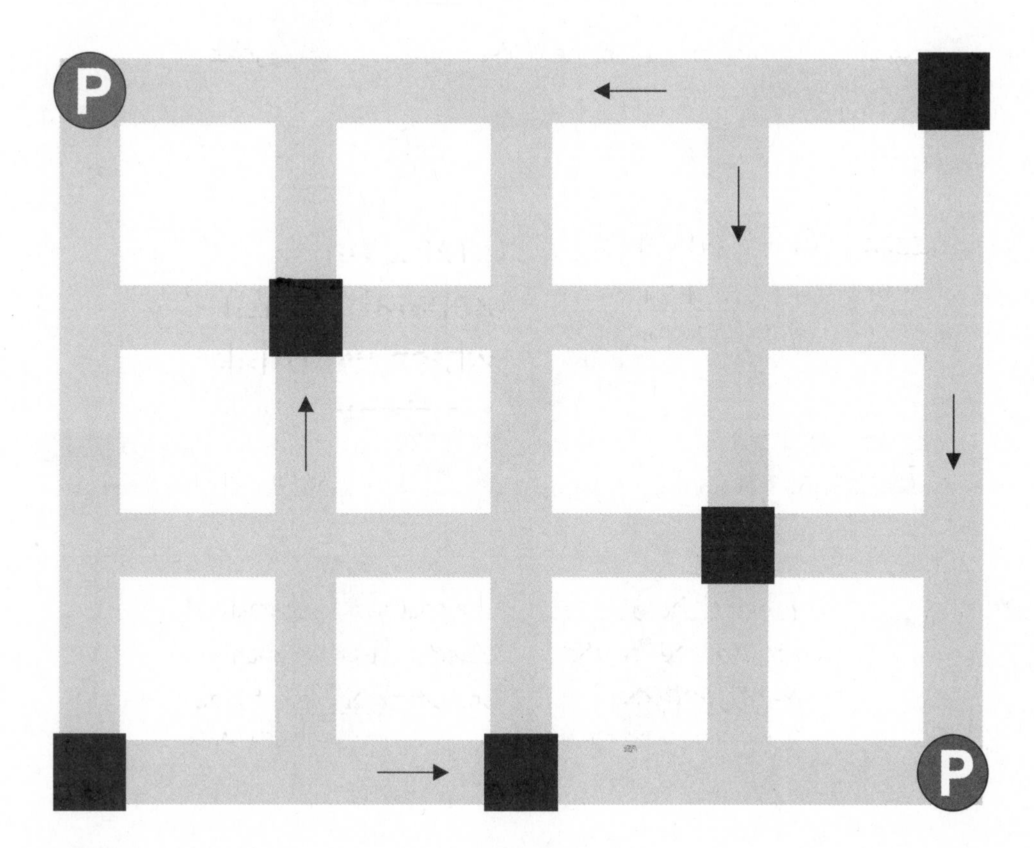

SOUND THINKING

There is only one common uncapitalized word whose consonant sounds are R, D, and W, in that order. What is it?

____

★ Elementary by Sally R. Stein

ACROSS

1 TV host Philbin
6 __ Raton, FL
10 Well-behaved
14 Make adjustments
15 Not closed
16 Internet auction site
17 Eskimo dwelling
18 Narrow part of a bottle
19 Carryall bag
20 Misnamed writing implement
22 Mrs. Dick Tracy
23 Take a load off your feet
24 Jeans maker Strauss
26 Air-conditioner meas.
29 The one over there
32 Metallic visitor to Oz
36 "Yikes!"
38 Raison d'__
40 Dexterous
41 Second-place Olympic athletes
44 Look of contempt
45 Appear to be
46 Orderly
47 Off the path
49 Scissors sound
51 Train lines: Abbr.
52 Right away, in memos
54 Oxygen or hydrogen
56 Stylish
59 Exact duplicate
65 Iron corrosion
66 Informal greeting
67 Calf, to a cowboy
68 Stare at
69 Breakfast-in-bed need
70 Major blood vessel
71 Lawn invader
72 Employee IDs, at times
73 Javelin

DOWN

1 Banister
2 Outer border
3 Elaborate party
4 Digital music players
5 "Cut that out!"
6 German city
7 Oil cartel
8 Director __ B. DeMille
9 Short sock
10 Arriving, informally
11 Woodwind instrument
12 Meal for a horse
13 Colors for Easter eggs
21 Old-time anesthetic
25 Perfume bottle
26 __ nova (Brazilian dance)
27 Gets slimmer
28 Not yet rented
30 S&L devices
31 Sources of shade
33 Greedy one
34 Church platform
35 Homes for hawks
37 Performed like a ham
39 Biblical paradise
42 Chapters of history
43 Friend, to Fernando
48 Billionaires' boats
50 Bearlike beasts
53 Twosomes
55 Ice-cream serving utensil
56 Cornfield bird
57 Enormous
58 Aruba or Maui
60 Seacrest of *American Idol*
61 Large coves
62 Very mean boss
63 Bread with a pocket
64 Desk-calendar capacity

★★ Tanks a Lot

Enter the maze, pass over all tanks from behind (thereby destroying them), then exit. You may not pass through any square more than once, and may not enter a square in the line of fire of a tank you have not yet destroyed.

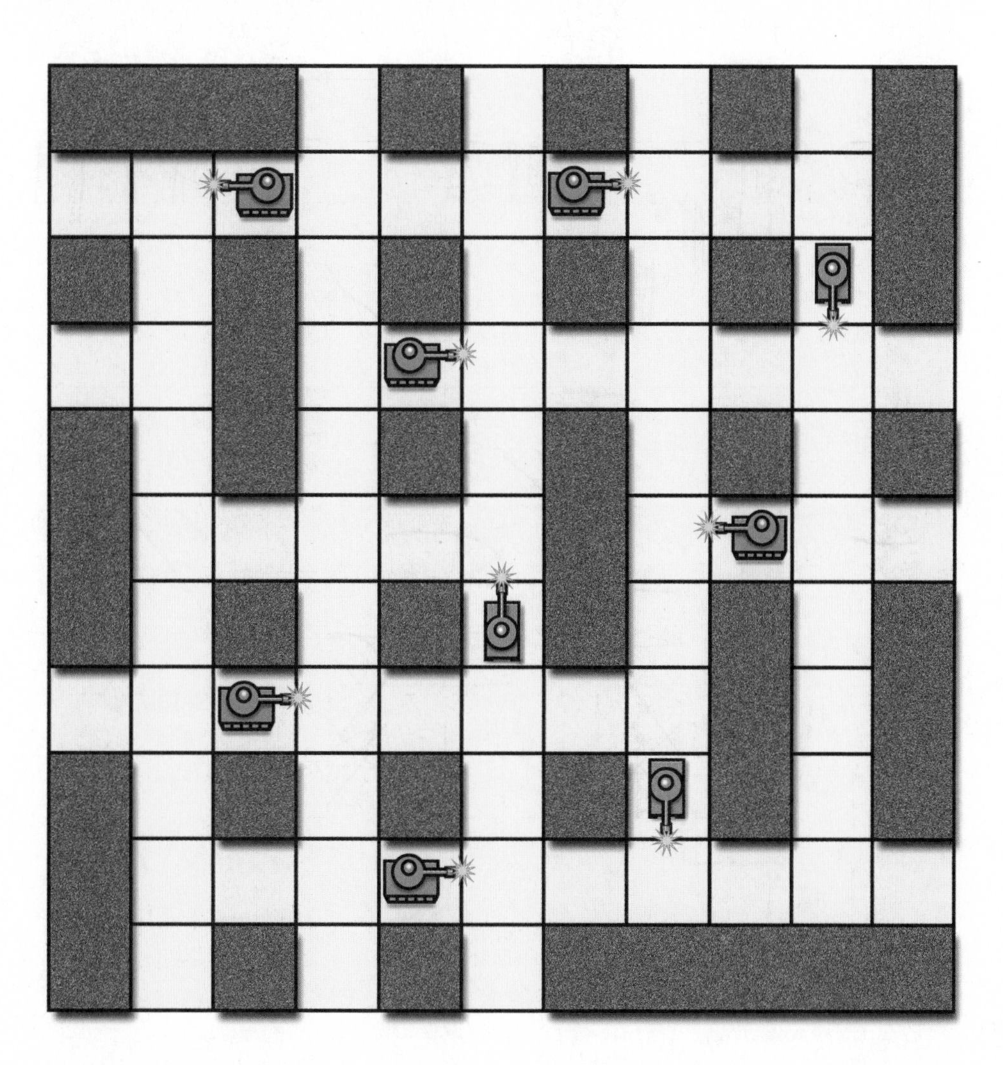

SMALL CHANGE

Change one letter in each of these two words, to form a common two-word phrase.

PET BOAST

____

★★ Star Search

Find the stars that are hidden in some of the blank squares. The numbered squares indicate how many stars are hidden in the squares adjacent to them (including diagonally). There is never more than one star in any square.

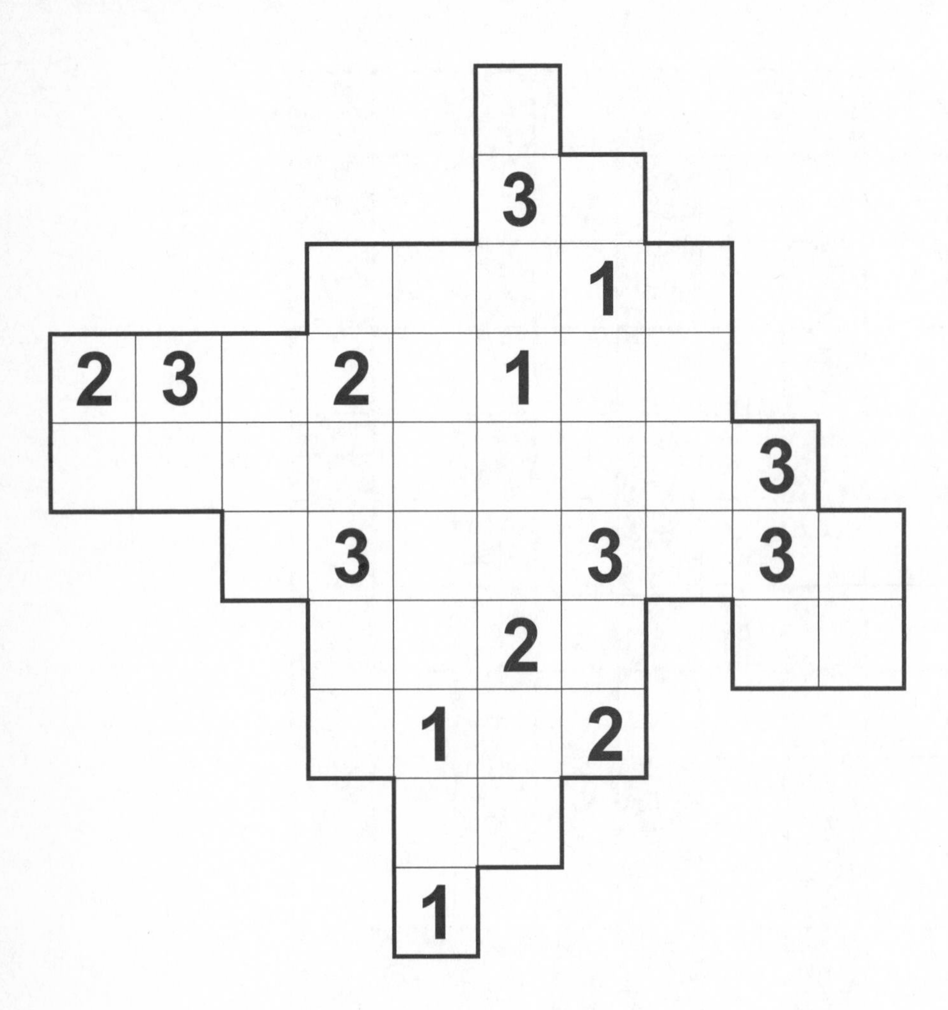

CHOICE WORDS

Form three six-letter words from the same category, by selecting one letter from each column three times. Each letter will be used exactly once.

B	R	I	B	U	L	_ _ _ _ _ _
D	U	M	K	E	G	_ _ _ _ _ _
H	U	N	V	U	M	_ _ _ _ _ _

★★ Triad Split Decisions

In this clueless crossword puzzle, each answer consists of two words whose spellings are the same, except for the consecutive letters given. All answers are common words; no phrases or hyphenated or capitalized words are used. Some of the clues may have more than one solution, but there is only one word pair that will correctly link up with all the other word pairs.

TRANSDELETION

Delete one letter from the word SKETCHY and rearrange the rest, to get a type of tool.

____

★★ Engineering Majors by Fred Piscop

ACROSS

1 Painter's topper
6 Goblet feature
10 Cutting remark
14 Be wild about
15 Runner's goal
16 Bassoon cousin
17 Gum chewing, for some
18 Graph line
19 Weevil's lunch
20 Ride in a country bar
23 Close down
24 Choir members
25 Turn aside
29 Sculptor's medium
32 Blissful spot
33 Shocking
34 A/C stat
37 Lightning producer
41 __ capita
42 Take another stab at
43 Classic toon Betty
44 Gift getter
45 Italicizes, e.g.
47 Traffic tie-up
50 Acapulco aunt
51 Freedom of speech, etc.
58 Yoked team
59 Actor Epps
60 Sign up for
62 Fried-rice option
63 Bear's digs
64 Chain unit
65 Tolkien tree creatures
66 Wheel shaft
67 Relating to pitch

DOWN

1 Scroogian cry
2 Red-coated cheese
3 Judicial attire
4 10th-century explorer
5 Pet restraint
6 Witness' place
7 Hailer's shout
8 Cast-of-thousands film
9 Butte relative
10 Fielder's flub
11 Roughly
12 Nancy's rich friend
13 Shipboard time indicators
21 Wee colonist
22 Comes to earth
25 Like a basso's voice
26 Twiddling one's thumbs
27 Zig or zag
28 Ltr. add-in
29 A Bolivian capital
30 Carhop's load
31 Dressing ingredient
33 Lo-cal
34 Timely benefit
35 Race pace
36 Ballpark arbiters
38 Fish, in a way
39 Stimpy's pal
40 TV-sked placeholder
44 Bar servings
45 Title for Churchill
46 Up-to-the-minute
47 Examine, with "out"
48 Ford predecessor
49 Turn aside
50 __ Haute, IN
52 Singer Falana
53 Giant-screen film format
54 Pretrial payment
55 Fascinated by
56 School on the Thames
57 Blood fluids
61 Fam. tree member

ABC

Enter the letters A, B, and C into the diagram so that each row and column has exactly one A, one B, and one C. The letters outside the diagram indicate the first letter encountered, moving in the direction of the arrow. Keep in mind that after all the letters have been filled in, there will be two blank boxes in each row and column.

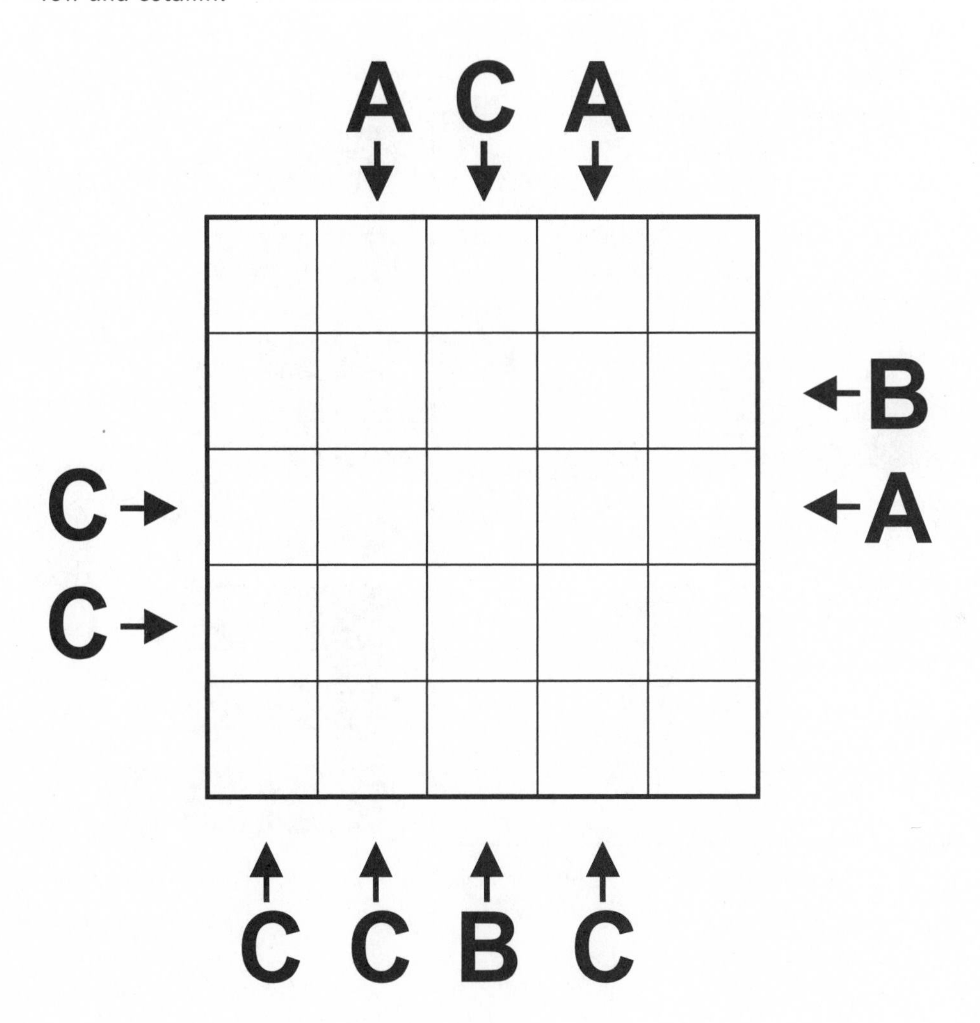

NATIONAL TREASURE

Of the common four-letter words that can be formed from the letters in KOREAN, only one is something edible. What is it?

— — — —

★★ Find the Ships

Determine the position of the 10 ships listed to the right of the diagram. The ships may be oriented either horizontally or vertically. A square with wavy lines indicates water and will not contain a ship. The numbers at the edge of the diagram indicate how many squares in that row or column contain parts of ships. When all 10 ships are correctly placed in the diagram, no two of them will touch each other, not even diagonally.

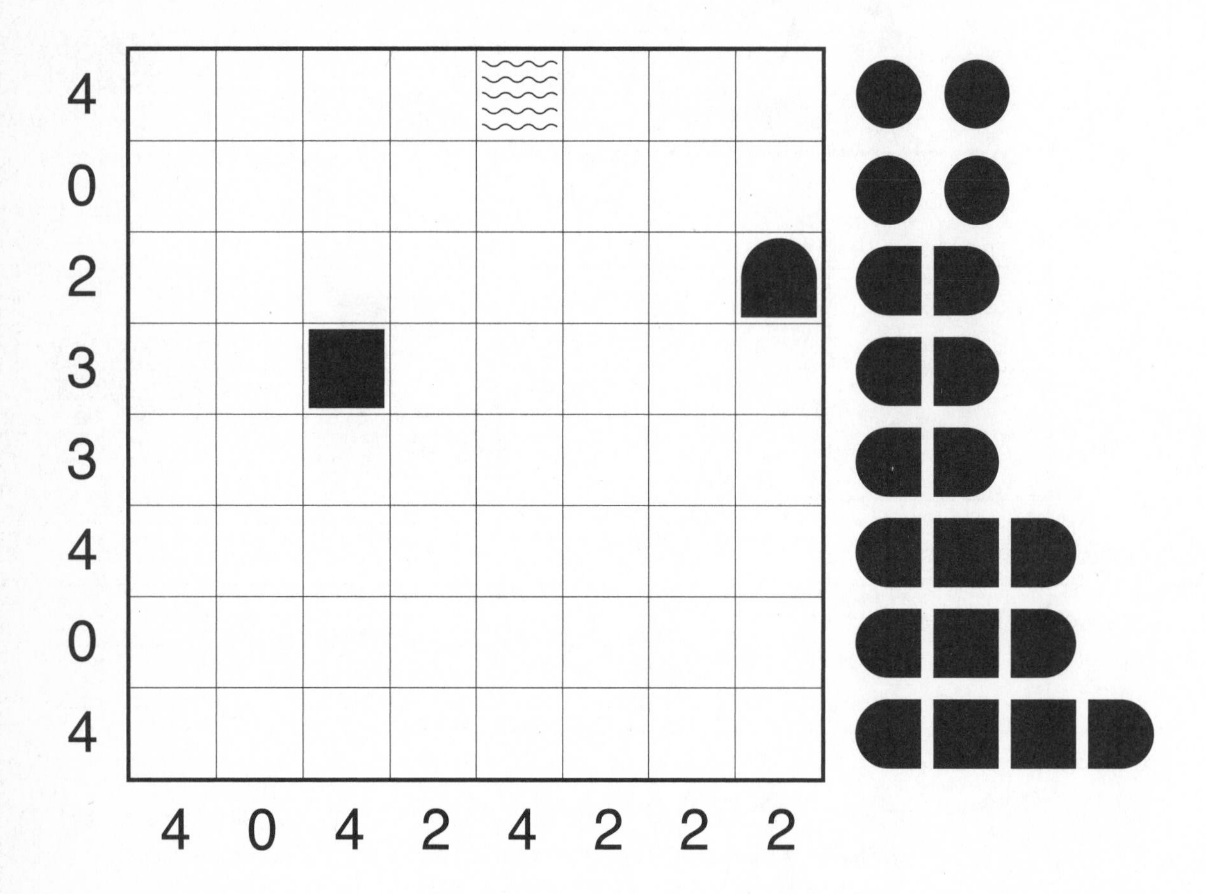

TWO-BY-FOUR

The eight letters in the word LAYABOUT can be rearranged to form a pair of common four-letter words in only one way. Can you find the two words?

_ _ _ _ _ _ _ _

★★ Drink Up by Shirley Soloway

ACROSS

1 Core group
6 From square one
10 Workout venues
14 Hunter constellation
15 Liquid rock
16 Composer Weill
17 Bouquet
18 Running pace
19 *Picnic* playwright
20 Sort of saltine
23 Dairy dweller
24 One score
25 Novelist Segal
27 Sushi fish
30 Did nothing
33 Rambler
37 Shakespearean villain
39 Slave girl of opera
40 Graph line
41 Not to be done
42 Peevish mood
43 Assail
44 Perry's creator
45 Greek letter
46 Asian/European capital
48 *Harper's Bazaar* artist
50 *Ninotchka* name
52 Detonate
57 One in office, for short
59 Living-room furniture
62 Monomaniacal whaler
64 Shrewd
65 Trojan War epic
66 Maggie's older sister
67 Sight from Sandusky
68 DC's subway
69 Maximally
70 Rents out
71 German industrial city

DOWN

1 Move via gravity
2 Quiver item
3 Part of LED
4 Brutus, e.g.
5 Passed, as legislation
6 Utah resort
7 Kind of cop
8 Call forth
9 Undoing, figuratively
10 Something to do at 6 Down
11 Gag ender
12 Mythical ship
13 Hodgepodge
21 Scotch alternative
22 Where Ipanema is
26 Don't go well
28 Untrustworthy one
29 Weasel-like animal
31 Tinker with prose
32 Statistics
33 California county
34 Wagon pullers
35 Vase material
36 __ *Is Born*
38 Movie or party ender
41 British kitchen accessory
45 When a round starts
47 Video-remote button
49 "Prufrock" monogram
51 Blazing
53 Tall stories
54 Some newspaper bios
55 Bell-bottom feature
56 Ate
57 Where to get dates
58 Oberlin's home
60 Skim along
61 Blinkers
63 Cave dweller

★★ Two Pairs

Among the 16 pictures below, find the two pairs of pictures that are identical to each other.

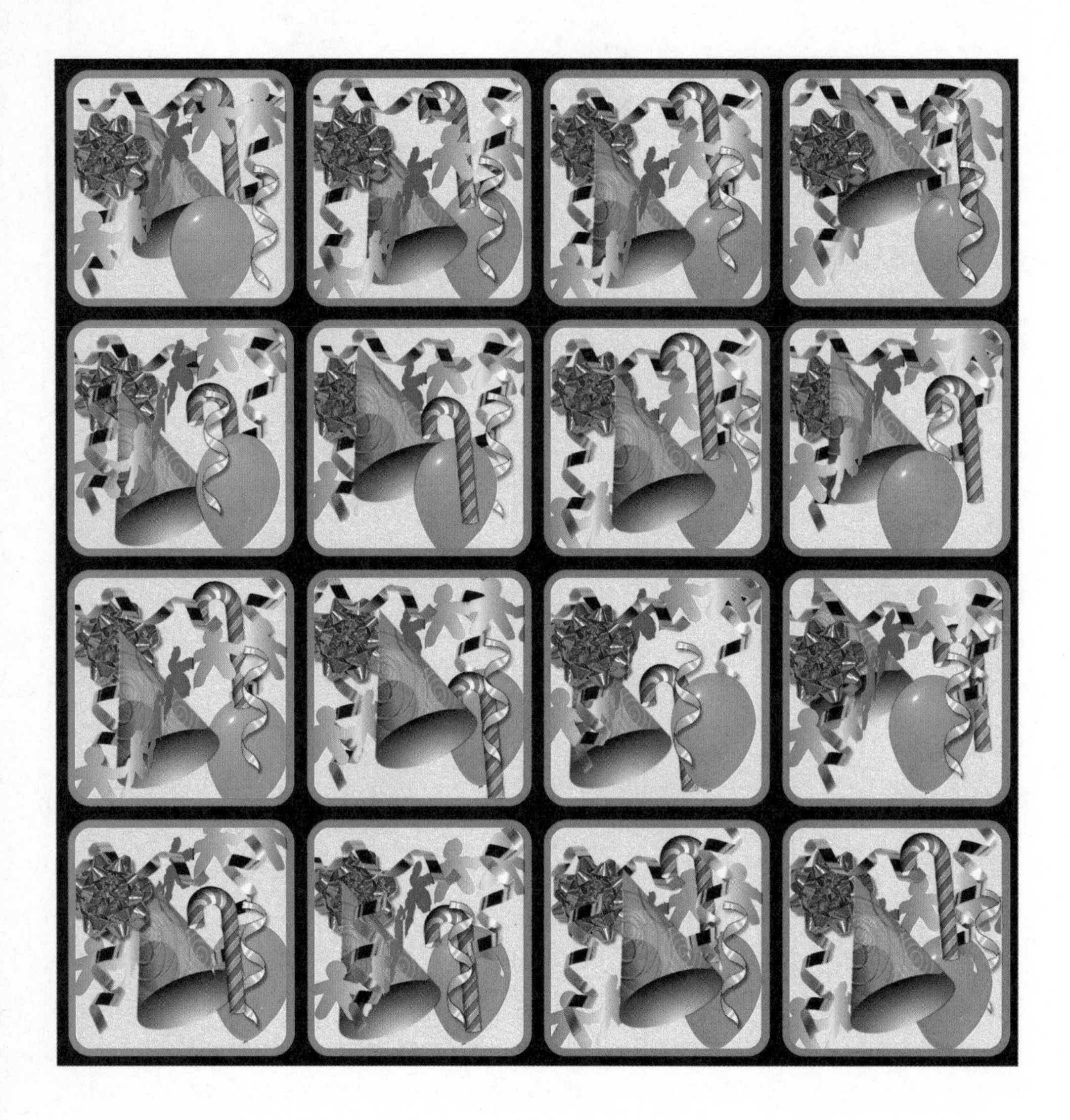

BETWEENER

What four-letter word belongs between the word at left and the word at right, so that the first and second word, and the second and third word, each form a common compound word?

DATA __ __ __ __ BALL

★★ Sudoku

Fill in the blank boxes so that every row, column, and 3x3 box contains all of the numbers 1 to 9.

	7						8	
2				8				5
3			6		1			4
		1		6		5		
	8		2		9		7	
		9		5		2		
9			4		5			2
4				1				7
	3						5	

MIXAGRAMS

Each line contains a five-letter word and a four-letter word that have been mixed together (the order of the letters in each word has not been changed). Unmix the two words on each line and write them in the spaces provided. When you're done, find a two-part answer to the clue by reading down the letter columns in the answers.

CLUE: Knives and forks

M A W O T E D I F = _ _ _ _ _ + _ _ _ _

T A P E T C A L K = _ _ _ _ _ + _ _ _ _

C U R L T I R A B = _ _ _ _ _ + _ _ _ _

G A M E M U S T A = _ _ _ _ _ + _ _ _ _

★★ Fences

Connect the dots with vertical or horizontal lines, so that a single loop is formed with no crossings or branches. Each number indicates how many lines surround it; squares with no number may be surrounded by any number of lines.

0		3		2	3	1	2
							2
		2					
3		3		3			1
1			0		0		2
					3		
2							
2	1	3	1		3		2

WRONG IS RIGHT

Which of these four words is misspelled?

A) abhorrent B) belligerent

C) fragrent D) incoherent

★★ Video Store by Fred Piscop

ACROSS

1 IOUs
6 Boston hoopster, for short
10 Breakfast side dish
14 Biblical brother
15 Mayberry tyke
16 West Coast sch.
17 One prone to emotional display
19 Hang around
20 Cushy gig
21 Homegrown
23 Hobbyist's buy
24 Tart fruits
25 Bounced back
29 Becloud
32 A way to read
33 Earring sites
34 Took the reins
37 Basis of a suit
38 Gadded about
39 Actress Sorvino
40 Damascus' land: Abbr.
41 Make merry
42 Lord's domain
43 Dickens-based musical
45 Most wise
46 Junkyard stuff
48 Anthem contraction
49 Takes a bite of
51 Gilbert and Sullivan work
56 Tennis great Arthur
57 The Three Stooges, for one
59 MGM beast
60 Mideast's Gulf of __
61 Film director from France
62 Bad-weather systems
63 Department-store department
64 Actress Burstyn

DOWN

1 No-goodniks
2 Mata __
3 Shahs' land
4 Hefty volume
5 Had a nosh
6 56 Across' workplace
7 Blunted blade
8 Tell a whopper
9 Knoxville's loc.
10 Disco dance
11 Consumer-help phone number
12 Toil away
13 President after Grant
18 __ pro quo
22 Shows curiosity
25 Chows down
26 Be too sweet
27 Distressing experience
28 Away from home
29 Delaware's capital
30 Biblical brother
31 Color of embarrassment
33 Be gaga over
35 Bow-toting god
36 Pub missile
38 Pastor, informally
39 *SI* or *GQ*
41 Ready to harvest
42 Wooer's words
44 Nears midnight
45 Raspberry bit
46 Play for time
47 Timex rival
48 Begins the bidding
50 Shell game
51 Sign to heed
52 List-ending abbr.
53 Archer of legend
54 Tall story
55 "You said it!"
58 Poem of praise

★★ Number-Out

Shade squares so that no number appears in any row or column more than once. Shaded squares may not touch each other horizontally or vertically, and all unshaded squares must form a single continuous area.

6	4	5	6	1	3
5	6	2	2	2	4
1	3	2	1	6	5
2	1	2	5	2	3
3	5	6	4	3	2
4	3	3	3	5	6

THINK ALIKE

Unscramble the letters in the phrase HIT FOYER to form two words with the same or similar meanings.

________________ ________________

★★ Hyper-Sudoku

Fill in the blank boxes so that every row, column, 3x3 box, *and* each of the four 3x3 gray regions contains all of the numbers 1 to 9.

5	2	3	1					
			5		4	8	9	
	4					1		
			2					
		5				9		
6					7			
2	5		7		3	6	8	
3	1	8						
	9					3		

CENTURY MARKS

Select one number in each of the four columns so that the total adds up to exactly 100.

9	+	60	+	12	+	8	= 100
26		19		6		39	

★★ Looking Tidy by Fred Piscop

ACROSS

1 Mine passage
6 Winter footwear
11 Sault __ Marie, MI
14 South Pacific island group
15 Choreographer Ailey
16 Faux __
17 Parmesan or Romano
19 Drs.' orders
20 Longest-serving
21 Draw forth
23 Comic Carvey
26 Pyramid bottom
27 Scout's job, for short
28 Slanted type
30 Tricky pool shot
32 Spoiled, with "on"
33 Santa's landing spot
35 Composer Stravinsky
38 Toronto's loc.
39 Prism bands
42 Bullring cheer
43 Answer sheets
45 Place to build
46 Chip away at
48 Get going
50 Wiped away
51 Not so crooked
53 Play the lead
56 Sawbucks
57 St. Pete neighbor
58 Pick-me-ups
60 "Alley __!"
61 Clever sort
66 One in a litter
67 Prefix meaning "stone"
68 Inn patron
69 __-mo replay
70 Dutch painter Jan
71 Prized violin, informally

DOWN

1 Draft org.
2 "That's a laugh!"
3 Drs.' org.
4 On the market
5 Sheet repairer
6 Brazilian state
7 Dairy-aisle products
8 Really ham it up
9 "__ the season . . ."
10 Villainous looks
11 Hughes' wooden plane
12 Mexican silverworks city
13 German industrial center
18 *Power Lunch* channel
22 Lucie Arnaz's dad
23 Performed satisfactorily
24 Make amends
25 *The Deerslayer* hero
29 Proofs of age
31 Chad's cont.
33 Put back on the job
34 Beer-festival mo.
36 Bygone
37 Orchestra section
40 Air-pump letters
41 __ Lingus
44 Flow slowly
47 Tells on
49 Gets a grip on
50 Novelist Ambler
51 Sporty car roofs
52 Diplomat Wallenberg
54 Former Yankee manager
55 Composer Bruckner
59 Gear teeth
62 Bumped into
63 Plop or flop lead-in
64 "... __ penny earned"
65 Likely takeoff hr.

★ Look Both Ways

Find these palindromes (words spelled the same forward and backward) that are hidden in the diagram, either across, down, or diagonally. (We didn't dream up RÊVER; it's the French word for "to dream.")

```
R D E P V A H R D O B E N G H
C E E W T J O A T T X Q E Y U
B E V E S T G T N E R E V E R
P C N I O E O D J N O T W O Y
O E Z R V W Y A X T A S O S S
T R J K W E U D T A R H L O G
P T N A D P R E M O E S H L T
T O T Y K E T K T A F R E D E
R M P A I T E A U F E F C E E
M P X K O F T D L T R M U M S
I U P M X O R Z P R R C D N X
B E V I R J Q A I E N I H I B
P K C N E L L E D O B V L O D
B I B I A H A D O A Z I B S W
K I P M V A E N O D R C Q S Q
L E V E L R A B B A M A D A M
```

ABBA
AHA
BIB
BOB
CIVIC
DAD
DEED
DID
ELLE
EWE
EXE
HANNAH
KAYAK
LEVEL
MADAM
MINIM
MUM
NOON
OTTETTO
OTTO
PEEP
PEP
POP
RADAR
REDDER
REFER
RÊVER
REVIVER
ROTATOR
ROTOR
SEES
SOS
TENET
TOOT
TOT

INITIAL REACTION

Identify the well-known proverb from the first letters in each of its words.

R. W. B. I. A. D. ______________________________

★★ Sets of Three

Group all the symbols into sets of three, with each set having either all the same shape and three different colors, or all the same color and three different shapes. The symbols in each set must all be connected to each other by a common horizontal or vertical side.

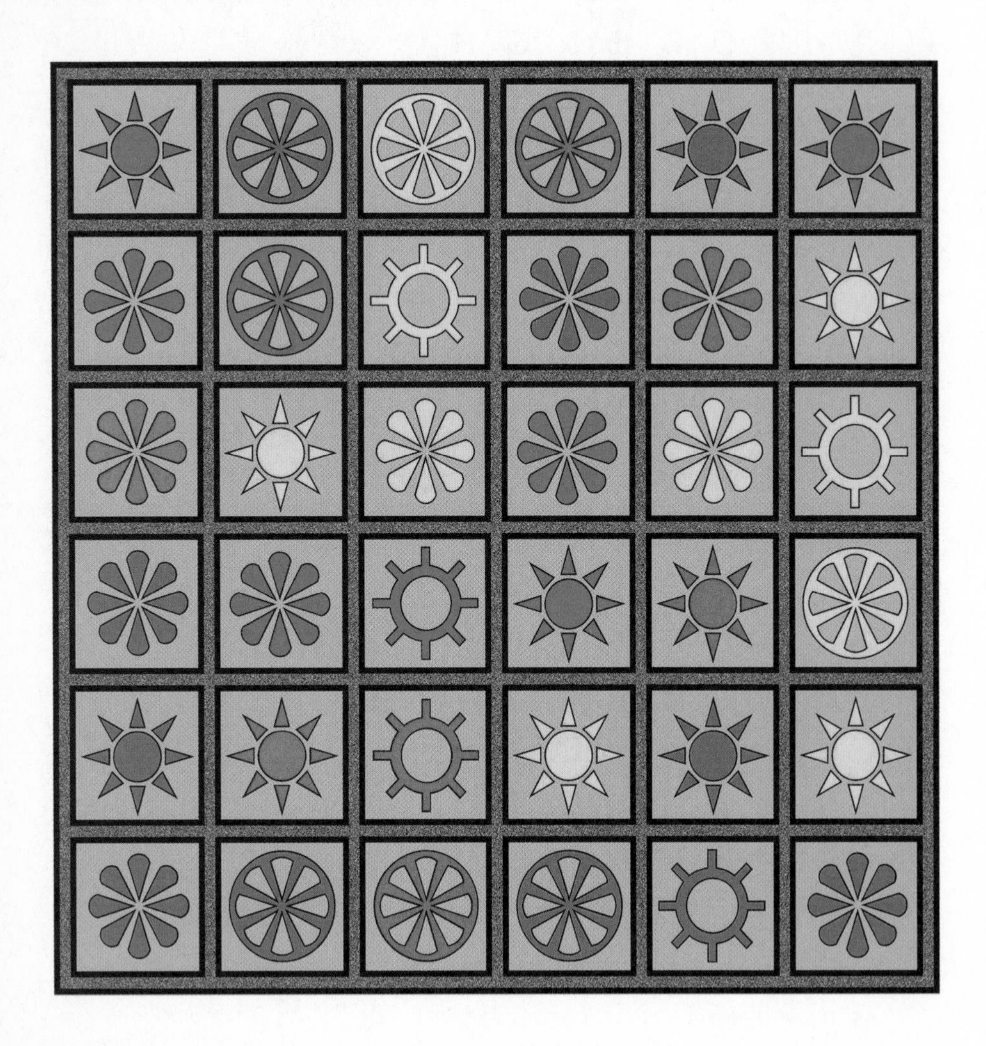

SAY IT AGAIN

What four-letter word can mean either "come ashore" or "capture"?

— — — —

★★ In Hot Water by Norma Steinberg

ACROSS

1 Fundamental
6 Cries out loud
10 Playing hooky, militarily
14 Unaccompanied
15 Word after karate or lamb
16 Latvian capital
17 Singer Rimes
18 Gun-shop purchase
19 "... and __ well!"
20 Seer's capability
21 Don Ho tune
24 Starts the bidding
26 Asserts it
27 Send into exile
29 "What he said!"
31 Lumber-camp implements
32 Marlon's *On the Waterfront* director
34 Mustard type
39 Swamp
40 Hungarian composer
42 Ill-mannered
43 Treasure trove
45 Pooch's annoyance
46 Where Mongolia is
47 Entr'__
49 Holding a grudge
51 Lash out at
55 Like a fillet
56 Freeload from
59 Annapolis monogram
62 Convinced
63 Seth's brother
64 Roast VIP
66 Pennsylvania city
67 Pear-shaped tomato
68 Bake-sale offerings
69 Danson and Kennedy
70 Sofa or stool
71 Secret rendezvous

DOWN

1 Farm package
2 Brewery products
3 Afternoon TV fare
4 B&B
5 Football position
6 Reads, as a bar code
7 "Oops!"
8 Broadway flop
9 Husband or wife
10 Sheik's domain of song
11 British prince, familiarly
12 Gives the eye to
13 Lariat
22 CIA's stock in trade
23 Music group
25 Stances
27 Hydroelectric structures
28 Way out
29 "Two on the" place
30 Labyrinth
33 Brit's elevator
35 Seeing red
36 Sarcastic "Fine!"
37 Cartoon canine
38 Close at hand
41 Forbidden
44 Reagan cabinet member
48 Frees from suspicion
50 Fill with germs
51 Portfolio holding
52 Fungus beginning
53 Unbroken
54 Peruvian heights
55 Key of Beethoven's 4th
57 Woodwind
58 Disaster aid org.
60 Witnesses
61 Fit within one another
65 Damage

★★ One-Way Streets

The diagram represents a pattern of streets. P's are parking spaces, and the black squares are stores. Find the route that starts at a parking space, passes through all stores exactly once, and ends at the other parking space. Arrows indicate one-way traffic for that block only. No block or intersection may be entered more than once.

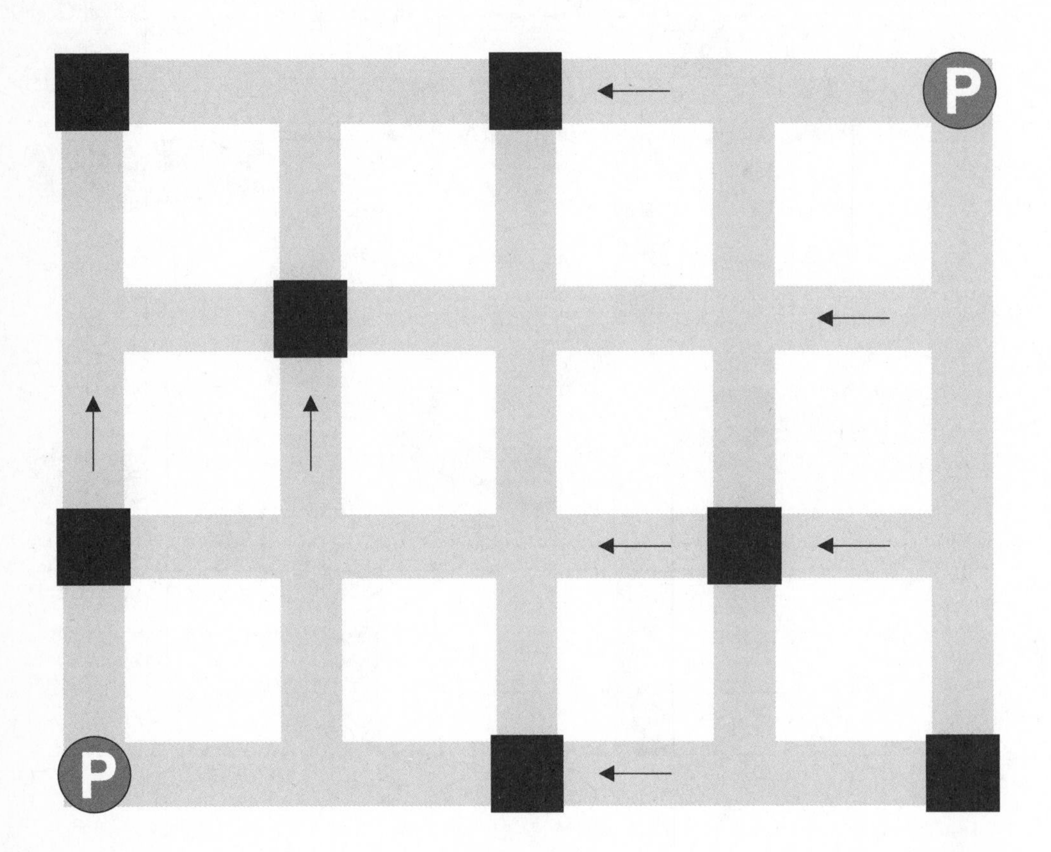

SOUND THINKING

There is only one common uncapitalized word not ending in D whose consonant sounds are S, B, and D, in that order. What is it?

____

★★ 123

Fill in the diagram so that each rectangular piece has one each of the numbers 1, 2, and 3, under these rules: 1) No two adjacent squares, horizontally or vertically, can have the same number. 2) Each completed row and column of the diagram will have an equal number of 1s, 2s, and 3s.

	1				3			
		3						
			2					
2				2				
	2							1
		3						
						3		
	2		2				1	

SUDOKU SUM

Fill in the missing numbers from 1 to 9, so that the sum of each row and column is as indicated.

	13	16	16
19	4		
16		3	
10			2

★★★ Line Drawing

Draw three straight lines, each from one edge of the square to another edge, so that the numbers in each region have something in common.

78
270
117
108
225
52
13
133
154
112
23
121
98
69
22
115

THREE OF A KIND

Find the three hidden words in the sentence that go together in some way.

Their kids were in danger, I learned.

★★ B-to-B Directory by Fred Piscop

ACROSS

1 Armada members
6 Goblet part
10 Thin nail
14 Radioactivity researcher
15 Miner's bonanza
16 Move out of town, in real-estate slang
17 Without a date
18 Eden figure
19 Enthralled by
20 Anti-nuke slogan
22 Letter starter
23 Pothook shape
24 Landscaping tools
26 Tonal quality
30 "Gay" city
32 Rock guitarist Van Halen
33 Coop brooder
34 Deep-six
38 And
39 Social bug
40 Celeb's wheels
41 Faints, with "over"
43 Sew up
44 Henry VIII's house
45 Chicago hub
47 "Rules of order" guy
48 Play producer
51 Indy entrant
52 Redcoat supporter
53 Tidbit for a bird
60 Illegally off base
61 Galley tools
62 Pay tribute to
63 Homeland Security agcy.
64 Frosty coating
65 Upper-crust
66 Exercise target
67 Overwhelm with humor
68 Ward off

DOWN

1 Picket-line crosser
2 Luau dance
3 Mineral in spinach
4 Ale serving
5 "Now, look …"
6 Bacon hunks
7 Hoo-ha
8 Red-coated cheese
9 Dues payer
10 Card players' group
11 Actress Zellweger
12 Rite place
13 Means of access
21 Language suffix
25 __ Moines, IA
26 Deck wood
27 Twiddling one's thumbs
28 Gds.
29 High-school class
30 Canterbury coins
31 Chip in
33 Salon sweepings
35 Depend (on)
36 Roman love god
37 Left, at sea
42 That ship
44 Burned down
46 Shady nooks
47 "Way cool!"
48 Shepherd's stick
49 Quitter's toss-in
50 Wine's bouquet
51 Mudville's slugger
54 Track border
55 Witty Bombeck
56 Part to play
57 Workbook segment
58 Tiny speck
59 __ Rabbit (Harris character)

★★ Star Search

Find the stars that are hidden in some of the blank squares. The numbered squares indicate how many stars are hidden in the squares adjacent to them (including diagonally). There is never more than one star in any square.

CHOICE WORDS

Form three six-letter words from the same category, by selecting one letter from each column three times. Each letter will be used exactly once.

C	U	P	E	C	P	_ _ _ _ _ _
S	H	P	I	O	B	_ _ _ _ _ _
T	I	O	T	R	E	_ _ _ _ _ _

★★ Dicey

Group the dice into sets of two or more whose sums equal nine. The dice in each set must be connected to each other by a common horizontal or vertical side.

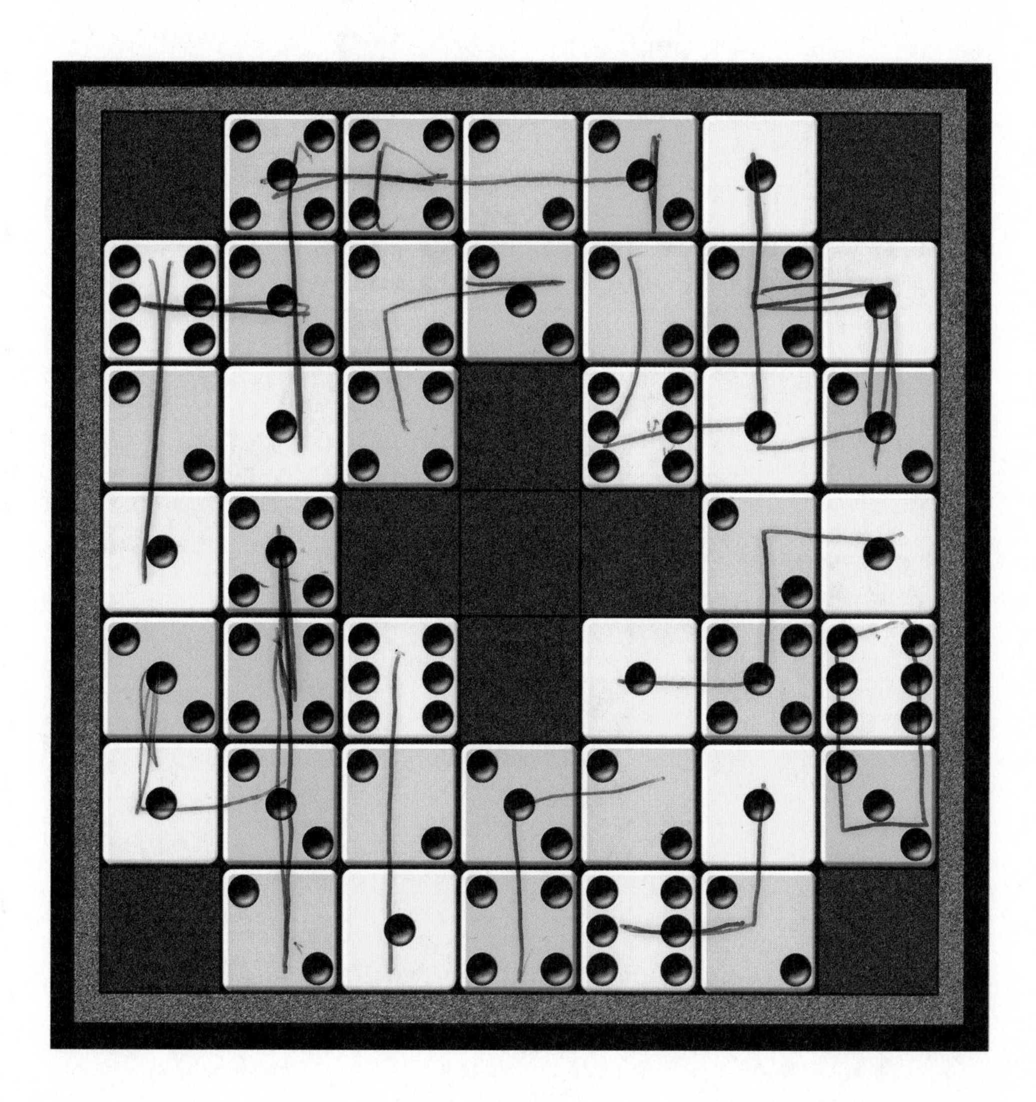

SMALL CHANGE

Change one letter in each of these two words, to form a common two-word phrase.

SEND TRAY

____

★★ Followings by Daniel R. Stark

ACROSS

1 Duffel filler
5 Quartet member
9 The C in C.S. Forester
14 Supermodel Macpherson
15 Brand for Bowser
16 Originated
17 Diamond or Simon
18 Zen riddle
19 Feels concern
20 Advantageous position
23 Soccer goal
24 Food consumers
25 Cameos, for example
27 Paddock youngsters
30 Flower product
33 Long-armed beast
36 Tablecloth pattern
38 Liquid-Plumr alternative
39 Writer Angelou
41 Sign up for
43 Forearm bone
44 Big occasion
46 Fists, slangily
48 Follett or Kesey
49 Made a home
51 Gnats and mice
53 Marsh wader
55 Strand components
59 Jungle crusher
61 Type of butterfly
64 Conductor Previn
66 It may be bounding
67 Madame Bovary's first name
68 Tavern perch
69 Barely made, with "out"
70 Subsides
71 Oater salutation
72 Caves, at times
73 Quick bite

DOWN

1 Wish granter
2 Actress Verdugo
3 Top choices
4 Change of pace
5 Popular fund-raiser
6 Oodles
7 Train for a match
8 Fish finder
9 Laughed shrilly
10 Geologic time division
11 Plant with ears
12 "Hmmm ..."
13 In case
21 Globule
22 Not pro
26 Tan shade
28 Secure, as a contract
29 Gym exercise
31 Green Gables girl
32 Certain horse coloring
33 Final word
34 Do road work
35 Cosmetic buy
37 Hockey feint
40 Pot starter
42 Gives one's reaction
45 Without wasted words
47 Brood
50 Jones' partner
52 Glossy fabric
54 Known as
56 Stallone role
57 They branch out
58 Cut drastically
59 Lavish party
60 Aware of
62 Trout habitat
63 Legal claim
65 Curtain holder

★★ Hyper-Sudoku

Fill in the blank boxes so that every row, column, 3x3 box, *and* each of the four 3x3 gray regions contains all of the numbers 1 to 9.

			3	9			1	
5				6	1		9	
				2	5	7		
	9							
	1		2			9	5	8
				5	9	4	7	
		6						
			9	3			8	7
			8					

MIXAGRAMS

Each line contains a five-letter word and a four-letter word that have been mixed together (the order of the letters in each word has not been changed). Unmix the two words on each line and write them in the spaces provided. When you're done, find a two-part answer to the clue by reading down the letter columns in the answers.

CLUE: Road work?

M E L O D I N A G = _ _ _ _ _ + _ _ _ _

A M A S K E M A W = _ _ _ _ _ + _ _ _ _

C A P O L L K A M = _ _ _ _ _ + _ _ _ _

P O G O L O F E Y = _ _ _ _ _ + _ _ _ _

★★ ABC

Enter the letters A, B, and C into the diagram so that each row and column has exactly one A, one B, and one C. The letters outside the diagram indicate the first letter encountered, moving in the direction of the arrow. Keep in mind that after all the letters have been filled in, there will be two blank boxes in each row and column.

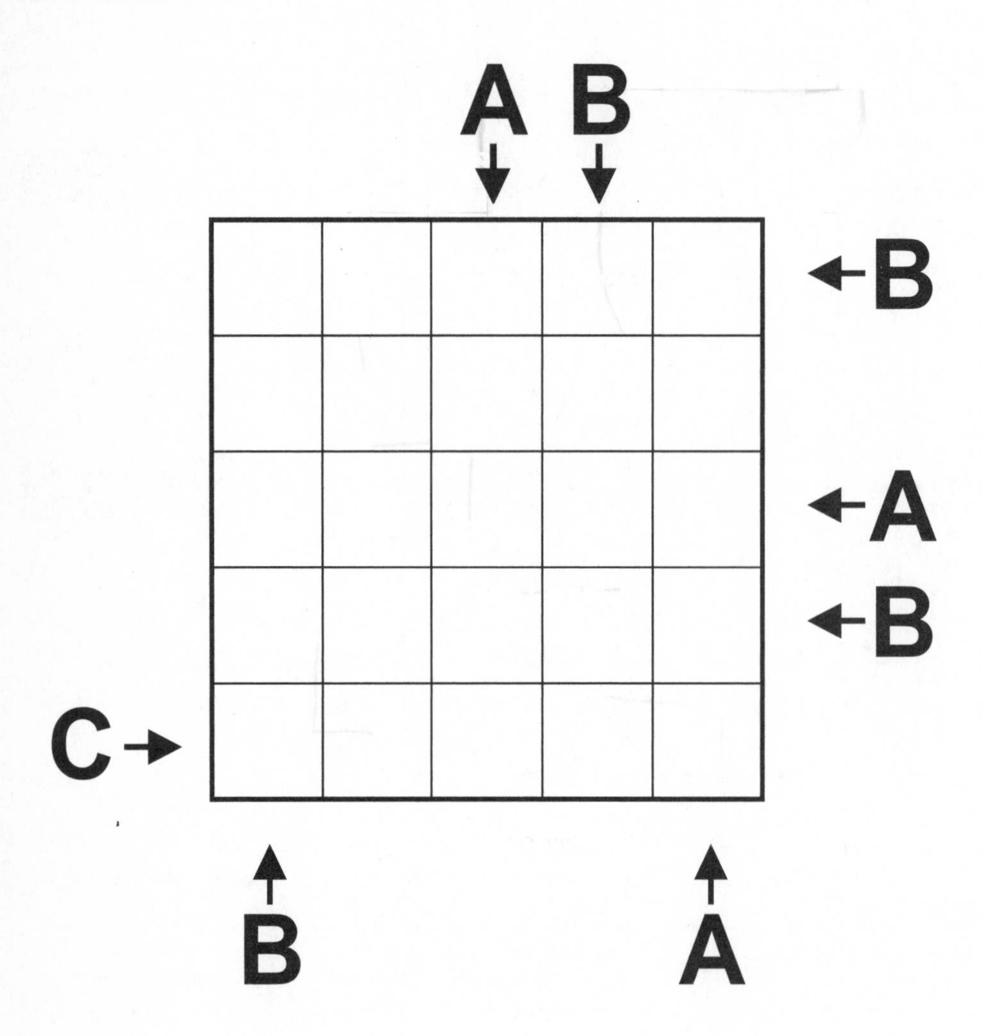

NATIONAL TREASURE

Find the one common six-letter word that can be formed from the letters in GAMBIAN.

_ _ _ _ _ _

★★ Two Pair by Fred Piscop

1	2	3	4	5	■	6	7	8	9	■	10	11	12	13
14					■	15				■	16			
17					18					■	19			
20								■	21	22				
■	■	■	■	23			■	■	■	24				
25	26	27	28			■	29	30	31				■	■
32					■	33					■	34	35	36
37				■	38					■	39			
40			■	41					■	42				
■	■	43	44					■	45					
46	47				■	■	■	48			■	■	■	■
49					50	■	51				52	53	54	55
56				■	57	58								
59				■	60				■	61				
62				■	63				■	64				

ACROSS

1 Rich strikes
6 Parcel (out)
10 Flower stalk
14 Mentally quick
15 Devil's doings
16 Asian cuisine
17 Duffers' expenses
19 They may be lively or fine
20 Academic period
21 Is in sync
23 Dinghy propeller
24 Each and __
25 Company lover
29 Titled ones
32 Chess player's octet
33 Serenades the moon
34 Cork sound
37 Iowa city
38 Lama locale
39 Prefix with conference
40 *The Simpsons* grandpa
41 Llama locale
42 Stockholm citizen
43 Subdued hue
45 Noiseless aircraft
46 Pug's weapons
48 Eight slices, often
49 Ivanhoe's love
51 Red shades
56 Till stack
57 First Amendment right
59 Try to slim down
60 Has a bug
61 Cornhusker State city
62 Stately trees
63 Went by bus
64 Barely defeated, with "out"

DOWN

1 Falls behind
2 Mean man
3 Per-__ worker
4 Gen. Robert __
5 Motion detectors, e.g.
6 Push back
7 In charge of
8 Tell a whopper
9 *Born Free* lioness
10 "... __ a fever"
11 Kind of bike
12 Beanery patron
13 Girl, informally
18 Hang around
22 Salon supplies
25 Movie-rating org.
26 Poetic foot
27 Ratings time, for networks
28 USNA grad
29 Swedish philanthropist
30 Is in hock
31 Diner sandwich
33 Lie low
35 Merrie __ England
36 Use a spyglass
38 Blaster's need
39 __-night doubleheader
41 Part of 25 Down
42 Ponder overnight
44 Nuclear experiments
45 Jazzman's jobs
46 Tolkien ring-bearer
47 Ancient Aegean region
48 Bel __ cheese
50 Way out there
51 Card combo
52 *Nautilus* skipper
53 Brewed beverages
54 Need liniment
55 Roe source
58 Copacabana locale

★★ Knot or Not?

When the mouse tails are pulled, which will knot, and which will not?

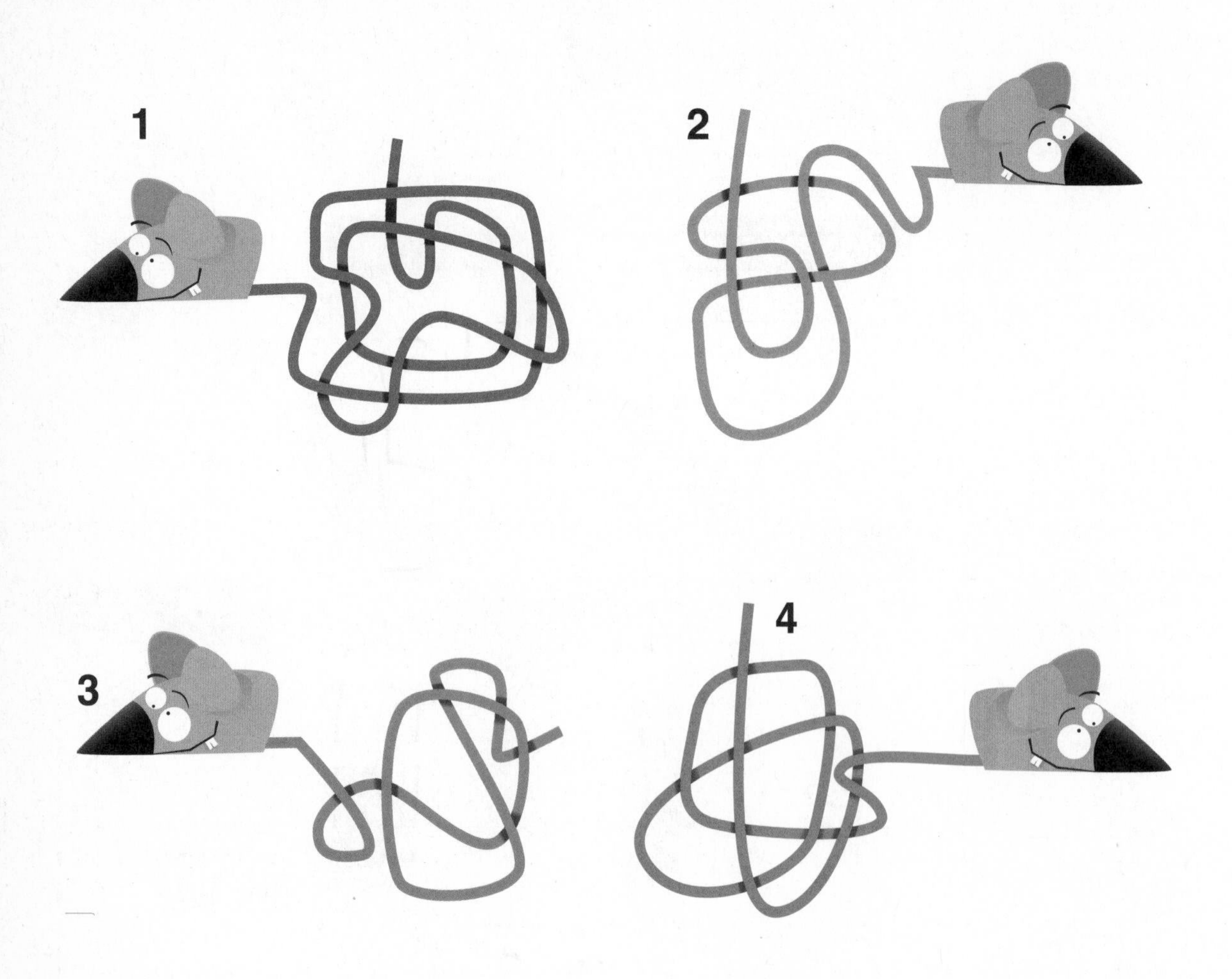

BETWEENER

What four-letter word belongs between the word at left and the word at right, so that the first and second word, and the second and third word, each form a common compound word?

PORK _ _ _ _ STICK

★★ Find the Ships

Determine the position of the 10 ships listed to the right of the diagram. The ships may be oriented either horizontally or vertically. A square with wavy lines indicates water and will not contain a ship. The numbers at the edge of the diagram indicate how many squares in that row or column contain parts of ships. When all 10 ships are correctly placed in the diagram, no two of them will touch each other, not even diagonally.

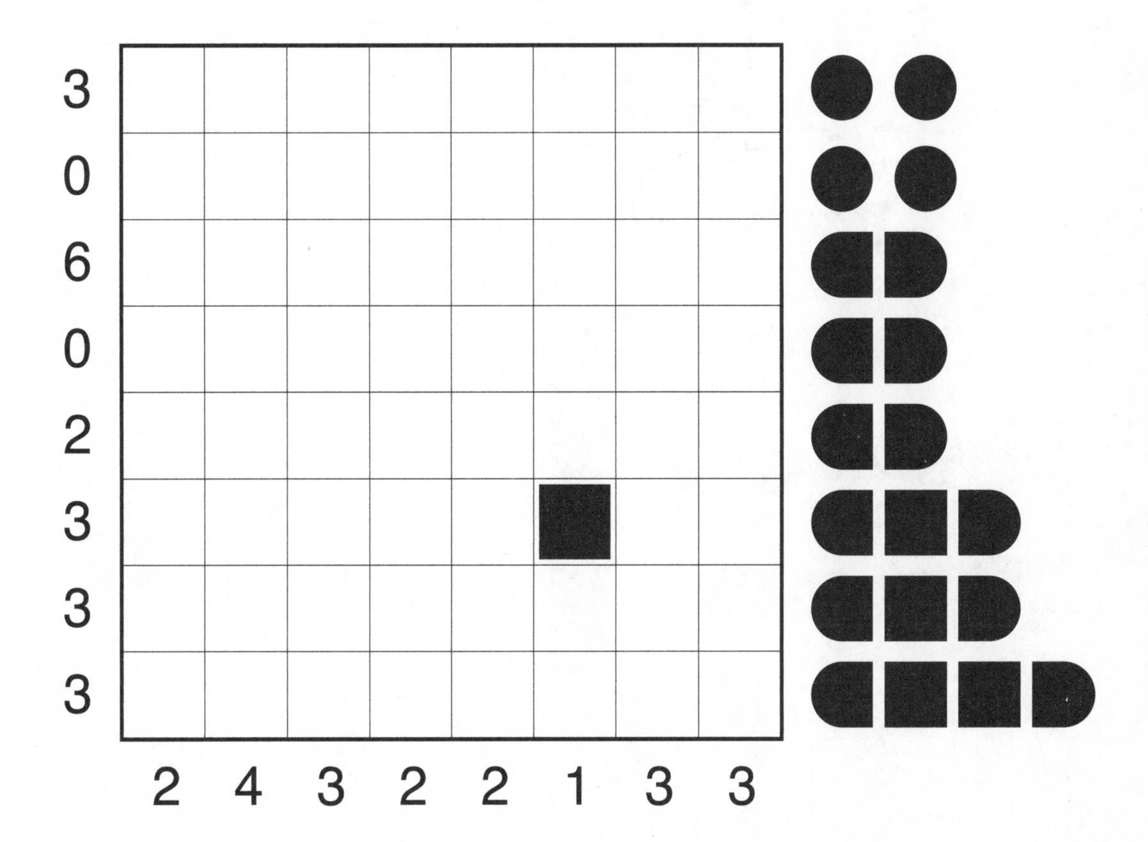

TWO-BY-FOUR

The eight letters in the word MOTORIZE can be rearranged to form a pair of common four-letter words in four different ways, if no four-letter word is repeated. Can you find them all?

_ _ _ _ _ _ _ _ _ _ _ _ _ _ _ _

_ _ _ _ _ _ _ _ _ _ _ _ _ _ _ _

★★ Triad Split Decisions

In this clueless crossword puzzle, each answer consists of two words whose spellings are the same, except for the consecutive letters given. All answers are common words; no phrases or hyphenated or capitalized words are used. Some of the clues may have more than one solution, but there is only one word pair that will correctly link up with all the other word pairs.

TRANSDELETION

Delete one letter from the word TRIPLES and rearrange the rest, to get an occupation.

____

★★ Street Smarts by Norma Steinberg

ACROSS

1 Sits in (for)
5 Majestic
10 Engrave with acid
14 __ pet (TV ad product)
15 Pueblo's exterior
16 Depend (on)
17 "One more thing ..."
19 PDQ relative
20 Oral Roberts University site
21 Parrot's pad
22 Eyelid annoyance
23 "__ baaaaack!"
25 Staggered
27 Wyatt of the Old West
29 Miscue
32 Churlish ones
35 Modern music genre
39 Little devil
40 Old hand
41 Fitness system
42 Vitality
43 Sense of self
44 Reveals
45 Complete collections
46 Shifty trick
48 Annoyance
50 Hue and cry
54 Spurts of energy
58 "Hold on there!"
60 Digital music player
62 Islamic Almighty
63 Chunk of time
64 Place for a nostalgic walk
66 About
67 Tehran citizen
68 Really, really bad
69 Fluffy and Fido
70 Poem division
71 Negotiation result

DOWN

1 Weatherman Willard
2 "Yeah!"
3 Authoritative book
4 Accepts a proposal
5 Cheer
6 Adam's address
7 Choreographer Champion
8 Humiliate
9 Philippine island
10 Pencil's end
11 Automotive tryout
12 Pottery material
13 Overdone promotion
18 Scarlett's place
24 Bert's kid-vid pal
26 Bottom-of-barrel contents
28 Assail vigorously
30 Leave out
31 Motor info
32 Kind of column
33 Jason's ship
34 Mall dining area
36 Used to be
37 On
38 Factors in heredity
41 Entreaty
45 Played for time
47 Shoots daggers (at)
49 Neuter
51 Sound like
52 Verdi work
53 Spartacus, for one
55 Spartacus, for one
56 Obsession
57 Beach find
58 Senate official
59 Sharpen
61 "__ even think it!"
65 River, in Spain

★★ 123

Fill in the diagram so that each rectangular piece has one each of the numbers 1, 2, and 3, under these rules: 1) No two adjacent squares, horizontally or vertically, can have the same number. 2) Each completed row and column of the diagram will have an equal number of 1s, 2s, and 3s.

			1					
					1		3	
	2							
1						1		
			3					
		2						
3					2			

WRONG IS RIGHT

Which of these four words is misspelled?

A) treatice B) tortoise

C) chalice D) porpoise

★★ Fences

Connect the dots with vertical or horizontal lines, so that a single loop is formed with no crossings or branches. Each number indicates how many lines surround it; squares with no number may be surrounded by any number of lines.

2	2		3			3	
2			0		0	1	2
					2		
		3	3				
				1	1		
		3					
1	1	3		3			2
	3			3		1	3

ADDITION SWITCH

Switch the positions of two of the digits in the incorrect sum at right, to get a correct sum.

```
  937
+ 473
-----
  816
```

★★ Thriller by Fred Piscop

ACROSS

1 Bit of bread
6 Flat floaters
11 Black gunk
14 Daily delivery
15 Hearing-related
16 Tick off
17 Thrilled
19 Undercover agcy.
20 Granny or half hitch
21 Meandered
23 Dietary need
27 Humdinger
28 Go back
29 Midnight rider of yore
32 Starts the bidding
33 Civic leader
34 Corp. alias
37 Database function
38 Egg purchase
39 Joyride
40 Ballpark fig.
41 Fodder storers
42 Wall covering
43 One at the plate
45 What's happening
46 Fancy flapjack
48 High-tech door-opener
49 Shark hanger-on
51 Crow's-nest spot
52 Commotion
53 Thrilled
59 Cheyenne's state: Abbr.
60 River of Tours
61 Worker's reward
62 Actor Cariou
63 Phased out
64 Linen item

DOWN

1 Ens.' subordinate
2 Sought office
3 Merchandise ID
4 Singer Tormé
5 Investment intermediaries
6 Dangerous inert gas
7 Polly, to Tom Sawyer
8 TGIF part
9 Catches some rays
10 Trim-figured
11 Thrilled
12 Disney mermaid
13 All set
18 Measurement standard
22 Put on TV
23 Plain writing
24 Bank takebacks
25 Thrilled
26 Jamboree setup
29 Stubble remover
30 Potato features
31 Wernher __ Braun
33 Suburban burrower
35 Jag
36 Inclined to fidget
38 Morse click
39 Expressed aloud
41 Germ-free
42 Baggage handlers
44 Wall St. launch
45 Short race
46 Slow pace
47 Color yet again
48 Not roaming free
50 "Auth. unknown"
51 Twist's request
54 Covered up
55 Satisfied sound
56 Compete
57 Language suffix
58 Aerialist's protection

★★ Cockatoo Maze

Enter the maze where indicated at bottom, pass through all the stars exactly once, then exit at top left. You may not retrace your path.

SAY IT AGAIN

What word that's a four-letter pronoun can also mean "abundant source"?

_ _ _ _

bRaIn BREathER

GOLDEN RULES OF CLEANING

In cleaning, your goal is to remove dirt. But you don't want to hurt yourself or what you're cleaning, and you want to make the job as quick and easy as possible. Follow these rules, and you're golden.

The sooner the better Most spills and stains, including food stains, clothing stains, and carpet stains, are much easier to clean up when you attack them right away, or at least as soon as possible. A rare exception to this rule: Mud tracked on your carpet is much easier to vacuum up once it's bone dry and crumbly.

Clean from the top down Start at the top floor (to avoid tracking through cleaned rooms) and the top of each room—first ceilings and cobwebs, then fans, light fixtures, windows and walls, furniture, baseboards, and floors. The exception: Wash walls from the bottom up.

Think dry, then wet In each room, dust and vacuum first, then do the mopping, mirror-cleaning, and other all-purpose-cleaner jobs. The result: less dirt floating around to cling to wet surfaces.

Let time work for you First, spray on cleaning chemicals, and let them work while you do something else. In the kitchen, spray counters and appliances, then remove old food from the fridge, while the cleaner soaks in. When you're ready to wipe clean, you'll hardly have to scrub.

Carry your supplies with you Some helpful items include a plastic cleaning caddy for your supplies, a large plastic bucket, a rolling supply cart, and an apron with roomy pockets. But keep one-job products where they'll be used—e.g., toilet bowl cleaner in the bathroom.

Use the stealth test When using a new technique or product, test it on an inconspicuous area of the object you're cleaning to make sure it doesn't suffer damage.

Don't saturate easily damaged items When cleaning items that might be harmed by liquid products (computers, electronics, art work, etc.), spray the cleaner on your cleaning cloth rather than directly on the object to be cleaned.

Read the directions Keep in mind that manufacturers know best how to clean their products; and makers of cleaning products know best how to use *their* products. Save the cleaning tips that come with appliances, rugs, etc. Similarly, don't remove the care labels from clothes, linens, or other washables.

Protect thyself Some cleaning products contain ingredients that can damage your eyes, skin, nose, and lungs. Use rubber gloves; cover your arms, legs, and hair; and make sure the room you're in is well ventilated. And never mix cleaning products together. Some combinations can produce poisonous gases.

★ At the Theater

Try to find these cinema terms that are hidden in the diagram either across, down, or diagonally, and you'll find that one of them has left the building and isn't there. What's the missing answer? (MOTION and PICTURES are hidden separately.)

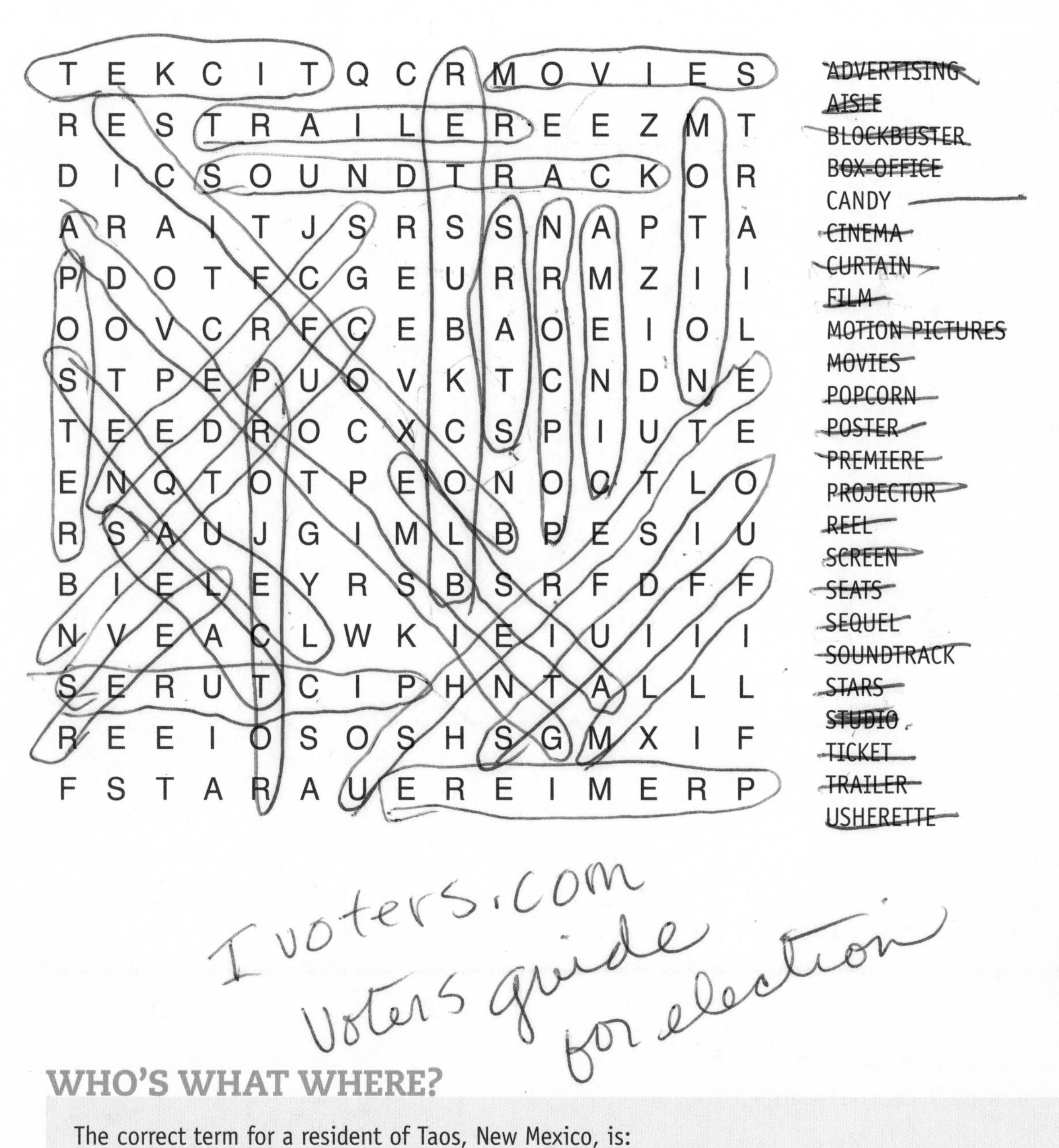

WHO'S WHAT WHERE?

The correct term for a resident of Taos, New Mexico, is:

A) Taosian

B) Taoseno

C) Taosite

D) Taoser

★★ Hyper-Sudoku

Fill in the blank boxes so that every row, column, 3x3 box, *and* each of the four 3x3 gray regions contains all of the numbers 1 to 9.

				6		1		
8	6				5			
					4		7	
5				9	8	6	1	
								9
9	4			7			2	3
	3		6			5		8
			2				4	
		4			9			

MIXAGRAMS

Each line contains a five-letter word and a four-letter word that have been mixed together (the order of the letters in each word has not been changed). Unmix the two words on each line and write them in the spaces provided. When you're done, find a two-part answer to the clue by reading down the letter columns in the answers.

CLUE: Chuckleheads

S E W A R T A P H = _ _ _ _ _ + _ _ _ _

S K I A R Z E M A = _ _ _ _ _ + _ _ _ _

E S P I T E L C H = _ _ _ _ _ + _ _ _ _

B R U I S E S E F = _ _ _ _ _ + _ _ _ _

★★★ On the Job by Daniel R. Stark

ACROSS

1 Show amazement
5 Uptight
9 Turn aside
13 Give off, as light
14 Rhett's home, for a time
15 Hindu Trinity member
16 Chaucer offering
17 Movie mogul
18 Brought to bay
19 Numero __
20 Masterpiece
22 New parts of old jeans
24 Computer-memory unit
25 Speak highly of
26 Did a salon job
28 Up-to-date
31 Primitive weapon
33 Metamorphose
35 For pick-up
36 Mergers and buyouts
37 Burnoose wearer
38 Steady devotion
40 Arrests, so to speak
41 Even so
42 What's more
43 Hay parcel
44 Sunflower yield
45 Frothy desserts
48 Cut up
53 Like a cool cat
54 Punch server
55 Dobbin's dinner
56 Graceful wrap
57 Left off
58 Former National League park
59 Cleveland's lake
60 Song or slug follower
61 Autobahn vehicle
62 Supplemented, with "out"

DOWN

1 Outfit
2 Westinghouse alternative
3 Gas-range feature
4 Cousteau's summer
5 Drew with acid
6 Benumbs
7 Sabatini rival
8 Length unit
9 Shoulder gesture
10 Ukrainian capital
11 Eternally
12 Cross the creek
15 Mighty mounts
20 Engine sound
21 Shaman's findings
23 White-water craft
26 Big Dipper neighbor
27 Ivy League member
28 Saltwater predator
29 Coup d'__
30 Fly catchers
31 Command to Rover
32 Mineral deposit
33 Gymnasts' goals
34 Handles roughly
36 Singer Reese
39 Came down
40 Modem-speed unit
43 Horticultural art
44 Immature raptor
45 Toned down
46 Ghostly
47 Was a mole
48 Music notation
49 Country road
50 Track postings
51 Santa __, CA
52 Kauai neighbor
56 Meet, in poker

★★ One-Way Streets

The diagram represents a pattern of streets. P's are parking spaces, and the black squares are stores. Find the route that starts at a parking space, passes through all stores exactly once, and ends at the other parking space. Arrows indicate one-way traffic for that block only. No block or intersection may be entered more than once.

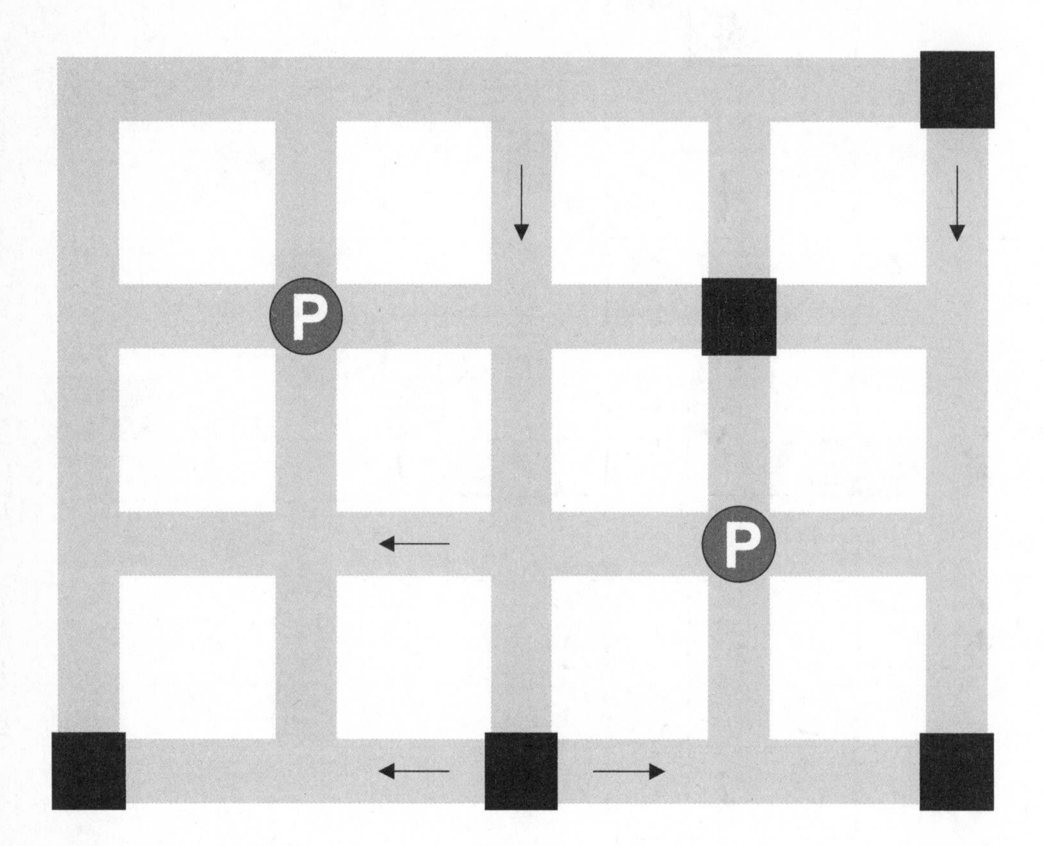

SOUND THINKING

Common words whose consonant sounds are TH, N, and K include THANK and THINK. The longest such word has six letters. What is it?

____

★★ Star Search

Find the stars that are hidden in some of the blank squares. The numbered squares indicate how many stars are hidden in the squares adjacent to them (including diagonally). There is never more than one star in any square.

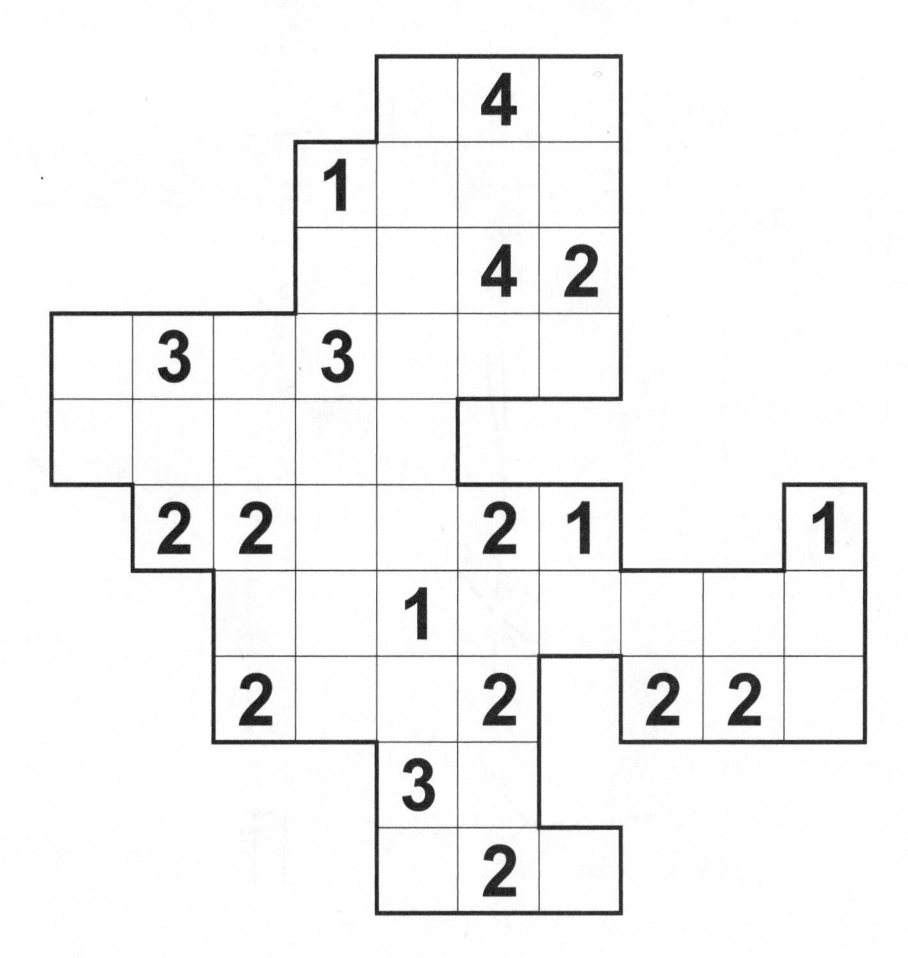

CHOICE WORDS

Form three six-letter words from the same category, by selecting one letter from each column three times. Each letter will be used exactly once.

B	N	N	I	O	G	_ _ _ _ _ _
I	M	P	B	R	Y	_ _ _ _ _ _
U	A	T	I	N	E	_ _ _ _ _ _

★★★ Three-Peats by Fred Piscop

ACROSS

1 Box office hits
6 Is in hock
10 Sealing material
14 Bee-related
15 Soccer legend
16 Genesis son
17 Jane Fonda film of '68
19 "It's been __!"
20 Usher's offering
21 Monthly expense
22 Blotch of color
24 Thoroughbreds' homes
26 __ monster (large lizard)
27 Brit. lexicon
28 Put up with
32 Touch up
35 Links alert
36 Fly's undoing
37 Hit or miss
38 Long-eared bounders
39 Choir member
40 Ticklish character
41 Chester __ Arthur
42 Writer Sontag
43 Myles from Plymouth
45 Tic-toe connection
46 Aswan Dam's river
47 Church devotions
51 Saskatchewan's capital
54 Hawaiian coffee region
55 Uncommon sense
56 Mean one
57 "The Queen City"
60 Petri-dish gel
61 Square footage
62 Teacher for one
63 Baseball great Sandberg
64 Cry out loud
65 Keep for later

DOWN

1 Rummy cakes
2 Eye-bending designs
3 Terra __
4 Swell
5 In a tangle
6 Starts the bidding
7 Cobbler's strip
8 Right-angle bend
9 Maritime distances
10 Fish condiment
11 Assist in a scam
12 Ring out
13 Fashion mag
18 Sax player's buy
23 Corrida cry
25 Sweet seller
26 *Contract Bridge Complete* author
28 Temple scroll
29 Hole-making tools
30 Londoner's "later"
31 Prince Harry alma mater
32 Nights before
33 Cheesy sandwich
34 Columnist Bombeck
35 Treacherous
38 Cry "Taxi!"
42 Learned ones
44 Cacophony
45 Actress Collette
47 For dieters
48 "Peachy keen!"
49 Early American tycoon
50 Cathedral topper
51 Crowd sound
52 Like soufflés
53 Mom's mom
54 Had down pat
58 Lyricist Gershwin
59 Filbert, e.g.

★★ Color Paths

Find the shortest path through the maze from the bottom to the top, by using paths in this color order: red, blue, yellow, red, blue, etc. Change path colors through the white squares. It is okay to retrace your path.

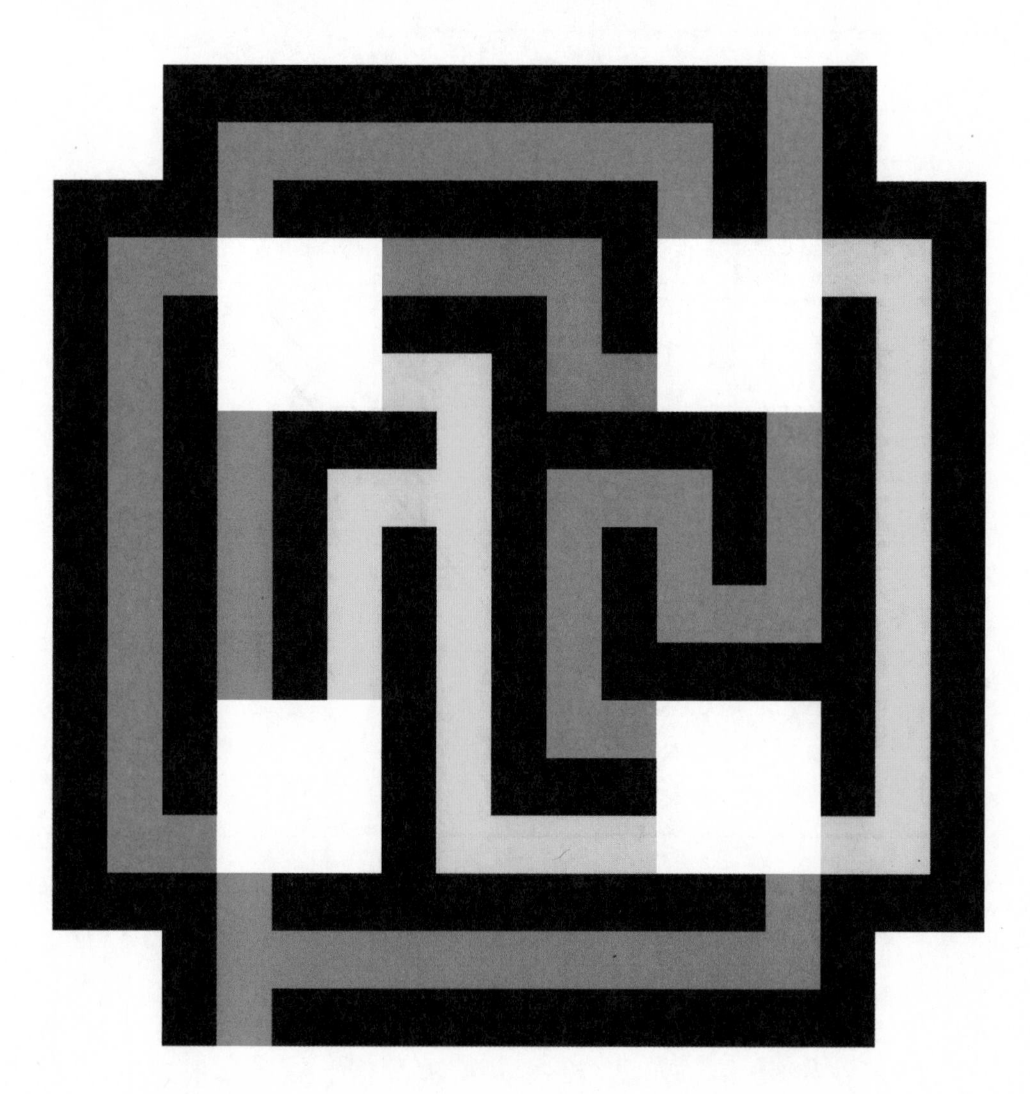

SMALL CHANGE

Change one letter in each of these two words, to form a common two-word phrase.

TOWS DRIER

____

★★ Sudoku

Fill in the blank boxes so that every row, column, and 3x3 box contains all of the numbers 1 to 9.

	8	3				5	1	
				7				
		4	3		2	8		
		5	9		8	7		
	9						2	
		6	2		7	4		
		8	6		4	9		
				9				
	5	7				6	4	

CENTURY MARKS

Select one number in each of the four columns so that the total adds up to exactly 100.

37	+	21	+	36	+	27	=	100
29		15		34		12		

★★★ Veggie Plate by Shirley Soloway

1	2	3	4	■	5	6	7	8	9	■	10	11	12	13
14				■	15					■	16			
17				18						■	19			
20			■	21					■	22				
23			24						■	25			■	■
■	■	■	26				■	27	28				29	30
31	32	33			■	■	34				■	35		
36				■	37	38				■	39			
40			■	41				■	■	42				
43			44				■	45	46			■	■	■
■	■	47			■	48	49					50	51	52
53	54				■	55					■	56		
57				■	58						59			
60				■	61					■	62			
63				■	64					■	65			

ACROSS

1 Brown shades
5 Not very enthusiastic
10 Funnel shape
14 Poetic planets
15 Lunar valley
16 Form of quartz
17 Grade-school toy
19 Water carrier
20 Suffix meaning "like"
21 Cash-barrelhead link
22 Red Riding Hood locale
23 Redhead
25 Operate
26 Creative thought
27 "That's fine!"
31 Bogart's ... *Sierra Madre* role
34 Visibility obstacle
35 Primary
36 Small strings
37 Preparations
39 Cleaner scent
40 Age
41 Revolver, perhaps
42 Smooths, as a shelf
43 Juicy fruit
45 Exploitative one
47 Moral lapse
48 Spicy soup
53 Upscale
55 Did battle with
56 Potsdam pronoun
57 Sistine Chapel ceiling figure
58 Picnic activity
60 Venetian explorer
61 Upscale
62 Heavy weight
63 Expresses disdain
64 Trait sources
65 Eroded

DOWN

1 Subject
2 Gladiatorial venue
3 Rocket or Raptor
4 Former draft org.
5 Literary family name
6 Joe Jackson in *Field of Dreams*
7 Shortened preposition
8 Gets up late
9 Occupational ending
10 Lame excuse
11 Sort of paper
12 Lt. Kojak's employer
13 Once-wedded ones
18 Mob members
22 Judicial order
24 Teases
28 Aircraft-carrier designation
29 Repair
30 Swiss-cheese holes
31 Tune for two
32 Gumbo ingredient
33 Fairy-tale ladder
34 Spoil
37 Officeholder, for short
38 Legal out
39 Henry VIII's VIth
41 Call false
42 Handle
44 Whatchamacallits
45 Make current
46 Outpourings
49 Dine at home
50 Jazz instrument
51 Transpire
52 "__ are the times that try men's souls"
53 Fully attentive
54 Altar exchanges
58 Brit's clothespin
59 Commotion

★★ Split Decisions

In this clueless crossword puzzle, each answer consists of two words whose spellings are the same, except for the consecutive letters given. All answers are common words; no phrases or hyphenated or capitalized words are used. Some of the clues may have more than one solution, but there is only one word pair that will correctly link up with all the other word pairs.

TRANSDELETION

Delete one letter from the word EQUALITY and rearrange the rest, to get something to drink.

____

★★ Number-Out

Shade squares so that no number appears in any row or column more than once. Shaded squares may not touch each other horizontally or vertically, and all unshaded squares must form a single continuous area.

3	1	5	2	4	3
5	2	2	2	1	1
4	3	1	6	6	2
1	2	4	4	6	5
4	6	4	1	5	1
2	4	3	5	5	6

THINK ALIKE

Unscramble the letters in the phrase PESTO CASE to form two words with the same or similar meanings.

______________________ ______________________

★★★ Searches by Bruce Venzke

ACROSS

1 Minor players
5 Tooth trouble
9 Aristotle's teacher
14 Bruins' sch.
15 Ichabod's rival
16 Ready to be played
17 Place for supplies
19 Dye-job choice
20 Searches
22 Gridiron gains: Abbr.
23 "You da __!"
24 Like falling off a log
25 Accomplished
26 Talk online
28 Kiwi's extinct kin
31 His and her
34 Not of the cloth
35 Ones in office
36 Searches
39 Microbrewery output
40 Till compartment
41 Evaluate, as ore
42 72, often
43 Grub
44 "Ta-ta!"
45 Polite fellow
47 Sharp turn
48 Tach letters
51 Searches
55 Painter Matisse
56 Legendary swashbuckler
57 One in a rush
58 Memo-starting phrase
59 Part of AD
60 Shoe fabric
61 Samoa studier
62 Predicament

DOWN

1 Like some jobs
2 Group of eight
3 Paint finish
4 '30s First Mother
5 Across the sea
6 Sing like Bing
7 Smee's boss
8 Austen novel
9 WWII vessel
10 Whoppers
11 Unknown
12 Keep an eye on
13 Unmatched
18 Twain's New York home
21 Get through to
25 Makes indistinct
26 Social worker's load
27 Top songs
29 Gymnast Korbut
30 Very pale
31 Duffer's worry
32 Storytelling dance
33 Coming-out
34 Season of repentance
35 Affectation
37 Unwilling blame-takers
38 Sci-fi zapper
43 Intact
44 Treated gently
46 Like some pitchers
47 Football ref
48 French river
49 Lowly laborers
50 Early PC program
51 Swain
52 Tonsorial touch-up
53 Sharpen
54 Pillow cover
55 Day divs.

★★ ABC

Enter the letters A, B, and C into the diagram so that each row and column has exactly one A, one B, and one C. The letters outside the diagram indicate the first letter encountered, moving in the direction of the arrow. Keep in mind that after all the letters have been filled in, there will be two blank boxes in each row and column.

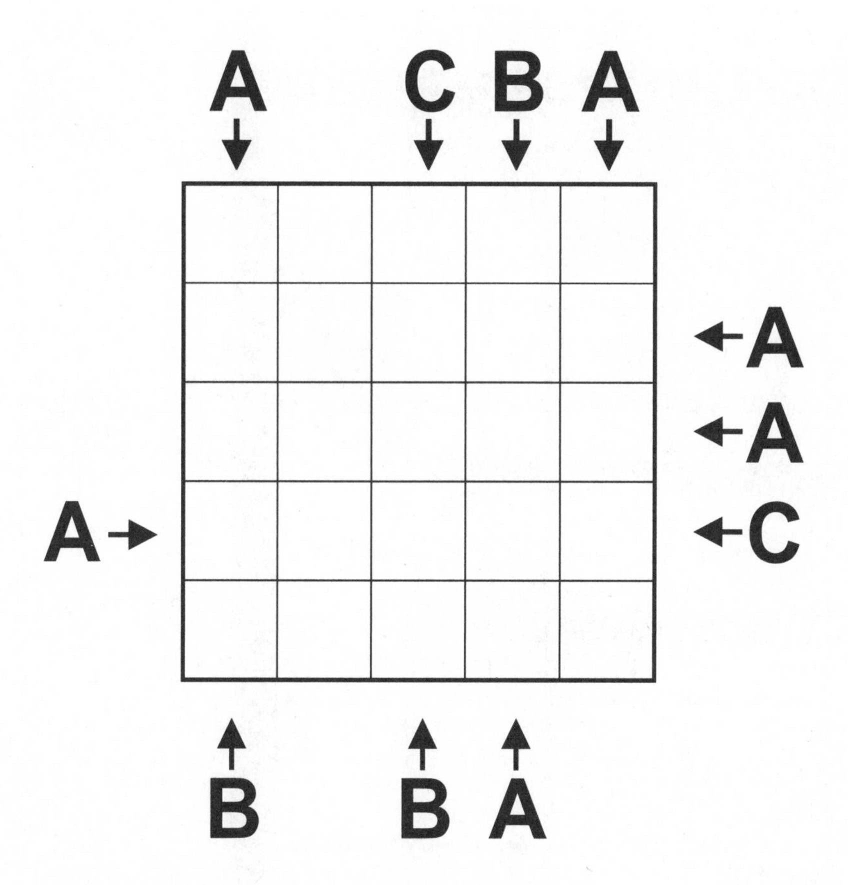

CLUELESS CROSSWORD

Complete the crossword with common uncapitalized seven-letter words, based entirely on the letters already filled in for you.

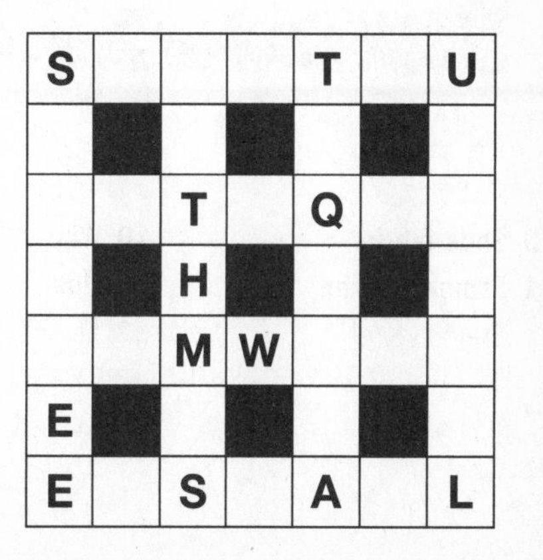

★★ Looped Path

Draw a continuous, unbroken loop that passes through each of the red, blue, and white squares exactly once. Move from square to square in a straight line or by turning left or right, but never diagonally. You must alternate passing through red and blue squares, with any number of white squares in between. To get you started, part of the path is drawn.

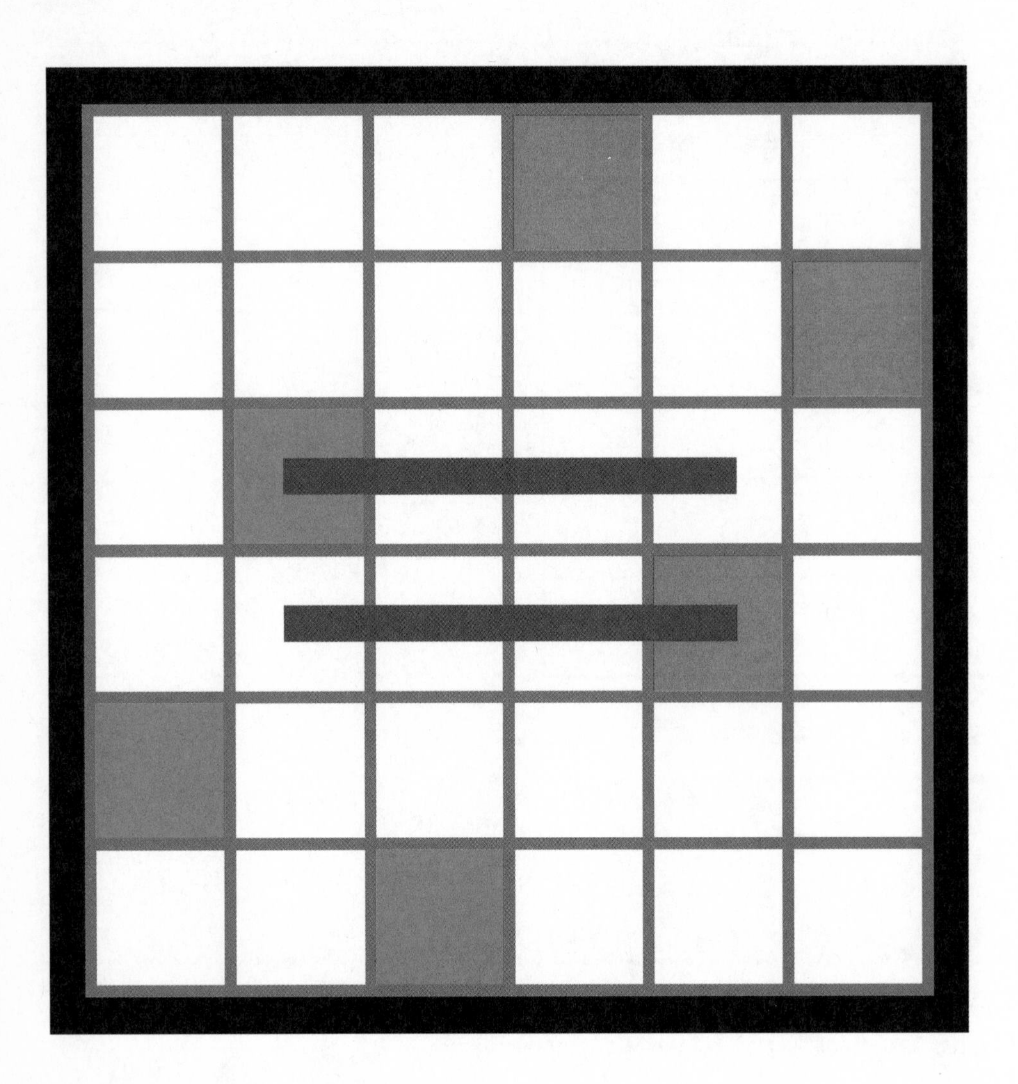

BETWEENER

What four-letter word belongs between the word at left and the word at right, so that the first and second word, and the second and third word, each form a common compound word?

LEAP _ _ _ _ MAN

★★★ Line Drawing

Draw three lines, each from one edge of the square to another edge (all of which will intersect at the same point), so there are figures of the same size and shape in all six of the regions.

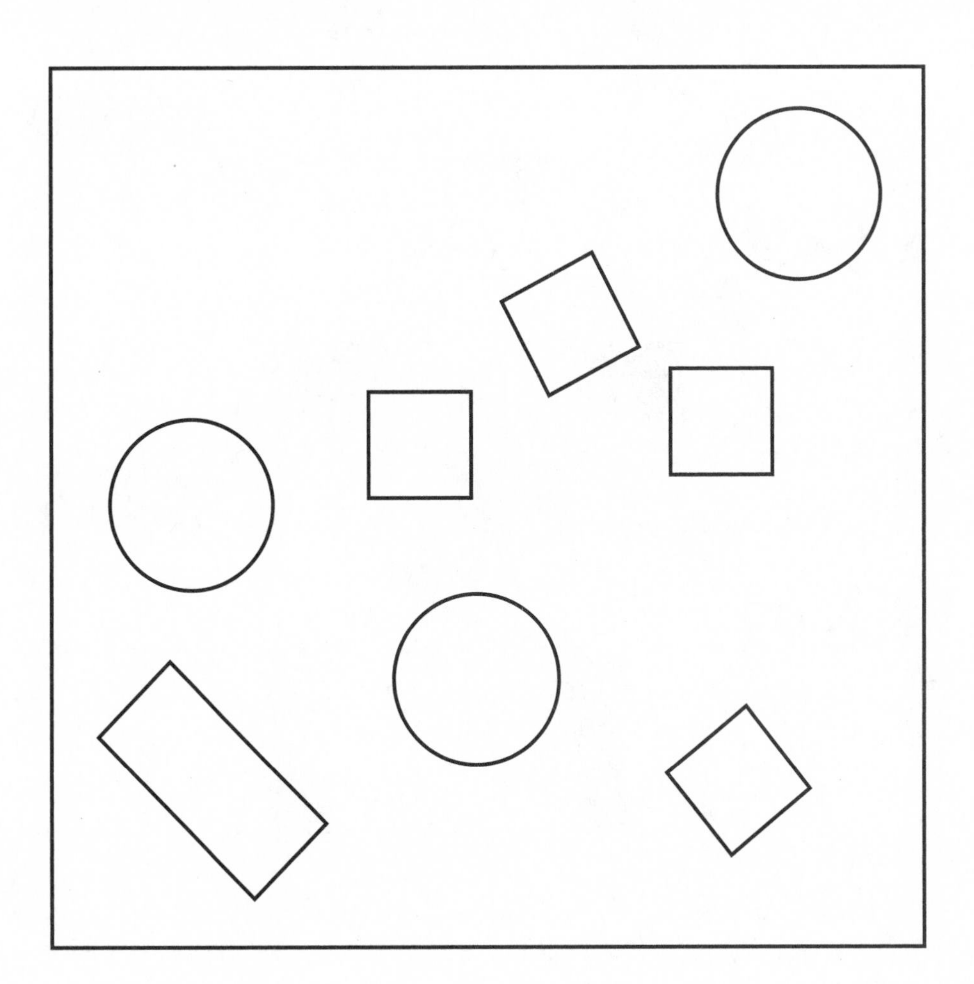

THREE OF A KIND

Find the three hidden words in the sentence that go together in some way.

For most Americans, skin diving requires diligent lessons.

★★★ Toppings by Robert H. Wolfe

ACROSS

1 Picket-line crosser
5 Little rascals
9 Lose control
14 "Tall" story
15 Non-pro sports org.
16 Angular pipe
17 Cost to play
18 Dye
19 Personal preference
20 Race for kids
23 For this reason
24 Forever and __
25 Haddock relative
28 Small measure
30 "I've had enough!"
32 Word of surprise
35 Detonator
38 Wholesale quantity
40 South American resort
41 Shed
42 Thoroughbred's quest
47 Timber tree
48 Give priestly authority to
49 New Mexico city
51 Bread buy
52 Big times
55 Athens rival
59 John Singleton film
61 Mideast hot spot
64 Box-office receipts
65 Filled with enthusiasm
66 Flexible
67 Get an __ effort
68 Move, to a Realtor
69 Very cold
70 Ornery one
71 AMA part

DOWN

1 Hide away
2 Wooden craft
3 Church area
4 Paged
5 Counting everythng
6 1109, once
7 Bamboo lover
8 Filled up
9 Make do with
10 Neutrogena competitor
11 Workout target
12 Earthenware vessel
13 Sheepish one
21 Wire feature, perhaps
22 Indian queen
25 Hot drink
26 Doctoral hurdles
27 Oceanic measurement
29 Artist Chagall
31 *Gigi* studio
32 Role seeker
33 Annoy continually
34 Stage comment
36 Formal address
37 Horn sound
39 Ecol. watchdog
43 Be postponed
44 Higgins, to Eliza
45 Dryers' partners
46 "Uh-uh!"
50 African hot spot
53 Ancient Mexican
54 Muddle
56 Wanders about
57 Works hard
58 Append
59 *Ed Wood* role
60 Ring decisions
61 Short time out
62 Self-importance
63 Jazz pianist Evans

★★ Find the Ships

Determine the position of the 10 ships listed to the right of the diagram. The ships may be oriented either horizontally or vertically. A square with wavy lines indicates water and will not contain a ship. The numbers at the edge of the diagram indicate how many squares in that row or column contain parts of ships. When all 10 ships are correctly placed in the diagram, no two of them will touch each other, not even diagonally.

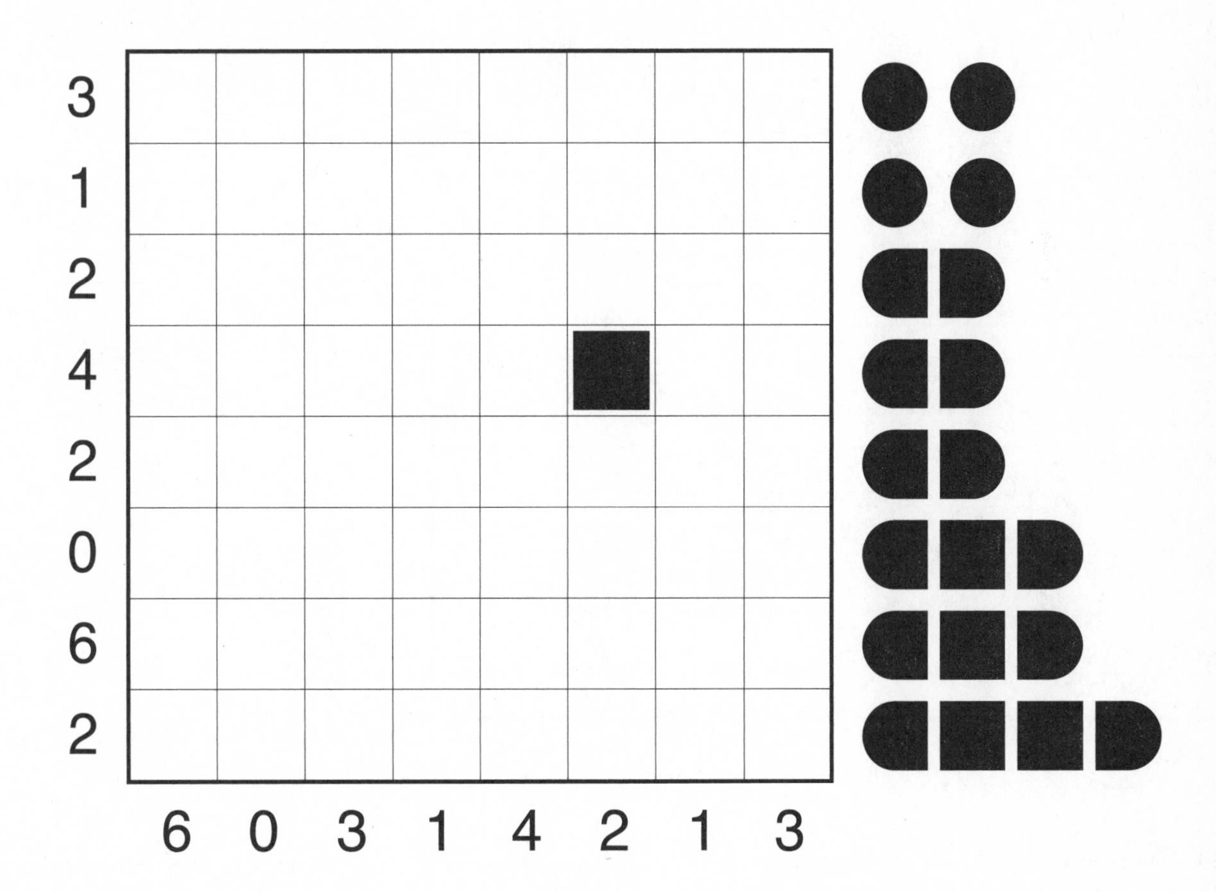

TWO-BY-FOUR

The eight letters in the word NOTIFIED can be rearranged to form a pair of common four-letter words in only one way, if no four-letter word is repeated. Can you find the two words?

_ _ _ _   _ _ _ _

★★★ Hyper-Sudoku

Fill in the blank boxes so that every row, column, 3x3 box, *and* each of the four 3x3 gray regions contains all of the numbers 1 to 9.

	9			1		8	5	
3			2	8	6		7	
9	2	1						
			4			3		
	8			6		9		
					4			
	3	4	9	7				5

MIXAGRAMS

Each line contains a five-letter word and a four-letter word that have been mixed together (the order of the letters in each word has not been changed). Unmix the two words on each line and write them in the spaces provided. When you're done, find a multipart answer to the clue by reading down the letter columns in the answers.

CLUE: Confident comment

A B H O R L E R N = _ _ _ _ _ + _ _ _ _

S O N A C L E V E = _ _ _ _ _ + _ _ _ _

A C I N G T E L E = _ _ _ _ _ + _ _ _ _

S T E A K I N G Y = _ _ _ _ _ + _ _ _ _

★★★ Name of the Game by Kevin Donovan

ACROSS

1 Ask for opinions
5 Shady deal
9 Porky's pal
14 Medicinal plant
15 Fashionable Chanel
16 Simone's school
17 Orange skin
18 Choir part
19 Tiler's filler
20 Conspirator's line
23 Begat
24 Payable
25 Ad ender
28 Possesses
29 Basketball shot
33 Dedicate, as time
35 Less reassuring, perhaps
37 In the past
38 Potential buyer's line
43 Socks
44 Ran off together
45 Move back
48 Getz of jazz
49 Cooling-system part
52 NATO member
53 It's found underground
55 Keep score
57 Salesman's line
62 Steamed
64 Baker's appliance
65 Corporate communication
66 It may be grand
67 Look after
68 Screen symbol
69 Neato
70 Cupid alias
71 Thomas Hardy girl

DOWN

1 Louisiana county
2 *Twelfth Night* character
3 Unsocial sorts
4 Cliff projection
5 "Beat it!"
6 Bubbly beverage
7 Successful legislation
8 Bellowed, as Bossy
9 Extent
10 Field measure
11 Ballpark frank
12 Winter ailment
13 Even so
21 More peculiar
22 Llama chew
26 Tingling sensation
27 Sugar source
30 Swiss canton
31 Riviera city
32 Ship structures
34 Empty space
35 Fencing piece
36 Laughfest
38 Drive-__
39 Garden gear
40 Intensify
41 Place to unwind
42 Oscar de la __
46 "Go on ..."
47 Work sites for RNs
49 Swindle
50 Los __, NM
51 WWII-era scarcity
54 Chew the scenery
56 Word on a ticket
58 List finisher
59 Assert as accurate
60 Game for gamblers
61 Objectives
62 A thing's
63 Noisy quarrel

★★★ Fences

Connect the dots with vertical or horizontal lines, so that a single loop is formed with no crossings or branches. Each number indicates how many lines surround it; squares with no number may be surrounded by any number of lines.

	3	3					1
				2			3
3			3				1
1	3						
						0	1
3				3			2
2			3				
3					3	3	

WRONG IS RIGHT

Which of these four words is misspelled?

A) pompadour
B) pomagranate
C) pomposity
D) pommel

★★ Dotty

Draw a line from square to square, moving either horizontally and vertically, so that all squares have been visited once. You may pass from one square to another only if it contains a dot of the same color and size. Note that many squares have small dots on top of large dots.

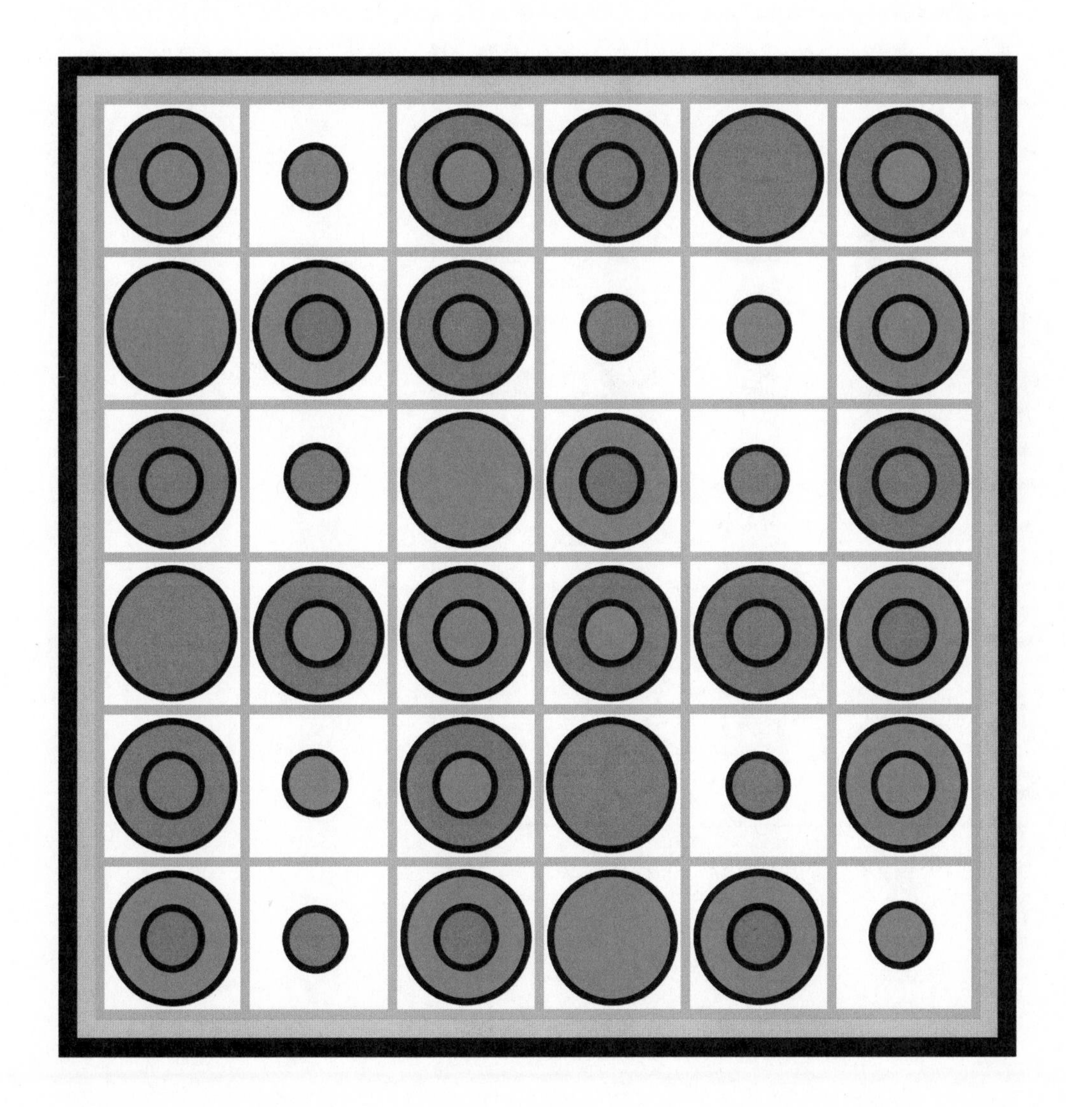

SAY IT AGAIN

What five-letter word can be either a mode of transportation or a type of tool?

_ _ _ _ _

★★ Number-Out

Shade squares so that no number appears in any row or column more than once. Shaded squares may not touch each other horizontally or vertically, and all unshaded squares must form a single continuous area.

6	4	5	2	1	2
3	1	4	2	3	3
5	2	2	2	6	3
2	5	3	6	4	3
1	4	3	1	2	5
4	2	6	3	5	4

THINK ALIKE

Unscramble the letters in the phrase JULEP MAP to form two words with the same or similar meanings.

________________ ________________

★★★ Sparklers by Doug Peterson

1	2	3	4	■	5	6	7	8	9	■	10	11	12	13
14				■	15					■	16			
17				■	18					■	19			
20				21						22				■
23			■	24			■	■	25					26
27			28		■	29	30	31			■	32		
■	■	■	33		34	■	35			■	36			
■	37	38				39				40				■
41				■	42			■	43			■	■	■
44			■	45				46	■	47		48	49	50
51			52			■	■	53	54		■	55		
■	56					57	58				59			
60				■	61					■	62			
63				■	64					■	65			
66				■	67					■	68			

ACROSS

1 Sheet size
5 Sedate
10 Munch on
14 Track event
15 Gung-ho
16 Robust
17 "Just __!"
18 Prefix for national
19 Pt. of some signatures
20 Valuable card in pinochle
23 '70s hoops grp.
24 Mock apple __
25 Soon
27 Bite playfully
29 Dull finish
32 "I'm impressed!"
33 eBay action
35 Science class, briefly
36 RCA rival
37 Basalt and pumice
41 Work on a road
42 Silent acknowledgment
43 "How dare __!"
44 Period of history
45 Laura of *ER*
47 Appt.-book headings
51 Rebel yell, for one
53 DSL co.
55 Guffaw syllable
56 Initiating a conversation
60 Warty critter
61 Fictional bell town
62 "Diana" singer
63 Chip in a chip
64 Alpine refrain
65 Go after
66 Lyrical tributes
67 Thrill to pieces
68 Sea swirl

DOWN

1 "Good" Roman emperor
2 Sushi-bar condiment
3 Glacial mass
4 Part of a guitar
5 Ray Bradbury genre
6 Type of bicycle
7 Not behind
8 Bright thought
9 College building
10 Porcelain ware
11 New employee's reference
12 Vocal shortcuts
13 Just painted
21 Sight-related
22 Small bill
26 Your, old-style
28 Up to the task
30 Put up with
31 Quirky trait
34 *Hans Christian Andersen* star
36 Stubby tail
37 Wanderer
38 Put too much stock in
39 Versailles veto
40 Vitality
41 Hyena's hand
45 Acct. for the future
46 Royal seal
48 Was a kvetch
49 Changed a yacht's course
50 Bizarre
52 Hands over
54 Swiped
57 Tinseltown favorite
58 Zilch, in Zacatecas
59 Alleviate
60 Eastern principle

★★★ 123

Fill in the diagram so that each rectangular piece has one each of the numbers 1, 2, and 3, under these rules: 1) No two adjacent squares, horizontally or vertically, can have the same number. 2) Each completed row and column of the diagram will have an equal number of 1s, 2s, and 3s.

							3	
		1						
1								
		3		1				
							1	
				3				
							2	
								3

SUDOKU SUM

Fill in the missing numbers from 1 to 9, so that the sum of each row and column is as indicated.

	15	11	19
19		8	
13	3		
13			4

★★★ Find the Ships

Determine the position of the 10 ships listed to the right of the diagram. The ships may be oriented either horizontally or vertically. A square with wavy lines indicates water and will not contain a ship. The numbers at the edge of the diagram indicate how many squares in that row or column contain parts of ships. When all 10 ships are correctly placed in the diagram, no two of them will touch each other, not even diagonally.

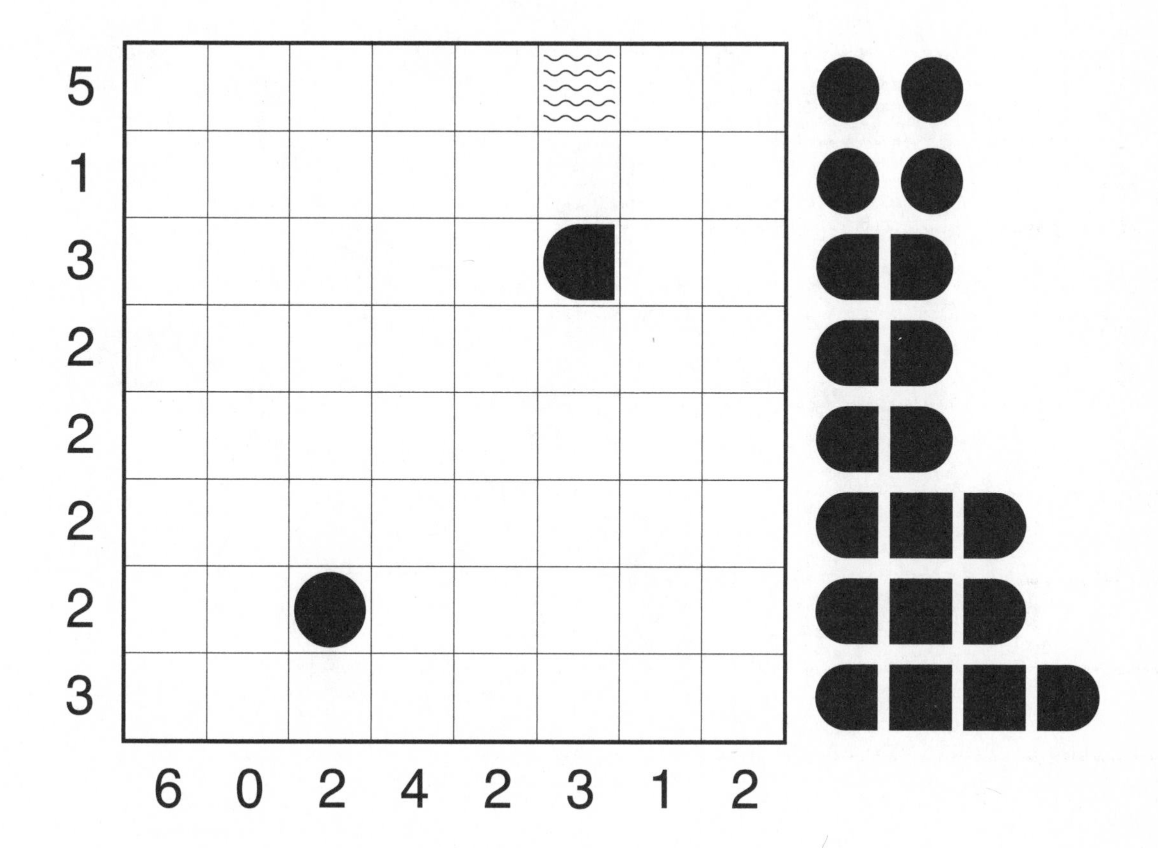

TWO-BY-FOUR

The eight letters in the word OFFICIAL can be rearranged to form a pair of common four-letter words in only one way, if no four-letter word is repeated. Can you find the two words?

_ _ _ _ _ _ _ _

★★★ Weather Report by Shirley Soloway

1	2	3	4	■	5	6	7	8	9	■	10	11	12	13
14				■	15					■	16			
17				18						■	19			
20						■	■	21		22				
23			■	24		25	26	■	27				■	■
■	■	■	28					29			■	30	31	32
33	34	35			■	36				■	37			
38					■	39			■	40				
41				■	42				■	43				
44			■	45					46			■	■	■
■	■	47	48			■	49				■	50	51	52
53	54					55	■	■	56		57			
58				■	59		60	61						
62				■	63					■	64			
65				■	66					■	67			

ACROSS

1 *Major Barbara* playwright
5 Sailor's pal
10 "Terrible" time
14 Central part
15 Limber
16 Dixieland trumpeter
17 Ticket buyers' insurance
19 Ancient Peruvian
20 Big name in soul
21 Eventually
23 GPs, e.g.
24 Yale students
27 Jazz phrase
28 Cake cover
30 Bottom-row keyboard key
33 Tough nut to crack
36 Florence's river
37 Unexciting
38 Prone to dripping
39 Harmful
40 Bisect
41 Arrow Shirt rival
42 List of choices
43 Ore evaluation
44 Lower a lawn
45 Moolah
47 Have on
49 Bastes or alters
50 Propellerless plane
53 Rock-concert souvenirs
56 Recessed space
58 Mouthful of moonshine
59 Conversation starter
62 Walkway
63 Soup alternative
64 Writes
65 Galley marking
66 TV actors' honors
67 Art Deco artist

DOWN

1 "Get lost!"
2 Secret stash
3 Celestial ram
4 Exited
5 Hawaiian's "thanks"
6 Ripen
7 __-tac-toe
8 Members of the deer family
9 "What is your answer?"
10 Larcenous one
11 Unexpected gains
12 Aquatic mammal
13 Command to a canine
18 Soda flavor
22 Russian fighter plane
25 Author Allende
26 Cord components
28 __ for oneself (manage alone)
29 Bring about
31 Flowing rock
32 He and she
33 Formally proper
34 Greek liqueur
35 Doc's friend
37 Dis
40 Pain in the neck
42 Carpentry joint
45 Passenger compartment
46 66 Across, for example
48 Poker card
50 Poker card
51 Something worth seeing
52 Wasting no words
53 Oz. fractions
54 Big blow
55 Fraudulent scheme
57 Part of Batman's costume
60 Stately shade source
61 At __ (no longer a threat)

★ Chef's Special

Find these words on a French menu that are hidden in the diagram, either across, down, or diagonally.
À LA CARTE

E T T E S I O N S E G S A L A C A R T E
R T W Q P C B N S L R L U D S E C Q S B
A P T A U R A I O U S U A N I T A R G M
G A T E I I A N O B A E E C L T L C R A
O I O O L N C F A E R L T O E E V U A L
U E C S R E S H C P G B A U G R A I T F
T H U A E T M L E A E N G L U G D S E E
E F E D I S A O S L I O T I M I O I N N
L B A T N I I E Y G O D E S K A S N L F
J Y E F R O M A G E F R A I S N E D L X
S P O X Z U F P D E L O R E T I F O R P
N V N N G H U E G N P C E A L V R P M T
O O E E N R N T B M A R U U I E P E R C
T L L B E A A I C A U L J I N N R P H O
U A R V M P I T V P G J L T S I E A B M
O U O N I O N S O U P U I O N I S I I P
R V H B M O B P E R A N E G H S N E S O
C E M M O S N O C Y E Q U T E V T E Q T
C N B C R U D I T E S E O U T A W R U E
F T Q M O U S S E U P E R C P E U K E Z

BAGUETTE
BÉARNAISE
BISQUE
BOMBE
BRIOCHE
CALVADOS
CANAPÉ
CHASSEUR
COMPOTE
CONSOMMÉ
COQ AU VIN
CORDON BLEU
COULIS
CRÊPE
CROUTONS
CRUDITÉS
CUISINE
ÉCLAIR
FLAMBÉ
FLORENTINE
FOIE GRAS
FONDUE
FROMAGE FRAIS
GÂTEAU
GLACÉ
GRATIN
HOLLANDAISE
JULIENNE
LÉGUMES
LYONNAISE
MERINGUE
MOUSSE
NOISETTE
OMELETTE
ONION SOUP
PATÉ
PETITS FOURS
PETITS POIS
PROFITEROLE
PURÉE
QUICHE LORRAINE
RAGOUT
SNAILS
VINAIGRETTE
VOL-AU-VENT

IN OTHER WORDS

There is only one common uncapitalized word that contains the consecutive letters TIY. What is it?

____

★★ Alternating Tiles

Starting at a yellow tile somewhere at top and moving either horizontally or vertically, draw a path through the yellow and red tiles to the bottom. You may not pass through two tiles of the same color consecutively.

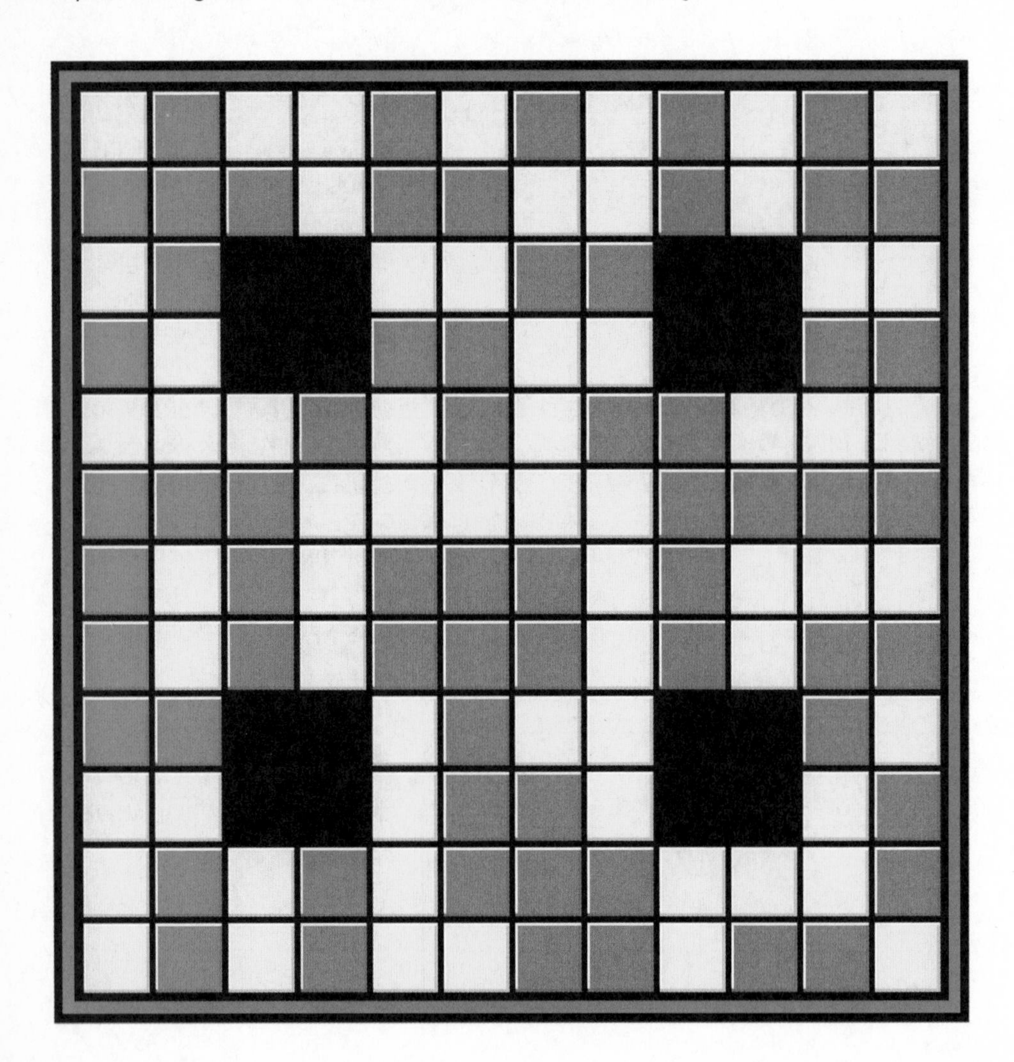

SMALL CHANGE

Change one letter in each of these two words, to form a common two-word phrase.

BAD HITTER

____

★★★ Star Search

Find the stars that are hidden in some of the blank squares. The numbered squares indicate how many stars are hidden in the squares adjacent to them (including diagonally). There is never more than one star in any square.

					2				
			1		4		2	1	
	3								
			1	4			1		2
				4					
	1	2						3	
					5				
			1		2		2		

CHOICE WORDS

Form three six-letter words from the same category, by selecting one letter from each column three times. Each letter will be used exactly once.

A	V	T	E	R	E	_ _ _ _ _ _
A	T	R	N	E	Y	_ _ _ _ _ _
S	R	E	E	U	T	_ _ _ _ _ _

★★★ Sign Language by Doug Peterson

1	2	3	4	5	■	6	7	8	9	■	10	11	12	13
14					■	15				■	16			
17					18					■	19			
20				■	21				■	22				
■	■	■	23	24			■	25	26			■	■	■
27	28	29	■	30			31					32	33	34
35			36					■	37					
38				■	■	39		40	■	■	41			
42				43	44	■	45		46	47				
48						49					■	50		
■	■	■	51				■	52			53	■	■	■
54	55	56			■	57	58			■	59	60	61	62
63				■	64					65				
66				■	67				■	68				
69				■	70				■	71				

ACROSS

1 *My Fair Lady* lady
6 Antidrug cop
10 Deep black
14 Sit in on
15 Dept. of Labor branch
16 *Peter Pan* dog
17 Animation technique
19 Level
20 Bark excitedly
21 Thom of shoedom
22 Fabled beauty
23 Fall birthstone
25 Sullen
27 Monastic title
30 Interrogation-room feature
35 Isaiah follower
37 Give comfort to
38 "__ off?"
39 Unrefined
41 Yucky stuff
42 Filmed again
45 Bank offering
48 Young tough guys in '30s films
50 Polished off
51 A fan of
52 Weary worker's cry
54 Succulent
57 Genealogy diagram
59 Tooth part
63 Inventor center?
64 Line for a bond analyst
66 Pesky insect
67 It means "everything"
68 *Carmen* composer
69 Levelheaded
70 Apportion, with "out"
71 Something to skip

DOWN

1 No trouble at all
2 Minstrel's instrument
3 Pedestal topper
4 Nothing
5 24/7 cash source
6 Hazy
7 Laos locale
8 Fleming of *Spellbound*
9 Has the wherewithal
10 Dovetail
11 Catch red-handed
12 Bouncing spot
13 Tall tale
18 Muscat citizen
22 Sci-fi award
24 Toy dog, for short
26 Cries of dismay
27 North Sea inlet
28 Zellweger of *Chicago*
29 Cooking byproduct
31 Belt
32 Hotel lobbies, often
33 Push aside
34 Marsh plant
36 Wipe out
40 Diplomatic deception
43 Disavow
44 Ending for absorb
46 Barely defeated
47 Police series
49 Serve a stretch
53 Lunchbox item
54 Binges
55 Arm bone
56 Director Reitman
58 Quarters cost
60 Pasta in some soups
61 Rack holder
62 Nantes noggin
64 __ Kippur
65 47 Down network

★★★ Sudoku

Fill in the blank boxes so that every row, column, and 3x3 box contains all of the numbers 1 to 9.

		4			8			
	6					9	1	
9				5	2		7	
						2		5
		7		8		3		
3		8						
	2		7	1				9
	1	5					4	
			4			6		

MIXAGRAMS

Each line contains a five-letter word and a four-letter word that have been mixed together (the order of the letters in each word has not been changed). Unmix the two words on each line and write them in the spaces provided. When you're done, find a two-part answer to the clue by reading down the letter columns in the answers.

CLUE: Wayne's Oscar film

L E T H U G E R E = _ _ _ _ _ + _ _ _ _

C L U R I M R E P = _ _ _ _ _ + _ _ _ _

B L U A R I T C H = _ _ _ _ _ + _ _ _ _

S I K E T Y E E D = _ _ _ _ _ + _ _ _ _

★★★ One-Way Streets

The diagram represents a pattern of streets. A and B are parking spaces, and the black squares are stores. Find the route that starts at A, passes through all stores exactly once, and ends at B. Arrows indicate one-way traffic for that block only. No block or intersection may be entered more than once.

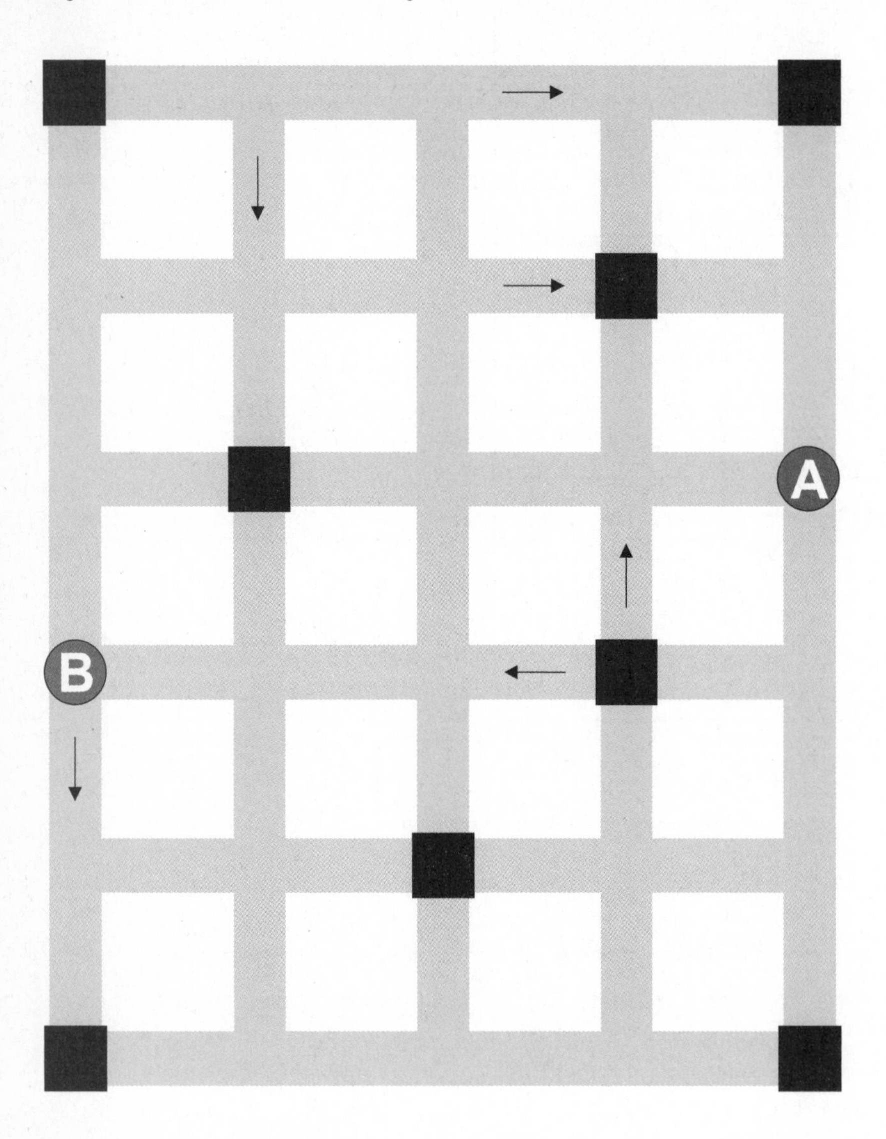

SOUND THINKING

There are two common uncapitalized words whose consonant sounds are V, R, N, and T, in that order. One of them is VARIANT. What's the other one?

____

★★★ ABC

Enter the letters A, B, and C into the diagram so that each row and column has exactly one A, one B, and one C. The letters outside the diagram indicate the first letter encountered, moving in the direction of the arrow. Keep in mind that after all the letters have been filled in, there will be two blank boxes in each row and column.

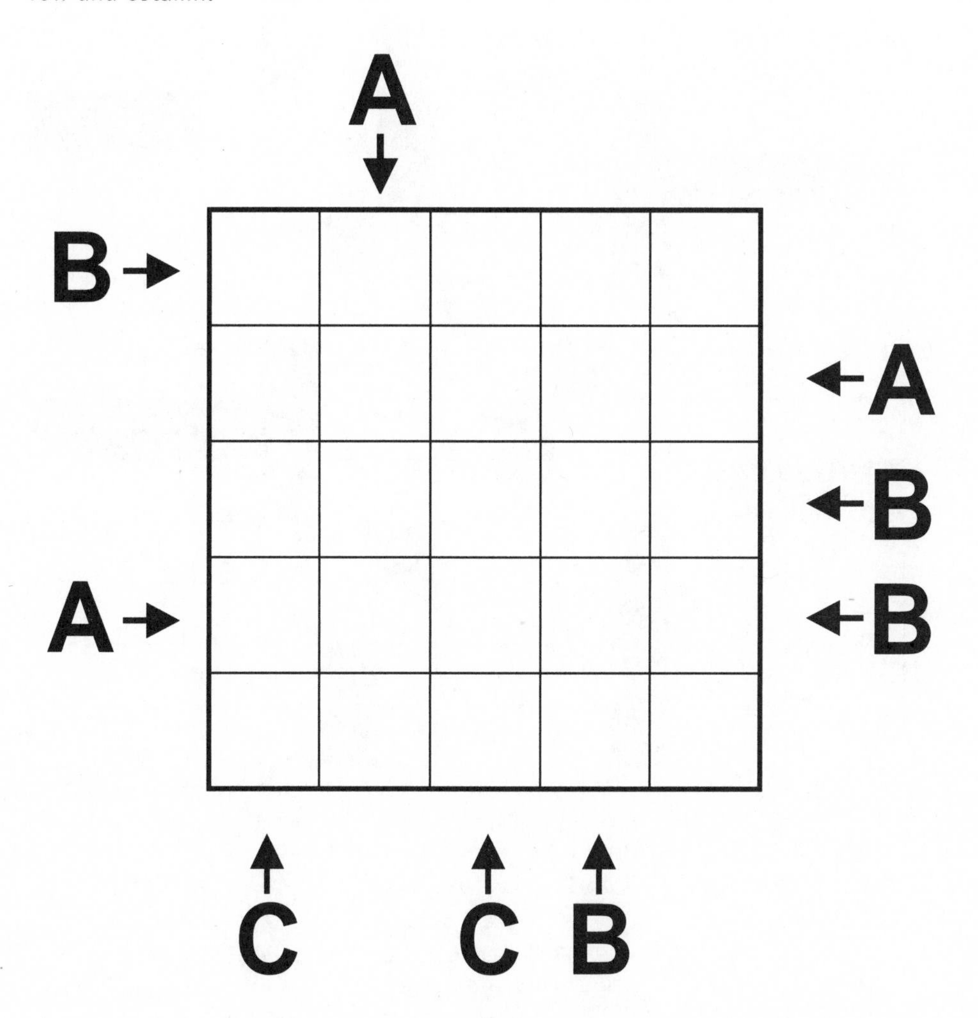

NATIONAL TREASURE

There is only one common eight-letter word that can be formed from the letters in AUSTRALIAN. If it's a plural noun, what's the word?

_ _ _ _ _ _ _ _

★★★ Making the Cut by Kevin Donovan

ACROSS

1 NL West player
6 Scandinavian reindeer herder
10 Economical
14 A as in Athens
15 Ranch unit
16 Additional
17 Martial-arts move
19 Place to stay in London
20 Atlantic island group
21 Little rascal
22 Military melody
23 Pulled apart
24 Foot ending
26 Arctic assistant
28 Magazine parts
29 They're found in digs
33 Letters' partner
37 Little ones
39 Fortune-teller's card
40 Story that's not straight
42 Catch
44 Like King's work
45 Level-headed
47 Was certain of
48 Chorus-line component
50 Explosive sound
51 Before
52 Eminent beginning
53 Widespread reputation
57 Norse god of thunder
60 HHS agency
62 Fish dish
64 Smidge
65 It often starts a fight
67 Big story
68 For all time
69 Class in Calcutta
70 Pupil's place
71 Food shop
72 Knight's ride

DOWN

1 Senegal capital
2 Cut, as a trail
3 Clothes protector
4 Visual aid
5 Bosworth or Winslet
6 Fond du __, WI
7 Most uncomfortable
8 Get-together for seniors
9 Grinder contents
10 Army-front section
11 Jazzy Fitzgerald
12 "Make it quick!"
13 Butterfly catchers
18 Pricey property
25 They're in the air
27 "Sure, I'll go along!"
30 Persia, today
31 Central part
32 Fret
33 Caused wonderment
34 Ostrich relative
35 Of two minds
36 Ginger's spot
38 Acapulco address
41 Take a good look
43 Most recent
46 Worn articles
49 Called the game
53 Parade presentation
54 Cause merriment
55 __ Carlo
56 Put a stop to
57 Evened the score
58 Crosby costar
59 Big name in elevators
61 Joint in bad condition
63 Orbital segments
66 __ Lanka

★★ Wheels and Cogs

When the crocodile turns the handle as shown, will he be rewarded with one steak or two?

BETWEENER

What five-letter word belongs between the word at left and the word at right, so that the first and second word, and the second and third word, each form a common compound word?

TOOTH _ _ _ _ _ BOARD

★★★ Find the Ships

Determine the position of the 10 ships listed to the right of the diagram. The ships may be oriented either horizontally or vertically. A square with wavy lines indicates water and will not contain a ship. The numbers at the edge of the diagram indicate how many squares in that row or column contain parts of ships. When all 10 ships are correctly placed in the diagram, no two of them will touch each other, not even diagonally.

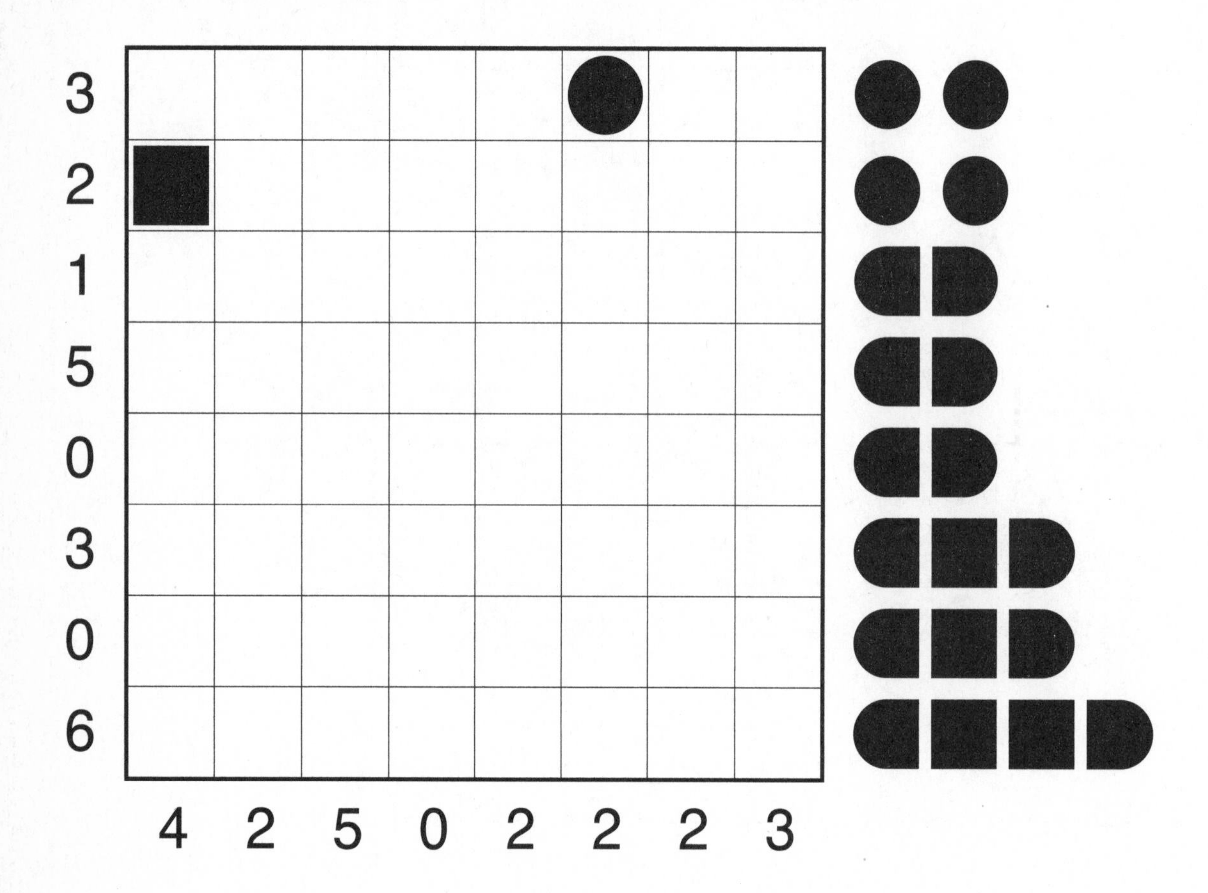

TWO-BY-FOUR

The eight letters in the word PAMPHLET can be rearranged to form a pair of common four-letter words in two different ways. Can you find both pairs of words?

_ _ _ _   _ _ _ _

_ _ _ _   _ _ _ _

★★★ 123

Fill in the diagram so that each rectangular piece has one each of the numbers 1, 2, and 3, under these rules: 1) No two adjacent squares, horizontally or vertically, can have the same number. 2) Each completed row and column of the diagram will have an equal number of 1s, 2s, and 3s.

				2				
							3	
		3			2			
3								
							1	
1								
					3			

ADDITION SWITCH

Switch the positions of two of the digits in the incorrect sum at right, to get a correct sum.

```
  478
+ 420
-----
  986
```

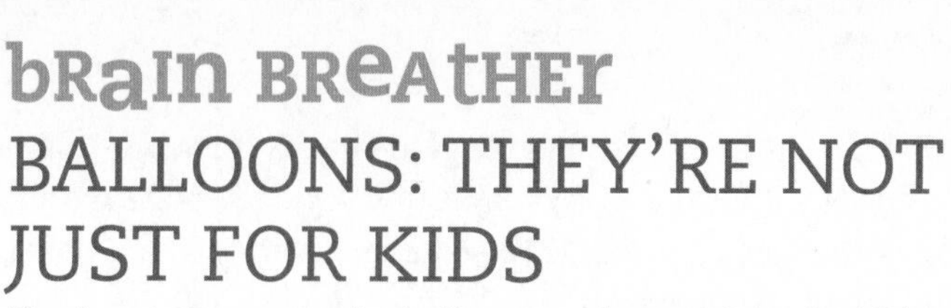

BRAIN BREATHER
BALLOONS: THEY'RE NOT JUST FOR KIDS

Check out these uses for balloons, at least a few of which we bet you never thought of!

Protect a bandaged finger
Bandaging an injury on your finger is easy; keeping the bandage dry is a different story. Try this tip: Slip a small balloon over your finger when doing the dishes, bathing, or even just washing your hands.

Make a party invitation How's this for an imaginative invitation? Inflate a balloon and pinch off the end, but don't tie a knot in it. Write the invitation details on the balloon with a bright permanent marker and let the ink dry. Then deflate the balloon, put it in an envelope, and mail it. When your guest receives it, he or she will have fun blowing up and reading this unique invitation.

Transport cut flowers When traveling with freshly cut flowers, don't bother with awkward, water-filled plastic bags. Simply fill a balloon with about ½ cup water and slip it over the cut ends of your flowers. Wrap a rubber band around the mouth of the balloon to keep it from slipping off.

Freeze for cooler punch To keep your party punch bowl cold and well filled, pour the beverage you're serving into several balloons (use a funnel) and place them in the freezer. When it's party time, peel the latex off the ice and drop a couple of "balls" into the punch bowl as needed.

Use as a hat mold To keep the shape in your freshly washed knit cap or cloth hat, fit it over an inflated balloon while it dries. Use a piece of masking tape to secure the balloon and keep it from tilting over or falling onto the ground.

Repel unwanted garden visitors
Put those old, deflated shiny Mylar balloons—the ones lying around from past birthday parties—to work in your garden. Cut them into vertical strips and hang them from poles around your vegetables and on fruit trees. They'll do a great job of scaring off invading birds, rabbits, and squirrels.

Keep track of your child The inexpensive helium-filled balloons sold in most shopping malls can be more than just a treat for youngsters; they could be invaluable in locating a child who wanders off in a crowd. Even if you keep close tabs on your kids, you can buy a little peace of mind by simply tying (not too tightly!) a balloon to your child's wrist on those weekend shopping trips.

★★★★ Scare Off by Merle Baker

ACROSS

1 Low island
4 In front
9 Sound of Washington
14 Doctors' org.
15 Alabama city
16 Period of history
17 Milk, to a pharmacist
18 They're packed up in a song
20 A way to recoil
22 For the most part
23 Easy Street's locale?
24 Greater part
25 Holds up
26 Some savings
30 Embarrass
32 Obviously contrived
33 *Norma* __
34 Brownish purple
35 Big cats
36 Brain scans
37 Mature
38 Post-lecture feature
39 Pigmented peeper parts
40 It's available to use
42 Quick ride
43 Lid attachment
44 Put on again
47 French physicist
50 Occurring near the sun
51 Farm workers' hero
53 Feel bad about
54 Preference
55 Cut back
56 HS subject
57 Samsung competitor
58 Celerity
59 Messy place

DOWN

1 Ariz. neighbor
2 Brand owned by Whirlpool
3 Sea battles of a sort
4 Attribute
5 Essential parts
6 George Jetson's son
7 Part of ACLU
8 Court figures
9 Price to pay
10 Angstrom creator
11 Ceremonial garb
12 Earth sci.
13 "So __ say"
19 Keeps happy
21 Carol start
24 Valley of Lebanon
26 __ guerre
27 '60s sitcom
28 Infatuated
29 Cong. period
30 Sail support
31 Titanic
32 Nagging suspicion
35 Astronomical distance
36 Madonna role
38 Find fault
39 Expanded
41 Soap ingredient
42 Moon goddess
44 Follies, e.g.
45 Very thin
46 Spenser's "Astrophel," for one
47 Play start
48 Stand for
49 "Hey, over here!"
50 Table-lamp part
52 Some printers, for short

★★★ Fences

Connect the dots with vertical or horizontal lines, so that a single loop is formed with no crossings or branches. Each number indicates how many lines surround it; squares with no number may be surrounded by any number of lines.

1							2
0			2	2	1	1	2
		1				3	
	2	3			1		
		1			1	1	
	3				0		
2	3	2	1	3			1
2							2

WRONG IS RIGHT

Which of these four words is misspelled?

A) ascetic
B) acetic
C) ascerbic
D) ascorbic

★★★ Number-Out

Shade squares so that no number appears in any row or column more than once. Shaded squares may not touch each other horizontally or vertically, and all unshaded squares must form a single continuous area.

2	3	1	4	5	2
5	6	6	6	1	2
6	1	4	5	3	2
6	5	4	1	2	3
1	5	5	6	6	4
4	2	3	1	6	4

THINK ALIKE

Unscramble the letters in the phrase BOW NOVICE to form two words with the same or similar meanings.

______________________ ______________________

★★★★ Differing Opinions by Ed Stein

ACROSS

1 Fountain order
5 Suns and stars
9 Confuse
14 Arraignment part
15 Claudius' successor
16 Clint's ... *Madison County* costar
17 Piltdown man, e.g.
18 Miss
19 New Zealand native
20 With 34 Across, "True!": Ptolemy/"False!": Galileo
23 Scallop's habitat
24 Sloth, for one
25 Jargon suffix
26 Flow partner
29 *Munich* actor Bana
32 CV
34 See 20 Across
39 Charlie Brown epithet
40 Help
41 Ill-wishers
43 "Definitely!": author Friedman/"Definitely not!": Columbus
48 Unlikely to happen
49 Rochester's love
50 Wall or well preceder
51 One-time go-between
54 Last in a series
56 Bran source
58 "Impossible headline!": inventor DeForest/"Future headline!": JFK
64 "Great" one
65 Recital performance
66 Def relative
68 Long-term investment
69 Utopia
70 Mitigating prefix
71 No-nos
72 Miss
73 Disorderly places

DOWN

1 Speed meas.
2 Loads
3 Jacob's first wife
4 Burdens
5 Wary
6 Part of a halter
7 Wintertime comment
8 Golf-club parts
9 Nitrogen-hydrogen compound
10 Game-show choice
11 Hit off the tee
12 Stringed instruments
13 Beethoven dedicatee
21 Spotted
22 Something sensed
26 Tonal sense
27 Dennis, to Mr. Wilson
28 The two
30 __-Tass
31 Patagonia locale
33 *Carmina Burana* composer
35 Pre-owned
36 Sea swirl
37 Spilled the beans
38 Get news of
42 Pen full of oink
44 Harry Potter et al.
45 Harbinger
46 Some decals
47 Where a shoulder meets an arm
51 Turned up the volume
52 Fitness regimen
53 Dramatist Chekhov
55 Henry Ford's son
57 Uris novel
59 Mardi Gras follower
60 Popular mixer
61 Cheers of a sort
62 [Groan!]
63 Defense acronym
67 McCourt work

★★ Straight Ahead

Enter the grid from the top; pass through all of the blue squares, then exit at right. You must travel horizontally or vertically in a straight line, and turn only to avoid passing through a black square. It is okay to retrace your path.

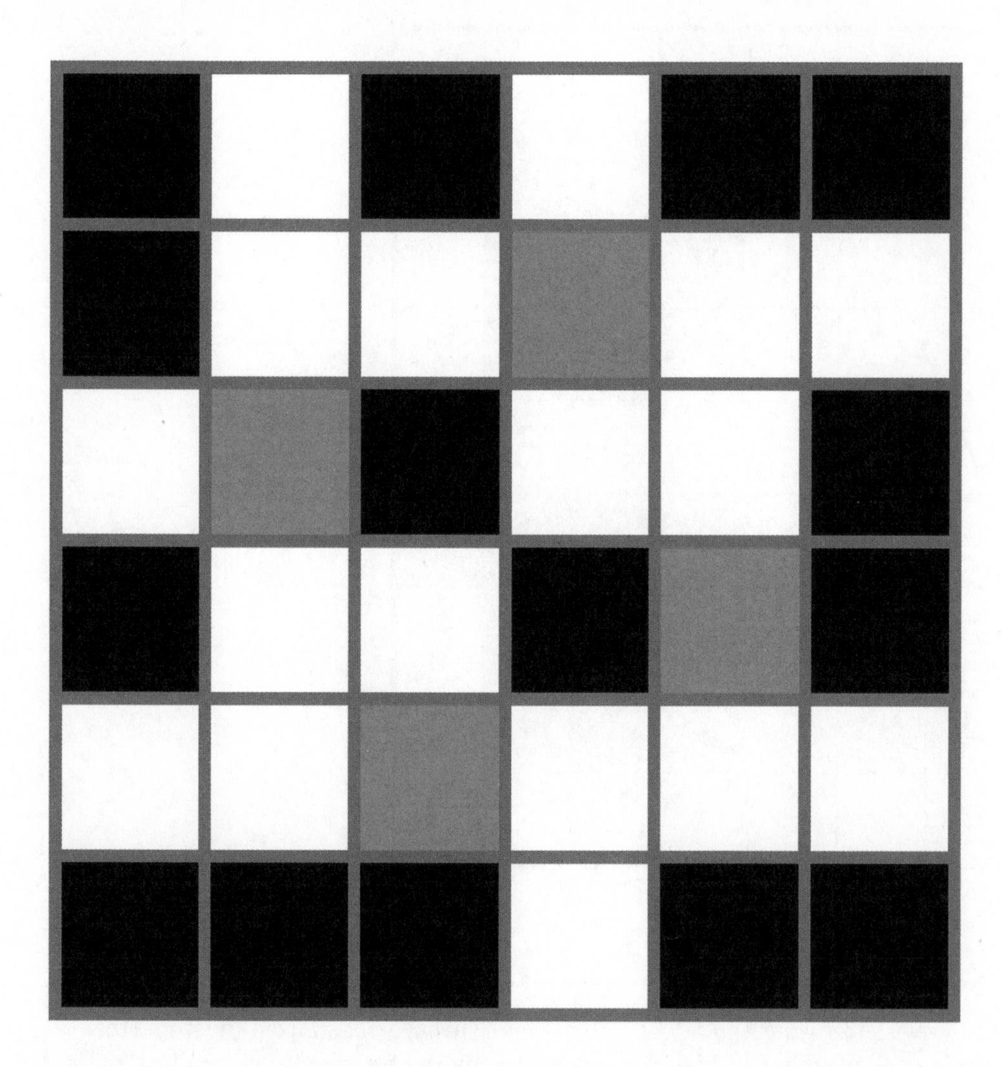

BETWEENER

What five-letter word belongs between the word at left and the word at right, so that the first and second word, and the second and third word, each form a common compound word?

APPLE _ _ _ _ _ PAN

★★★ Hyper-Sudoku

Fill in the blank boxes so that every row, column, 3x3 box, *and* each of the four 3x3 gray regions contains all of the numbers 1 to 9.

		6						
				5				2
1					8		9	
	3					1		7
		7				9	6	4
6							8	
	9		5					8
		4			7			
8		1						6

MIXAGRAMS

Each line contains a five-letter word and a four-letter word that have been mixed together (the order of the letters in each word has not been changed). Unmix the two words on each line and write them in the spaces provided. When you're done, find a two-part answer to the clue by reading down the letter columns in the answers.

CLUE: Truck driver's concern

T H E R A V I P E = _ _ _ _ _ + _ _ _ _

D E N O T E R R Y = _ _ _ _ _ + _ _ _ _

R O A C H E K A D = _ _ _ _ _ + _ _ _ _

D I S V A M O N G = _ _ _ _ _ + _ _ _ _

★★★ Wow!

Find these words starting with W that are hidden in various W shapes in the diagram. Two answers are shown to get you started.

```
R D T S P J O G F W Q W D E J A O E Z H
M Y E J H D Q Q H L H B O B D W D W C P
S W N R C P W I M R I W T R A B Z N Q L
P T O K E I S W E S K A O G K W E I U O
G M E R C E W T F K T W N N A E U F B E
W N G K C O S A E V J U O L D Y R N S W
Q J I A R H S H O O H W S O U L E U A L
W N K H W Y E W E B E R H S D F O K O P
C H E K T H R L B E W T Y I Q L U O R T
M G O T E I A A P T W T A D R P P S N W
W S A L U S D W L N W A X N E L C I R I
W O T R G E E E T O K A F F R K H E Z G
H A R H I I L R Z W G U L E P T P P A F
N I L F C S A I W T Z W S L D A X T W U
R I M L M H E A D S A W E E S F I A F E
Q X S L B J S L P D K W A T L U F X S Y
U P N A V H K W C E I W R R W H I U S H
Y G I C S N O C X T U C O O E X O C T J
V O K H Y R B X O V S C O R D S N I B Z
R V Z R E M I L F T G D D V D L M V L W
```

WADDLES
WAFER-THIN
WAFFLES
WAGTAIL
WAKEFUL
WALL CHART
WALLPAPER
WALNUTS
WAREHOUSE
WASHBASIN
WEIGHTS
WETSUIT
WHIRLPOOL
WHISPERED
WHOLESALE
WICKETS
~~WONDERFUL~~
WOODLOUSE
WOODSTOCK
WORCESTER
WORDSMITH
WORKBENCH
WORKING
WORRIED
WORSHIP
~~WRECKED~~
WRITTEN

INITIAL REACTION

Identify the well-known proverb from the first letters in each of its words.

T. P. I. M. T. T. S. ________________________________

★★★★ Platter Chatter by Raymond Hamel

1	2	3	4	■	5	6	7	8	9	■	10	11	12	13
14				■	15					■	16			
17				■	18					19				
20				21									■	■
22						■	■	23			■	24	25	26
27			■	28		29	30	■	31		32			
■	■	■	33					34						
35	36	37		■	■	38			■	■	39			
40				41	42				43	44		■	■	■
45						■	46				■	47	48	49
50			■	51		52	■	■	53		54			
■	■	55	56				57	58						
59	60									■	61			
62				■	63					■	64			
65				■	66					■	67			

ACROSS

1 Strikebreaker
5 Ones who exploit
10 For men only
14 Oxford part
15 KwaZulu-__ (South African province)
16 City founded by Pizarro
17 Puget Sound swimmer
18 Cow or chicken
20 Car-clutch component
22 NBAer
23 Piece of turf
24 Set fire to
27 "May I help you?"
28 Not __ many words
31 Brunch cocktail
33 Strange sighting
35 Melville novel
38 Shift, for one
39 Chain from Scandinavia
40 *The Dukes of Hazzard* car
45 Fluorescent paint
46 Othello, for one
47 Chinese tea
50 Hagiology subj.
51 "__ Yankee Doodle Dandy ..."
53 Went to Joe's, perhaps
55 Signal receiver
59 Foreordain
61 "Do __ others ..."
62 Gulf War missile
63 Partiality
64 Meaney of *Star Trek: Deep Space Nine*
65 ITAR-__
66 Doctorate hurdle
67 Fencing need

DOWN

1 Careless
2 Sarah Jessica TV role
3 It may be denied
4 Beauty lover
5 Far from amusing
6 River to the Mosel
7 French infinitive
8 Ways onto the highway
9 Zigzags on skis
10 Narrow cut
11 Vault mechanism
12 Drs.' org.
13 Fella's sweetie
19 First name in gymnastics
21 Dirty
25 "It's all clear to me now"
26 Where Scarlett lived
29 Turban wearer
30 Midnight follower
32 Sierra Club cofounder
33 Passepartout's boss
34 Greek sandwich
35 Chances
36 Zoo feature
37 King of Ithaca
41 Type size
42 Wakes
43 Short beards
44 Art Deco notable
47 Like some washing machines
48 Work hard
49 In
52 Wedding site
54 Bring forth
56 Includes later
57 *Simpsons* sister
58 Like some airpts.
59 Ore. clock setting
60 Sarnoff's co.

★★ Triad Split Decisions

In this clueless crossword puzzle, each answer consists of two words whose spellings are the same, except for the consecutive letters given. All answers are common words; no phrases or hyphenated or capitalized words are used. Some of the clues may have more than one solution, but there is only one word pair that will correctly link up with all the other word pairs.

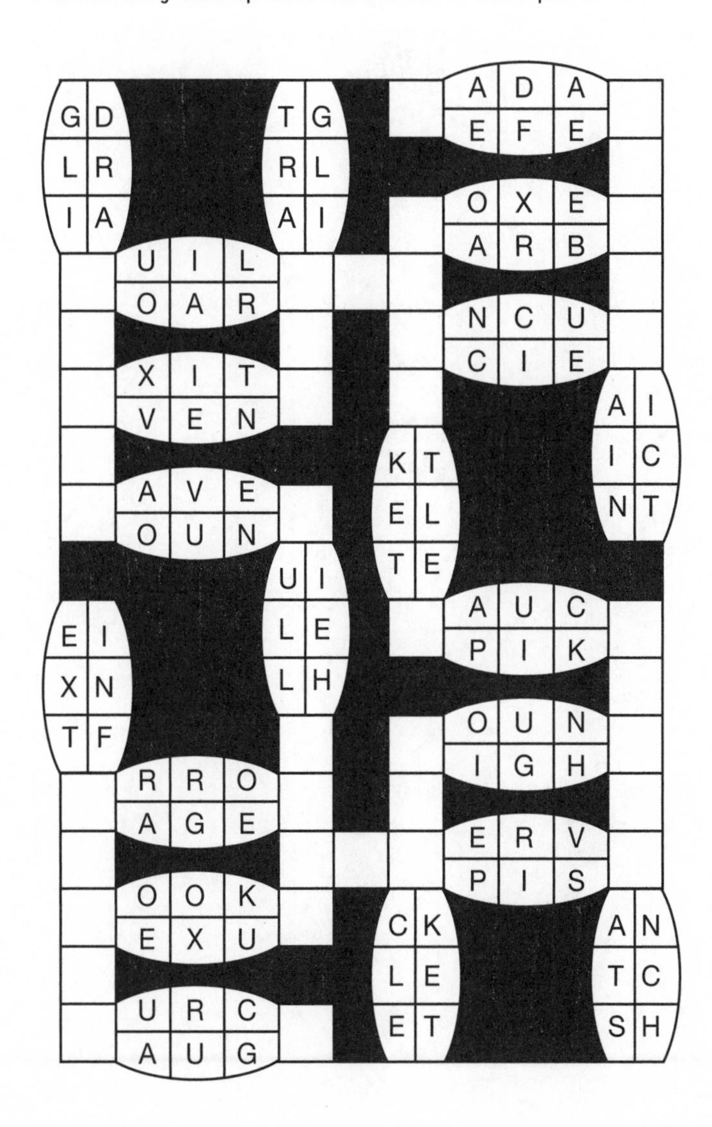

TRANSDELETION

Delete one letter from the word COLLAGEN and rearrange the rest, to get something associated with water.

____

★★★ One-Way Streets

The diagram represents a pattern of streets. A and B are parking spaces, and the black squares are stores. Find the route that starts at A, passes through all stores exactly once, and ends at B. Arrows indicate one-way traffic for that block only. No block or intersection may be entered more than once.

SOUND THINKING

Of the common uncapitalized words whose consonant sounds are W and N, in that order, only one doesn't start with a W. What's that word?

____

★★★★ Relatively Speaking by Doug Peterson

ACROSS

1 Tomato-impact sound
6 Phobos orbits it
10 *Ragtime* character
14 Artemis alias
15 NBA locale
16 Field mouse
17 Start of a quote by Abigail Van Buren
20 *House* actor
21 Most contemptuous
22 Grace ending
25 Furniture wood
27 Kitchy-__
28 Part 2 of quote
31 Specs component
35 Industrialist Hammer
36 Fraught with danger
38 Linoleum cleaner
39 More devious
40 Part 3 of quote
41 *Twelfth Night* role
43 Velvet finish
44 Beyond mischievous
46 Forwarded
47 Adds highlights to
49 Part 4 of quote
51 Towel ID
53 Street along the Seine
54 Vortex
55 Nero's first wife
59 Love: Sp.
61 End of quote
66 Arctic mass
67 *Little Mermaid* prince
68 Baseborn
69 Puts into words
70 Unit of force
71 Clog clearer

DOWN

1 Program proposed by RWR
2 Poe setting
3 Scale syllables
4 Feelers
5 Infield covering
6 Oats-and-fruit dish
7 JD holder
8 Sounds of encouragement
9 Raga master
10 Tube favorite
11 Sewing-machine inventor
12 "D'oh!" relative
13 Bridge seat
18 Invert
19 Colombian kin
22 Taken down a peg
23 *Kitty Foyle* author
24 Fur source
26 Easily reconfigured
29 Concerning
30 Drollery
32 Got melodramatic
33 Kind of mutual fund
34 Alfalfa's pal
37 Two days in December
40 Schick competitor
42 Appearing live
45 Called on
46 Holds back
48 Dishonors
50 Shade of meaning
52 Wall growth
55 Switch settings
56 Burger accompaniment
57 Weight system
58 Out of whack
60 Palette choices
62 "There's no __ team"
63 Onetime Lindbergh employer
64 Yellowstone grazer
65 Flour source

★★★ Sequence Maze

Enter the maze, pass through all the color squares exactly once, then exit, all without retracing your path. You must alternate between red and blue squares.

SAY IT AGAIN

What five-letter word can mean either "condition" or "speak"?

_ _ _ _ _

★★★ Star Search

Find the stars that are hidden in some of the blank squares. The numbered squares indicate how many stars are hidden in the squares adjacent to them (including diagonally). There is never more than one star in any square.

			1	1	1	1			
			1		2				
					2		2		1
			4		3				2
	2					3			2
			6						1
			3						
					1				
			1						

CHOICE WORDS

Form three six-letter words from the same category, by selecting one letter from each column three times. Each letter will be used exactly once.

A	A	R	O	G	R	_ _ _ _ _ _
L	O	C	N	O	E	_ _ _ _ _ _
P	L	U	L	V	E	_ _ _ _ _ _

★★★ Sudoku

Fill in the blank boxes so that every row, column, and 3x3 box contains all of the numbers 1 to 9.

		2	1		8	6		
			4		6			
3								7
1	8						3	6
5	2						1	4
4								8
			2		5			
		5	9		1	7		

CENTURY MARKS

Select one number in each of the four columns so that the total adds up to exactly 100.

31	+	16	+	19	+	20	=	100
40		28		17		22		

★★★★ Ex Factors by Richard Silvestri

1	2	3	4	■	5	6	7	8	■	9	10	11	12	13
14				■	15				■	16				
17				■	18				■	19				
20				21					22					
■	■	■	■	23			■	■	24			■	■	■
25	26	27	28			■	29	30			■	31	32	33
34					■	35				■	36			
37					38					39				
40				■	41				■	42				
43			■	44				■	45					
■	■	■	46			■	■	47			■	■	■	■
48	49	50				51	52				53	54	55	56
57					■	58				■	59			
60					■	61				■	62			
63					■	64				■	65			

ACROSS

1 Table extender
5 Prefix for bucks
9 Howled at the moon
14 __ buco
15 Norwegian royal name
16 Athenian forum
17 Pact acronym
18 PBS talk host
19 Unbending
20 Exposition?
23 Enzyme ending
24 Grazing spot
25 Word before paper or test
29 Luck personification
31 Lunar New Year
34 UFO crewman
35 Fit
36 He sang about Alice
37 Exact?
40 Nights before
41 Rosetta's river
42 Cardigan location
43 See it and seethe
44 Run out of gas
45 Tweety, for one
46 Podded plant
47 *Casablanca* pianist
48 Exchange?
57 Frequent
58 Zip
59 Curbside cry
60 Roomy dress style
61 Beat decisively
62 Stuff
63 Cosmetic purchase
64 Latin preposition
65 Rope fiber

DOWN

1 Protracted
2 Biblical twin
3 Wine area
4 Gull
5 Confusing situation
6 Take the honey and run
7 Response to a shock
8 Maintain
9 Bedrock name
10 Upset feeling
11 Mystical one
12 Leif's father
13 Miami-__ County
21 Cow
22 Church official
25 Four-time Wimbledon champ
26 *Amo*
27 Finished, as a wall
28 Interfere
29 Soup scoop
30 Skin soother
31 Refrain syllables
32 Bull in advertising
33 Stowe girl
35 It grows on you
36 __ end (over)
38 Early computer
39 Hindu master
44 Rock on the edge
45 Hoffman Oscar role
46 Ziti alternative
47 Parade about
48 "__ does it!"
49 Holy ring
50 Archaeology sight
51 Old Testament book
52 Light gas
53 Engrave with acid
54 Worry
55 Class ritual
56 Airhead

★★★ ABC

Enter the letters A, B, and C into the diagram so that each row and column has exactly one A, one B, and one C. The letters outside the diagram indicate the first letter encountered, moving in the direction of the arrow. Keep in mind that after all the letters have been filled in, there will be two blank boxes in each row and column.

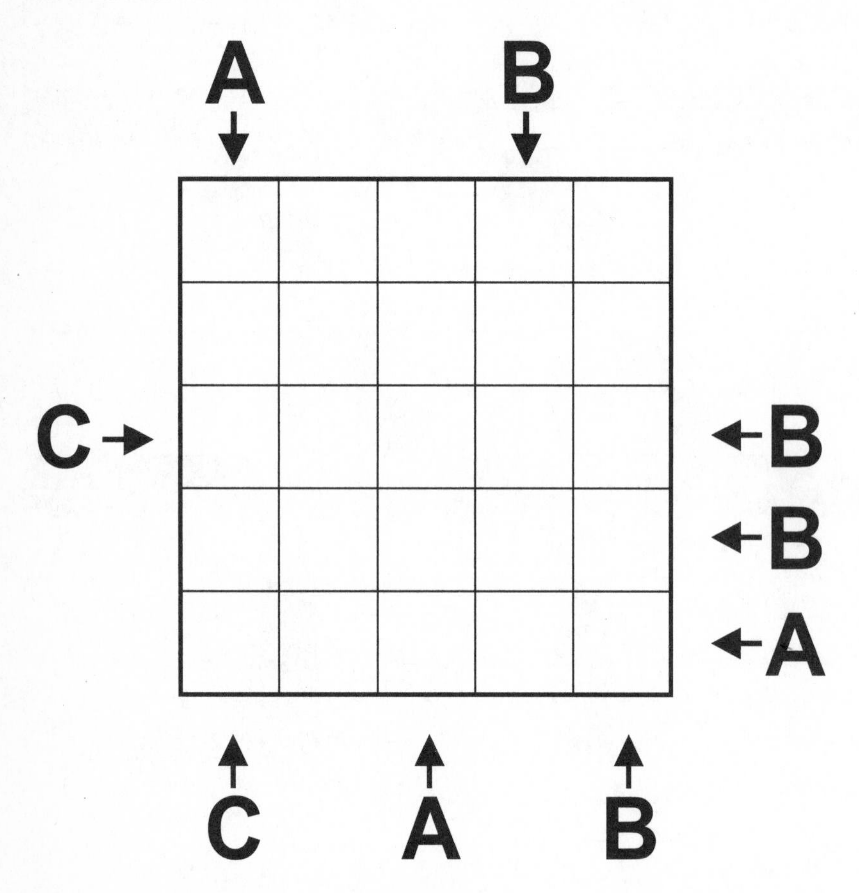

CLUELESS CROSSWORD

Complete the crossword with common uncapitalized seven-letter words, based entirely on the letters already filled in for you.

P			T	Z		
	■	C	■		■	
				G	H	T
	■		■	Z	■	
			F		H	
L	■	M	■		■	
A		Y				

★★★ Find the Ships

Determine the position of the 10 ships listed to the right of the diagram. The ships may be oriented either horizontally or vertically. A square with wavy lines indicates water and will not contain a ship. The numbers at the edge of the diagram indicate how many squares in that row or column contain parts of ships. When all 10 ships are correctly placed in the diagram, no two of them will touch each other, not even diagonally.

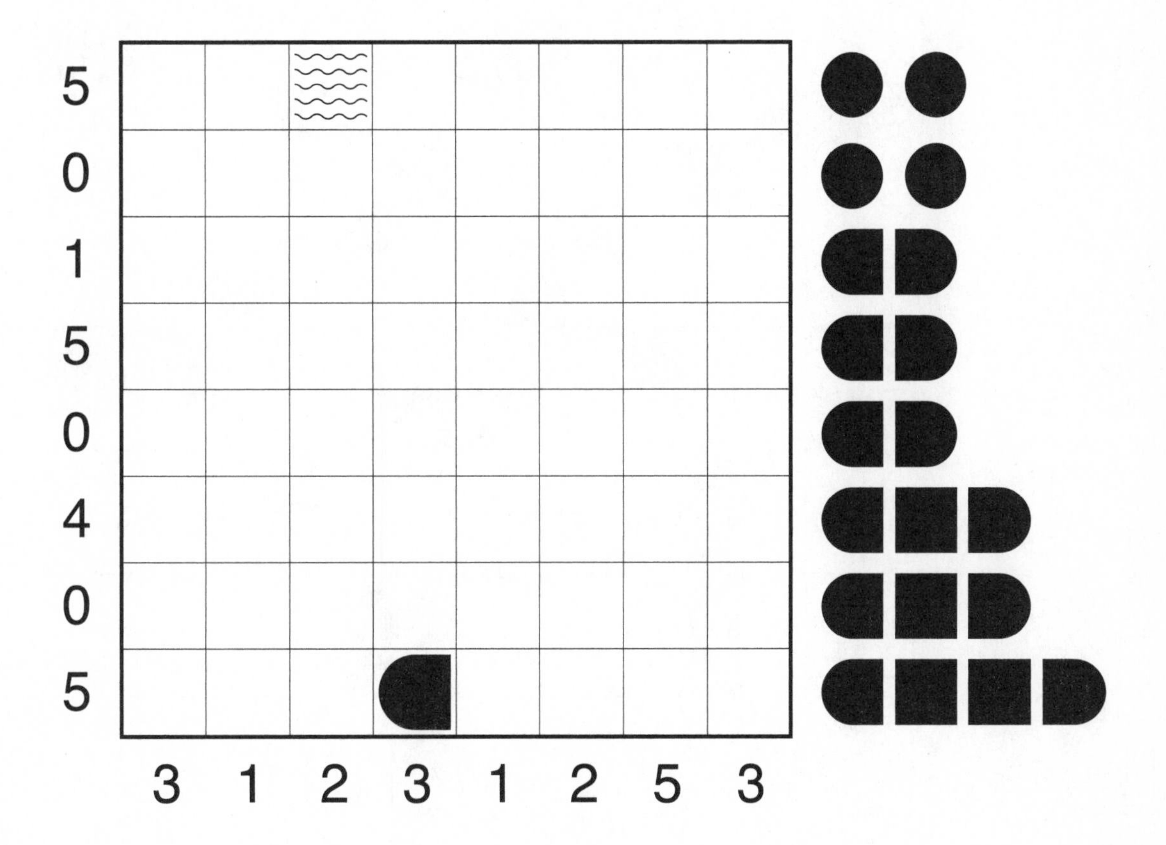

TWO-BY-FOUR

The eight letters in the word REVIEWER can be rearranged to form a pair of common four-letter words in only one way, if no four-letter word is repeated. Can you find the two words?

_ _ _ _   _ _ _ _

★★★★ Greenland by Shirley Soloway

1	2	3	4	5	■	6	7	8	9	10	■	11	12	13
14					■	15					■	16		
17					18						■	19		
20				■	21						■	22		
23				24		■	■	25			26		■	■
■	■	■	27			28	29			■	30		31	32
33	34	35	■	36				■	37	38				
39			40		■	41		42	■	43				
44					45	■	46		47		■	48		
49				■	50	51					52	■	■	■
■	■	53		54			■	■	55			56	57	58
59	60		■	61			62	63		■	64			
65			■	66						67				
68			■	69					■	70				
71			■	72					■	73				

ACROSS

1 "Blank" expression
6 Of John, Paul, etc.
11 100 pounds of nails
14 Slangy side dish
15 *Pal Joey* playwright
16 Significant span
17 Peace offering
19 *Garfield* girlfriend
20 Eight furlongs
21 Rice protagonist
22 Atticus Finch creator
23 Governor Spitzer predecessor
25 Instruct
27 Summer cooler
30 Retiree concerns
33 Presidential monogram
36 October birthstone
37 Type of writing
39 Grad student's rituals
41 Zenith
43 Youngest Marx
44 Numbers game
46 Center of activity
48 One in the viper family
49 Plan part
50 Vanity case
53 Annoyances
55 Defeats decisively
59 Telephonic trio
61 Non-nautical vessel
64 "Runaround Sue" singer
65 Top bond rating
66 Waterford's locale
68 B&B, e.g.
69 Sporting weapons
70 Certain sense of perception
71 Diminutive suffix
72 Heavy reading
73 Culottes kin

DOWN

1 Jazzy dance
2 Sly's screen spouse
3 Not vertical
4 Let on
5 Poetic preposition
6 Examine, with "over"
7 Sounds of surprise
8 Tried to catch one's breath
9 Gaming areas
10 *Chicago Hope* Emmy winner
11 Morning TV talk host
12 Perry victory site
13 1 Across kin
18 Super Bowl spectator
24 Place to purchase papers
26 Caveman creation
28 Take in
29 Lanai farewell
31 Web software, for short
32 With 33 Down, type of Wall Street order
33 See 32 Down
34 Champagne specification
35 Window-sill denizen
38 From Brno
40 Easy gait
42 Something snapped
45 Bouncy, to conductors
47 I, for one
51 Value greatly
52 Second-largest US island
54 Target game
56 Botch up
57 Completely opposite
58 Hägar's hound
59 Monopoly corner
60 Xanadu owner
62 Chestnut, for one
63 Highlands miss
67 JAMA readers

★★ Dot to Dot

Draw five squares in the diagram so that each corner of each square is on a dot. The squares may be at any angle. Dots may be used for more than one square, or not be used at all.

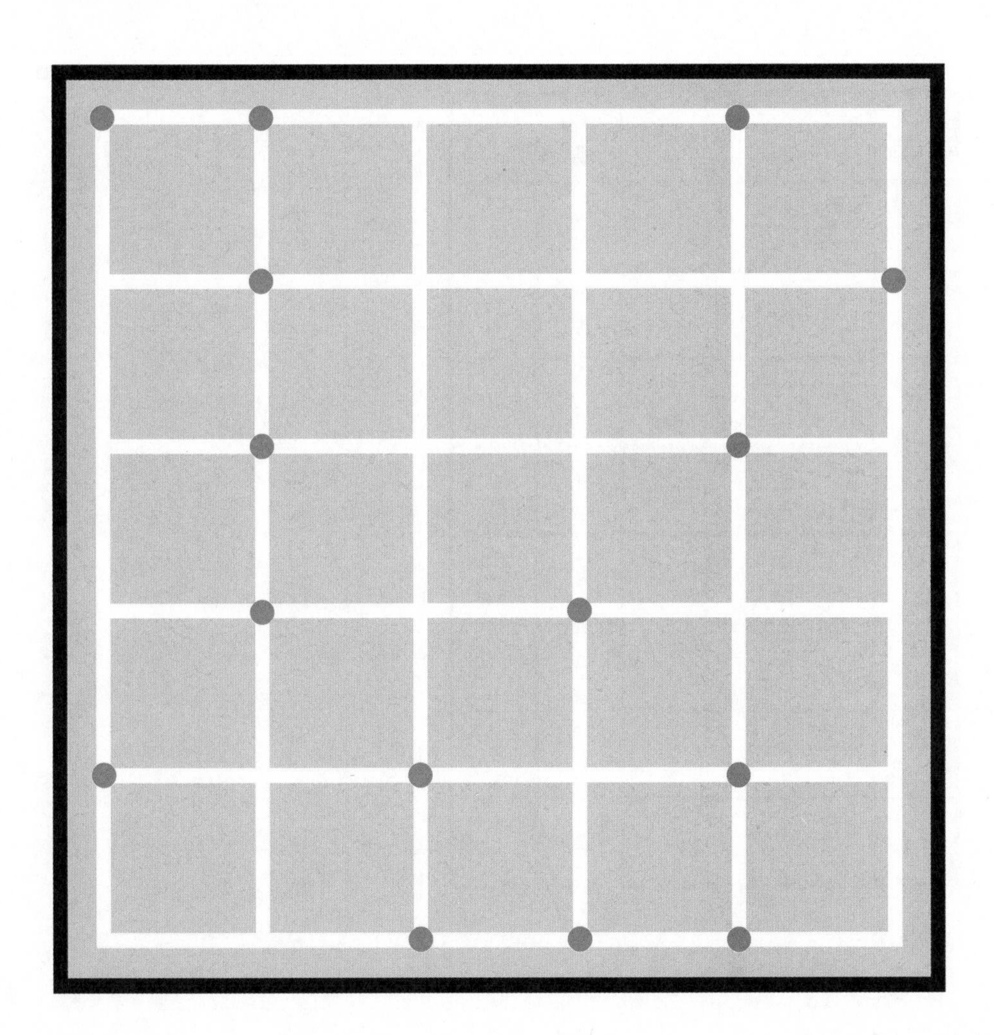

SMALL CHANGE

Change one letter in each of these two words, to form a common two-word phrase.

PRICE LOVER

____

★★★ 123

Fill in the diagram so that each rectangular piece has one each of the numbers 1, 2, and 3, under these rules: 1) No two adjacent squares, horizontally or vertically, can have the same number. 2) Each completed row and column of the diagram will have an equal number of 1s, 2s, and 3s.

							3	
		1		3				
1							2	
						3		
1								
								3
		1						
1								

SUDOKU SUM

Fill in the missing numbers from 1 to 9, so that the sum of each row and column is as indicated.

	13	16	16
13			2
13		3	
19	8		

★★★ Fences

Connect the dots with vertical or horizontal lines, so that a single loop is formed with no crossings or branches. Each number indicates how many lines surround it; squares with no number may be surrounded by any number of lines.

	0		1		3		1
3	2				3		
2							2
2			2		3		
		1		3			1
1							3
		3				2	3
3		3		3		1	

WRONG IS RIGHT

Which of these four words is misspelled?

A) cursory

B) corroboratory

C) conciliatory

D) chickory

★★★★ Around the Clock by Merle Baker

1	2	3	4	■	5	6	7	■	8	9	10	11	12	13
14				■	15			■	16					
17				18				■	19					
20								21				■	■	■
22					■	23				■	■	24	25	26
27			■	■	28				■	29	30			
■	■	■	31	32					33					
34	35	36				■	■	■	37					
38						39	40	41				■	■	■
42					■	43				■	■	44	45	46
47			■	■	48				■	49	50			
■	■	■	51	52					53					
54	55	56				■	57							
58						■	59			■	60			
61						■	62			■	63			

ACROSS

1 Luxuriate
5 Network absorbed by The CW
8 Acquire quickly
14 Minstrel's instrument
15 Mideast initials
16 Gives out
17 Settles
19 Rake over the coals
20 Funnel-shaped flower
22 Hunts, with "on"
23 Overcharge
24 Outburst from Homer
27 Discouraged
28 "New Look" designer
29 Be a bad winner
31 It may be dazzling
34 Newspaper piece
37 Really enjoys
38 Burt Reynolds series
42 Corolla part
43 Comic-strip penguin
44 Tempe sch.
47 Pizarro's quest
48 Word with silk or syrup
49 Styling shop
51 Crayon color
54 Like some paint
57 They're annoying
58 Not crazy about
59 College sr.'s test
60 Monthly pmt.
61 Tailor's measurement
62 Fashion monogram
63 Change the decor of

DOWN

1 Ad media
2 *Sleeping Beauty* princess
3 Put on a 48 Down
4 *South Park* kid
5 Versed in
6 Makes a connection
7 Counterfeit
8 Assent
9 Pirate, for one
10 Supporter
11 DC insider
12 Tony winner Hagen
13 L.A. setting
18 Family member
21 Zhivago's love
24 Follows persistently
25 Pearl Harbor locale
26 WWW address starter
28 Discouraged
29 Delighted
30 Lo-cal
31 One of a famous trio
32 Trompe l'__
33 Affirmative votes
34 Seized vehicle
35 Unceasingly
36 Nix
39 Henchman
40 Nicely resilient
41 Cravings
44 Alternate gene form
45 Became disenchanted
46 Paris-based intl. agcy.
48 Place for data
49 Norm: Abbr.
50 More adept
51 Underground mammal
52 Tiny bit
53 Bread part
54 Here, in France
55 Speaking start
56 Musical notes

★★★ Hyper-Sudoku

Fill in the blank boxes so that every row, column, 3x3 box, *and* each of the four 3x3 gray regions contains all of the numbers 1 to 9.

						7	2	
		6	5					9
			1			8		
1		8			9		5	7
2								
			7					8
		5	2	6				
	1							
		9		7	3		8	

MIXAGRAMS

Each line contains a five-letter word and a four-letter word that have been mixed together (the order of the letters in each word has not been changed). Unmix the two words on each line and write them in the spaces provided. When you're done, find a two-part answer to the clue by reading down the letter columns in the answers.

CLUE: Floor

E B D O B Z E D E = _ _ _ _ _ + _ _ _ _

T A V I O R S O D = _ _ _ _ _ + _ _ _ _

A W O L K E N S E = _ _ _ _ _ + _ _ _ _

A C L R E T A N S = _ _ _ _ _ + _ _ _ _

★★ Split Decisions

In this clueless crossword puzzle, each answer consists of two words whose spellings are the same, except for the consecutive letters given. All answers are common words; no phrases or hyphenated or capitalized words are used. Some of the clues may have more than one solution, but there is only one word pair that will correctly link up with all the other word pairs.

TRANSDELETION

Delete one letter from the word UNCLEARED and rearrange the rest, to get a color.

____

★★★★ The A List by Merle Baker

ACROSS

1 Zip
5 Tabula __
9 Long story
13 Simile words
14 Fly-ball paths
15 Gives notice
17 Hall of Fame football coach
19 Whirlpool brand
20 Oliver of *The West Wing*
21 First drawer of the Democratic donkey
23 Son of Noah
24 __ avis
26 Untrustworthy ones
28 To the extent that
31 Waker-upper
32 Smear
33 Pet welfare org.
35 Sharp flavors
38 Hoss' big brother
40 Alexander once of *60 Minutes*
43 WWII female
44 Andrews and Carvey
46 Chicken portion
48 Hearst's kidnappers: Abbr.
49 Altria spinoff of '07
52 Noble knight
54 Bottle storage spot
56 Hang-up
57 Nipper's co.
58 False god
60 Turkish military leaders
63 Constellation's brightest
65 *The Dragons of Eden* author
68 Corday's victim
69 Sitcom stopper
70 Ladies of Sp.
71 11-year gig for 42 Down
72 Mideast capital
73 Novel plantation

DOWN

1 Slangy denial
2 Memo directive
3 Boone, for short
4 Capital of Turkey
5 Dilapidated dwellings
6 Sheet-music abbr.
7 Look over
8 Capital of Eritrea
9 Tries to hit
10 USAF weapon
11 Performer at Woodstock
12 Yearly record
16 __ Club (Costco competitor)
18 Most Oscar presenters
22 Gene in *The Gene Krupa Story*
25 *The Nazarene* author
27 Sticking point?
28 Just slightly
29 Actress Thompson
30 *Arsenic and Old Lace* director
34 Sigh of contentment
36 Festive occasion
37 Great quantity
39 Signify
41 Complains constantly
42 Actor with six Golden Globe Awards
45 Day of rest
47 United Nations Plaza display
50 DOT part
51 Thomas Paine writings
53 Thunderstruck
54 Author Stoker
55 Happy as __
59 Hawaiian figurine material
61 Pearl Mosque site
62 Mosel River tributary
64 Consumes
66 Helmed
67 Org. employing cryptologists

★★★ Solitaire Poker

Group the 40 cards into eight poker hands of five cards each, so that each hand contains two pairs or better. The cards in each hand must be connected to each other by a common horizontal or vertical side.

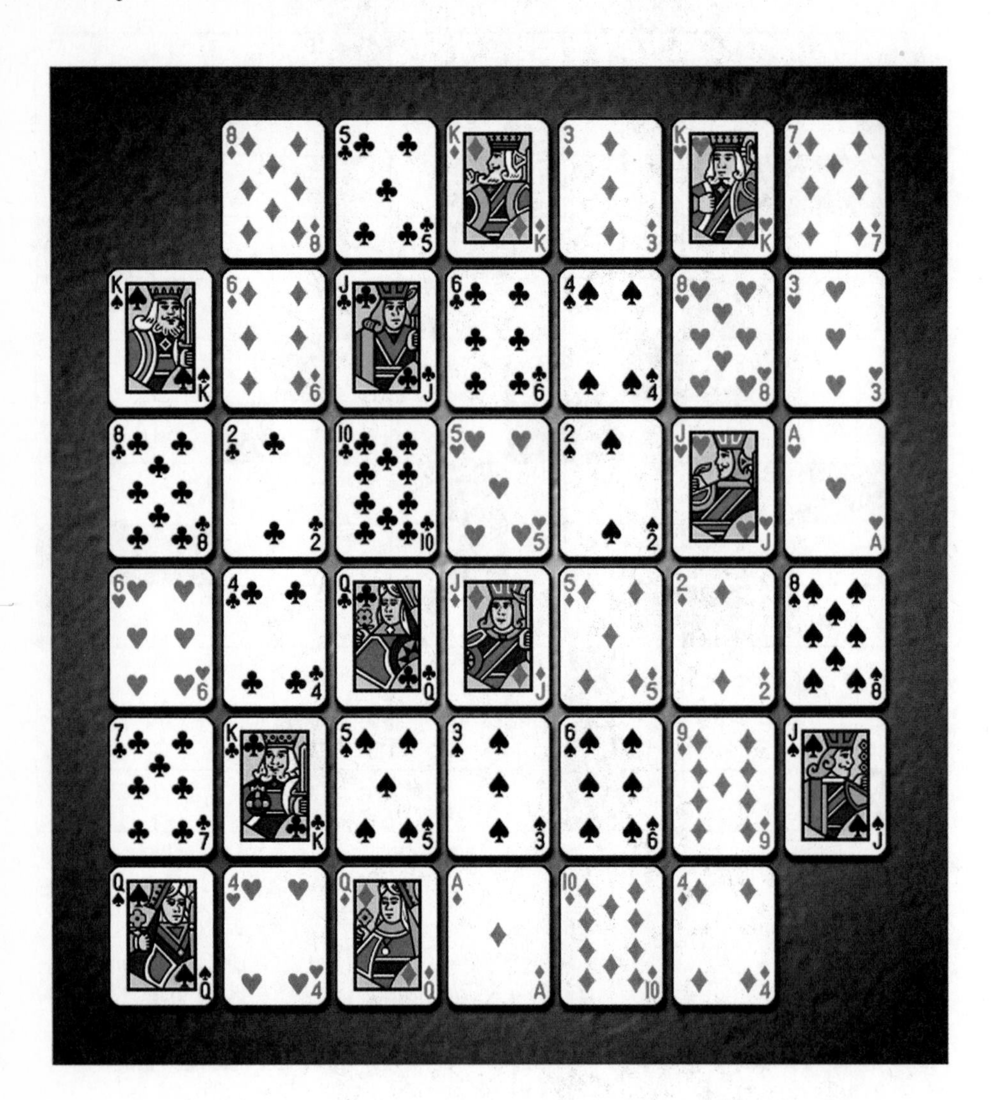

BETWEENER

What five-letter word belongs between the word at left and the word at right, so that the first and second word, and the second and third word, each form a common compound word?

WATER _ _ _ _ _ ROPE

★★★ Number-Out

Shade squares so that no number appears in any row or column more than once. Shaded squares may not touch each other horizontally or vertically, and all unshaded squares must form a single continuous area.

2	1	5	1	6	4
6	1	4	3	4	5
1	6	4	2	5	2
3	4	4	6	3	5
3	5	2	1	1	4
3	3	1	4	2	1

THINK ALIKE

Unscramble the letters in the phrase THREAD FAD to form two words with the same or similar meanings.

________________ ________________

★★★ One-Way Streets

The diagram represents a pattern of streets. A and B are parking spaces, and the black squares are stores. Find the route that starts at A, passes through all stores exactly once, and ends at B. Arrows indicate one-way traffic for that block only. No block or intersection may be entered more than once.

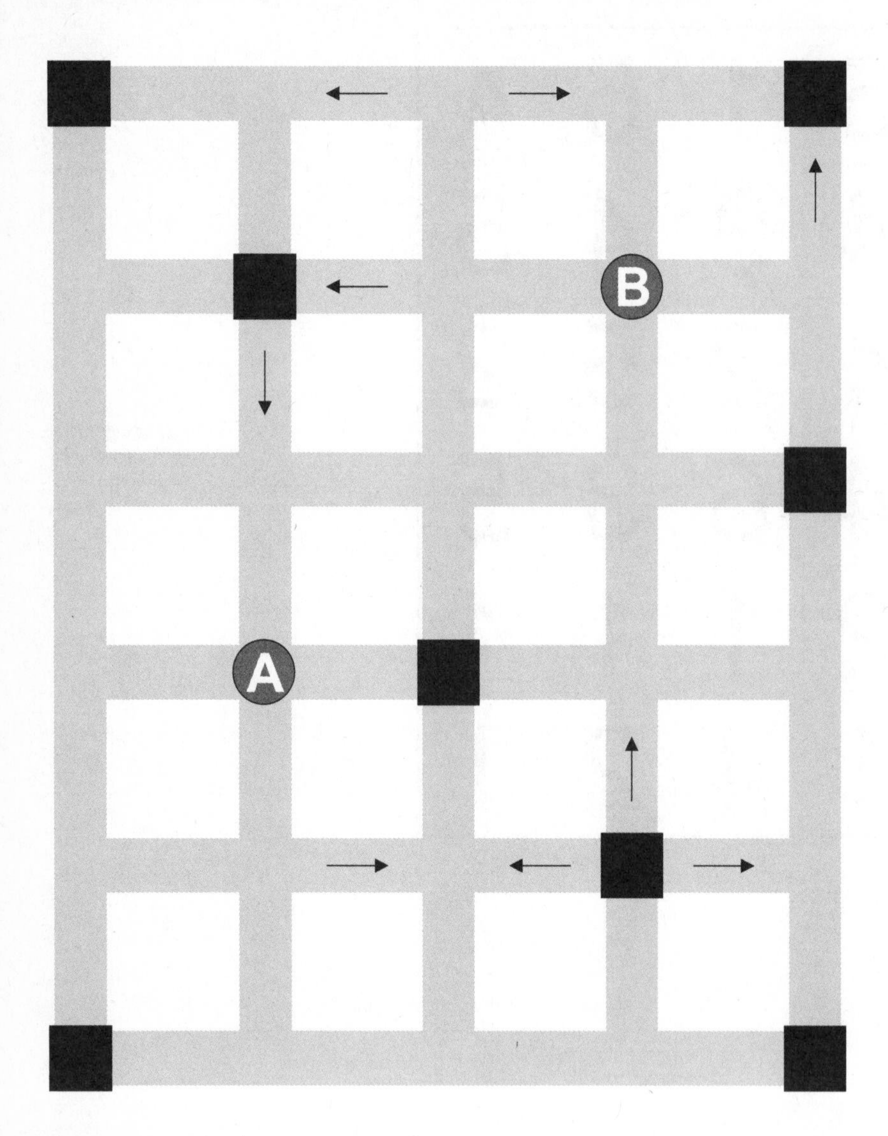

SOUND THINKING

There is only one common uncapitalized word whose consonant sounds are Y, N, Y, and N, in that order. What is it?

____

★★★★ Aural Antonyms by S.N.

ACROSS

1 Betray horror
5 Marine starter
9 Candy holders
14 Turkish title
15 Place to step
16 Quadruple-gold winner in Berlin
17 Inappropriate ceremony?
19 Noble gas
20 Sandra's costar in *Speed*
21 Clobbers
23 Talking Bible beast
24 Shows a preference
26 Tops without buttons
28 Pacific salmon
30 Chinese philosopher
34 On-the-go diva?
38 Where JFK served in WWII
39 Jai __
40 Lived
42 *Cope Book* aunt
43 Cooper character
46 Counterfeit film spool?
49 Rate
50 Wooden coaster
51 Broad belt
53 Cooper character
58 Hard to see
61 Model Campbell
63 Newlywed acquisition
64 Charlton Heston film
66 Interfere with a soft drink?
68 Backyard fare, for short
69 Word-processor purchaser
70 Oklahoma Indian
71 Urban-renewal candidates
72 Jersey remarks
73 For fear that

DOWN

1 Rubbernecks
2 Feel the same
3 Sand bar
4 Velvet fabric
5 Opp. of dep.
6 *Password*, for one
7 Golden Rule word
8 Rep
9 Stadium accommodation
10 Be short
11 Lucy Lawless TV role
12 Son of Seth
13 Certain IDs
18 Bag man
22 Large seaweed
25 Director Browning
27 Temperate
29 Six kings of Norway
31 Went fast
32 Unaltered
33 Footnote notation
34 __ ghanouj
35 Eskimo knives
36 Warship weapons: Abbr.
37 Cry of dread
41 *Rebel Without a Cause* Oscar nominee
44 Behavior, so to speak
45 Greek peak
47 Prefix for plunk
48 Money that sings
52 Sort of tame
54 Add to the register
55 Make smile
56 Carpentry grooves
57 Thoughtful
58 Entanglements
59 Its name means "To Above"
60 Brown shade
62 High-protein food
65 DJIA company
67 JAMA readers

★★★ Sudoku

Fill in the blank boxes so that every row, column, and 3x3 box contains all of the numbers 1 to 9.

3	5		2		6			1
	7						9	4
			4					
6						4		3
2		8						6
					7			
4	9						3	
1			8		5		6	7

MIXAGRAMS

Each line contains a five-letter word and a four-letter word that have been mixed together (the order of the letters in each word has not been changed). Unmix the two words on each line and write them in the spaces provided. When you're done, find a two-part answer to the clue by reading down the letter columns in the answers.

CLUE: Eliot work

C L O A N A B E L = _ _ _ _ _ + _ _ _ _

F I L D O L S E X = _ _ _ _ _ + _ _ _ _

E D U A D G E R S = _ _ _ _ _ + _ _ _ _

F A R M I E T S S = _ _ _ _ _ + _ _ _ _

★★★ Star Search

Find the stars that are hidden in some of the blank squares. The numbered squares indicate how many stars are hidden in the squares adjacent to them (including diagonally). There is never more than one star in any square.

				2		1			
		1							
1			3			4		2	
				2		1		1	
						1			1
		2		2					
							2		2
		2							
			2	2	2		2		

CHOICE WORDS

Form three six-letter words from the same category, by selecting one letter from each column three times. Each letter will be used exactly once.

C	A	R	N	S	T	_ _ _ _ _ _
R	U	R	I	O	P	_ _ _ _ _ _
T	A	D	R	I	H	_ _ _ _ _ _

★★★★ River Heads by Richard Silvestri

ACROSS

1 Paper holder
6 In oxfords, say
10 Practice in the ring
14 Fete
15 Silents star Negri
16 Evidence of lost ground?
17 Athenian marketplace
18 Over, in Heidelberg
19 Supreme Norse god
20 Free-for-all
22 Leave one's seat
23 Get the fare down
24 Xanadu, for one
26 Bee home
30 Best
32 Signs of hunger
33 Turn toward midnight
34 Wet behind the ears
37 Big beef purchase
38 Begat
39 Lost Dutchman, for one
40 Dot follower, at times
41 Power source
42 Far-reaching view
43 Maroon
45 Stumble
46 Cry on the set
48 Spigoted server
49 Toad feature
50 Politician, periodically
57 Oratorio song
58 Gets a move on
59 Camel kin
60 Type of horse
61 *Desperate Housewives* role
62 Boundary
63 Building wings
64 Car trouble
65 Helps, as a hood

DOWN

1 Niger neighbor
2 Ad art
3 Before too long
4 Eve's opposite
5 What the faithful say
6 Burst, as of energy
7 Rail rider
8 Sub in a tub
9 Grew dim
10 Tennis attire
11 Corn expert
12 Prime partygoers
13 First name of Bridget Jones' portrayer
21 A Camptown racer
25 State rep.
26 Church recess
27 Receipt stamp
28 Part of DJIA
29 Candles representation
30 Unit of capacitance
31 Agenda component
33 Legal claim
35 Start a pot
36 Become frayed
38 Stopped, as a flow
39 Big bucks, for short
41 Sign of a hit
42 Plain
44 Children of Uranus
45 Monastery address
46 Open-eyed
47 Sing in the snow
48 Perturbed
51 Staff member
52 Chow __
53 Silver-tongued
54 Application starter
55 Give off
56 "Phooey!"

★★★ Tractor Maze

Enter the maze where indicated at bottom, pass through all the stars exactly once, then exit at left. You may not retrace your path.

SAY IT AGAIN

What five-letter word can be either a piece of furniture or a verb meaning "postpone"?

_ _ _ _ _

★★★ Pathfinder

Starting from the shaded letter in the center, move up, down, left, or right one letter at a time, to trace a path of 19 chemical elements. Every letter will be used exactly once. To give you a hand, the initial letters of each element are listed below, in the order in which you'll find them.

U	I	N	A	N	S	U	H	P	S	O
M	Z	I	R	I	T	R	O	N	P	H
M	C	N	U	O	R	N	E	O	O	P
E	Y	H	N	G	E	N	S	A	T	N
R	D	M	O	L	I	I	S	M	G	O
C	R	U	C	I	S	U	I	U	R	A
U	O	I	D	A	R	M	D	K	E	L
R	G	E	L	A	N	U	O	C	I	N
Y	T	N	P	T	I	M	S	D	U	M
N	I	N	T	G	S	G	O	L	I	C
I	R	O	U	N	T	E	N	C	A	L

1. S__________
2. U__________
3. Z__________
4. M__________
5. T__________
6. I__________
7. T__________
8. C__________
9. N__________
10. A__________
11. P__________
12. N__________
13. N__________
14. P__________
15. R__________
16. H__________
17. P__________
18. G__________
19. S__________

WHO'S WHAT WHERE?

The correct term for a resident of the United Arab Emirates is:

A) Uaerian B) Emirian

C) Emirite D) Arabemiri

★★★ ABC

Enter the letters A, B, and C into the diagram so that each row and column has exactly one A, one B, and one C. The letters outside the diagram indicate the first letter encountered, moving in the direction of the arrow. Keep in mind that after all the letters have been filled in, there will be two blank boxes in each row and column.

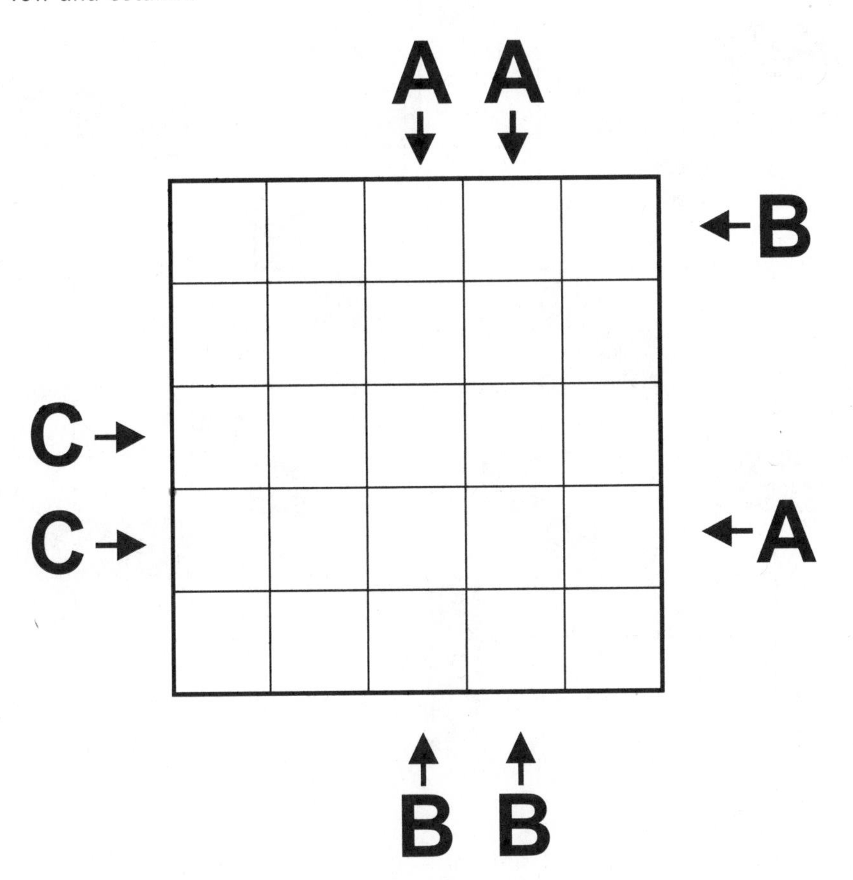

CLUELESS CROSSWORD

Complete the crossword with common uncapitalized seven-letter words, based entirely on the letters already filled in for you.

P			M	B		
	■		■		■	
L		C				C
	■	H	■		■	E
			G			D
I	■		■	Z	■	
M	U	S				

★★★★★ Themeless Toughie by Doug Peterson

ACROSS

1 Sure thing
8 Major pipeline
15 Pearson successor
16 Montmartre denizen
17 For whom loans are assets
18 Rode
19 Merger result of 1955
21 Energy source
22 Sweet refreshers
25 Old man
26 NBA nickname
27 Literature fellowship grp.
28 Sills et al.
33 Accurate
35 Down the drain
36 Wrecks, in Wimbledon
37 Fifth qtrs.
38 Wicker sporting equipment
39 Keep __ on (control)
40 Product first called I-Scream Bars
42 Loads of lettuce
44 Geometric prefix
45 Agcy. established in 1970
46 Opp. of "prescription"
47 Ft. Riley locale
48 "Bananaphone" artist
51 Stir
53 Makes reference
55 Silver Stater
59 Neighborhood near Copacabana
60 Rift
61 Bead on a blade
62 Marrow

DOWN

1 Code for Lambert Field
2 Have a life
3 Laughs
4 Ancient literary works
5 Squawk
6 Chester, for Charles
7 City on the Black Warrior River
8 Peruvian purrer
9 It's near Scorpius
10 White mouse
11 Kremlin Colonel relative
12 On
13 Something newsworthy
14 Edwards, sometimes
20 "Search me"
22 Waterproof wear
23 National Park since 1980
24 Needs a dishwasher, probably
26 Time piece
28 French pronoun
29 Denominator of Ohm's law
30 Muppet pal of Elmo
31 Nautical adverb
32 Lack of activity
34 Risky business
38 Website ending
40 BCE part
41 Roast participants
43 Website architect
47 Base character
48 Steal from
49 Mont Pelvoux, for one
50 Achilles heel
51 Posthaste
52 Impending times
54 Rock-music genre
56 Babel
57 Terps' org.
58 Christened

bRaIn BReAtHEr

CREATIVITY: THAT CERTAIN SOMETHING

Herewith, some observations about creativity from some very creative minds:

Some people see things that are and ask, Why? Some people dream of things that never were and ask, Why not? Some people have to go to work and don't have time for all that.

—GEORGE CARLIN

Creativity comes from trust. Trust your instincts. And never hope more than you work.

—RITA MAE BROWN

Creativity requires the courage to let go of certainties.

—ERICH FROMM

When inspiration does not come to me, I go halfway to meet it.

—SIGMUND FREUD

Creativity is allowing yourself to make mistakes. Art is knowing which ones to keep.

—SCOTT ADAMS

Rules are made for people who aren't willing to make up their own.

—CHUCK YEAGER

Originality is unexplored territory. You get there by carrying a canoe—you can't take a taxi.

—ALAN ALDA

Those who do not want to imitate anything, produce nothing.

—SALVADOR DALÍ

Punishing honest mistakes stifles creativity. I want people moving and shaking the earth and they're going to make mistakes.

—H. ROSS PEROT

★★★★ Find the Ships

Determine the position of the 10 ships listed to the right of the diagram. The ships may be oriented either horizontally or vertically. A square with wavy lines indicates water and will not contain a ship. The numbers at the edge of the diagram indicate how many squares in that row or column contain parts of ships. When all 10 ships are correctly placed in the diagram, no two of them will touch each other, not even diagonally.

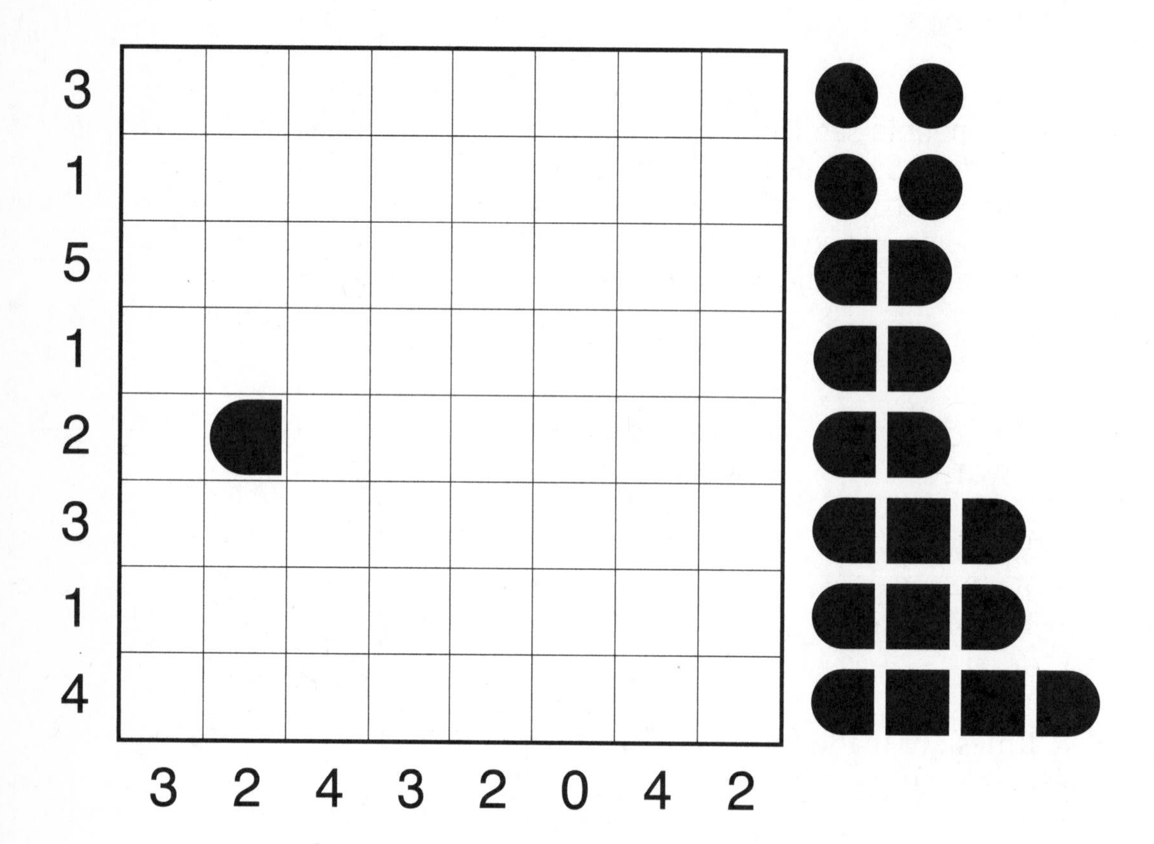

TWO-BY-FOUR

The eight letters in the word TABLEAUX can be rearranged to form a pair of common four-letter words in only one way, if no four-letter word is repeated. Can you find the two words?

_ _ _ _   _ _ _ _

★★★★ Hyper-Sudoku

Fill in the blank boxes so that every row, column, 3x3 box, *and* each of the four 3x3 gray regions contains all of the numbers 1 to 9.

			8					
								7
6				4			3	
5			2			8		
		6				5		9
		2	9					
8	7	5						
	9	3					7	1

BETWEENER

What six-letter word belongs between the word at left and the word at right, so that the first and second word, and the second and third word, each form a common compound word?

JACK _ _ _ _ _ _ HEAD

★★★★★ Themeless Toughie by S.N.

ACROSS

1 Bench sitters
9 Stay with
15 Withdrawn
16 Enthusiastic shout
17 Address of many bars
18 Retreats
19 Chemical not made since 1995
20 By the way
22 Some bears
23 Force
24 Bears' home
25 Rallies
26 Echo's punisher
27 Atomic
31 Vehicles first made in Switzerland
32 Don't give up
33 Extent
34 Popular twosomes
35 Experimenter's electromagnets
38 "Voyaging through strange __ of thought": Wordsworth
39 "Tut tut" singers
40 Ancient mariner
41 Well
42 Chihuahua chamber
46 A matter of when and where
48 Dynamo
49 Royal epithet
50 Future
52 Tasmania's highest point
53 Fan favorites
54 Felt
55 Strikes

DOWN

1 Goes like the wind
2 Opening
3 Out of line
4 Inappropriate behavior
5 Representation
6 It's lucky in Chinese culture
7 Something to order
8 Arch quality
9 Innovator of early TV
10 Lotus sports-car model
11 Jellied delicacy
12 '20s Hollywood idol
13 *Big Beat Heat* subject
14 Precedent setters
21 Eagle's objective
23 Eagle, for one
25 Driving-home results
26 *Les Contemplations* poet
27 Cork customs
28 Sit-down
29 Panasonic product
30 West African staple
31 Double-arc shape, in geometry
33 Say no to
35 __ bed
36 Force
37 Part of a Monet background
39 Brushed up on
41 Crammed
42 They usually leave two when they're done
43 Nitrogen/hydrogen radical
44 It sounds just like you
45 Major apprehension
47 Best-known part of the Caledonian Canal
48 Lightweight
51 __ *plaintif* (whine: Fr.)

★★ Plate Class

Which of the numbered pieces has broken off the plate?

SMALL CHANGE

Change one letter in each of these two words, to form a common two-word phrase.

STRONG BEAM

____

★★★★ Fences

Connect the dots with vertical or horizontal lines, so that a single loop is formed with no crossings or branches. Each number indicates how many lines surround it; squares with no number may be surrounded by any number of lines.

3		1		1		1	2
			2			2	
3	1					1	2
	0	2					
					2	1	
1	1					2	2
	2			3			
3	2		3		1		2

ADDITION SWITCH

Switch the positions of two of the digits in the incorrect sum at right, to get a correct sum.

$$\begin{array}{r} 957 \\ +\,189 \\ \hline 786 \end{array}$$

★★★★★ Themeless Toughie by Daniel R. Stark

ACROSS

1 Like some families
8 Contrived
15 Heighten
16 Superstar entertainer of the '20s
17 Brings forth
18 Signs on
19 Meted out
20 Time
22 Storage space
23 Congregation
24 Yacht units
26 In __ (as found)
27 Capitalize on
28 Place for papers
30 Two-time U.S. Open winner
31 Books that are written in
33 They're not with it
35 1040 deduction
36 Spanish one
37 Demand
41 Saw
45 Ring great
46 Some trails
48 *The Facts of Life* actress
49 Forbids
51 Planes
52 Rumple up
53 Gives aid to
55 Perform a certain operation
56 Sinatra collaborator
57 Profoundly different
59 Paul Revere, for one
61 Follow
62 Most uncanny
63 Narrowed down
64 Gray pieces

DOWN

1 Required
2 Set free
3 In the fridge
4 Spiked
5 *Idylls of the King* lady
6 Routine
7 Takes personally
8 Slinky dresses
9 Swindle
10 Pantomime dance
11 Spruces up
12 More hazy
13 License
14 Go over
21 Fabled flier
24 Bar activity
25 Shine source
28 Ancient underclass
29 Breathers
32 Angler's apt appellation?
34 Contented sound
37 Spot for shows
38 Yellowhammer State
39 In a row
40 Was equal to
41 Float alternatives
42 One on a board
43 Least involved
44 Just __
47 Merlot, for example
50 Turn ender
52 Sausalito's county
54 *The Lion King* villain
56 *Bundesstadt* of Europe
58 Absorbed
60 One of the fire signs

★★★★ 123

Fill in the diagram so that each rectangular piece has one each of the numbers 1, 2, and 3, under these rules: 1) No two adjacent squares, horizontally or vertically, can have the same number. 2) Each completed row and column of the diagram will have an equal number of 1s, 2s, and 3s.

						3		
1								
					3			
		2						
						1		
2								
							1	
					3			
	2							

WRONG IS RIGHT

Which of these four words is misspelled?

A) synergy

B) syncronize

C) synagogue

D) synthesis

★★★ Number-Out

Shade squares so that no number appears in any row or column more than once. Shaded squares may not touch each other horizontally or vertically, and all unshaded squares must form a single continuous area.

3	2	1	4	5	6
5	3	2	5	1	4
2	6	1	5	6	3
4	1	5	5	6	1
1	5	3	3	2	6
2	3	6	1	3	5

THINK ALIKE

Unscramble the letters in the phrase ROOK BRAWL to form two words with the same or similar meanings.

____________________ ____________________

★★★★★ Themeless Toughie by Merle Baker

ACROSS

1 Property
7 Slight hoarseness
11 Short trip
14 Occupies completely
15 Dieter's snack
17 Straighten up, perhaps
19 __ Plaines
20 An act of feeling
21 Nobel Prize presentation
22 Utmost
24 Work __
26 LEGO inventor, for one
27 Hurt
29 Former NOW president
31 Heel
32 Recognized to be
34 Look
36 Masthead credit
40 Joint parts
41 Moved heaven and earth
42 Former owner of Universal
44 Porter, at times
46 Monteverdi opera
47 Framework for improvisation
49 Religious grp.
51 Super conclusion
52 Brittany city
54 Single statistic
56 NFL linemen
58 Overload of a sort
61 Prize
62 Not any longer
63 Init.
64 Elbe tributary
65 Gives rise to

DOWN

1 Somewhat
2 Stills
3 Underlies
4 Tip of a tongue?
5 Bailiwick
6 Bacillus product
7 Obama in '08
8 Least secure
9 Line of work: Abbr.
10 HS class
11 It's most impressive
12 Olympic skating name
13 Took off
16 Helped out, in a way
18 They may be picked
23 Olympic skating name
25 Headlands
27 Comparison connector
28 Dialectical contraction
30 Inspired
33 Set upright
35 Overhead wisps
37 Come before
38 Reverse
39 Maxwell contemporary
42 Former *SNL* regular
43 French physicist
45 French roast
48 *Dilbert* intern
50 Elementary particles
53 Legitimate
55 Alphabet run
57 *Jeanne et Marie*: Abbr.
59 Sticker letters
60 ABC fixture since '75

★★★ Mythological Jigsaw

Find these names from Greek mythology that are arranged in jigsaw puzzle shapes in the diagram. One piece is shown to get you started.

AGAMEMNON

AMPHION
APHRODITE
APOLLO
ARTEMIS
ASTYANAX
BELLEROPHON
CASSIOPEIA
CLYTEMNESTRA
CYCLOPS
EOS
EURYDICE
~~GANYMEDE~~
GORDIUS
HERA
HERACLES
HIPPOLYTA
HYACINTHUS
HYPERION
IPHIANASSA
LYCOMEDES
LYSANDER
LYSEPPE
NEMESIS
OCEANIDES
ORCHOMENUS
ORESTES
PAN
PANDARUS
PERSEPHONE
PHILOCTETES
PITTACUS
POLYMESTER
POSEIDON
PROMETHEUS
PYGMALION
SALMONEUS
SCAMANDER
TROPHONIUS
ZAGREUS
ZEPHYR

```
O C E P O L Y N E S C A O R A S T P O S E
I N A T S E M E M N A M S E N A Y C A D I
D E C E R Z A S I D E E T E A X I S S O N
P S Y C L O G R S I R S S O C L O P E I A
R O M E S P U E P P H I A E T Y L Y C O M
U E H T H Y S N A A S A N M N E T S E D E
S H I P P P E R O P S A A R T S R O P H O
A T Y L O N O I L L P H I L S A R S U I N
L Y S P I T T A H O E T C O A E T P A N D
D N A P E R U C E O T E S M L M I E U R A
E R A P E S S A R R C H O O N H S Y R U S
D O R H P H O N E U N E M U E E R D I C E
I T E P Y A H Y A S G O R S L C A G A N Y
I L A M G M N I C S U I D B E S L Y S E M
O N Z E H P T H U S A G A E L L E R E D E
R Y H P I O N N O N M E M N O H P O P P E
```

IN OTHER WORDS

There is only one common uncapitalized word that contains the consecutive letters UIO. What is it?

____

★★★★ Sequence Maze

Enter the maze, pass through all the color squares exactly once, then exit, all without retracing your path. You must pass through the color squares in this sequence: red, blue, yellow, red, blue, etc.

SAY IT AGAIN

What six-letter word can mean either "go to" or "listen to"?

_ _ _ _ _ _

★★★★★ Themeless Toughie by Doug Peterson

ACROSS

1 Pitcher-plant habitat
8 Gets used to things
15 Inactive
16 Andover type
17 Lineup announcement
19 Super Bowl XXX city
20 Shoe accessories
21 Two-way preposition
22 Refuse
23 Play first
24 *The Nanny* role
25 Authoritative ref.
26 Compote flavor
27 Court star Marble
28 Hatch
31 Hitch
33 *The Secret of the Old Clock* sleuth
35 South-of-the-border spreads
37 Word of emphasis
41 "I'm on board!"
42 Culmination
44 Romantic beginning
45 Supporter
46 Diamond family name
47 Popeye's drawer
49 Start of an admission
50 State of mind
51 Rubberneck
52 Fruit-salad ingredients
55 Smith
56 Least consequential
57 AriZona rival
58 Supplies evidence of

DOWN

1 Fellow, often
2 One coming onstage
3 With a scoop
4 ACC team
5 "America the Beautiful" writer
6 Egg, in combinations
7 Mild
8 Faced the judge
9 Like some figs
10 Jacuzzi features
11 Bars for checkers
12 Globular
13 Haberdashery holder
14 Collected
18 Where fine fare is rare
24 Diamond devaluers
26 Part of Cambodia's capital
27 Cover for hoods
29 Miff
30 Fiesta fare
32 General Mills brand
34 *How Green Was My Valley* workplace
35 Pick up again
36 Home of Spelman College
38 Occupies
39 Most efficient
40 Some biomes
41 Family figures
43 Galilean moon
46 Sensory, in a way
47 Falling short
48 *My Three Sons* boy
50 Diary device
53 Fall off
54 Track in the ground

★★★★ ABCD

Enter the letters A, B, C, and D into the diagram so that each row and column has exactly one A, one B, one C, and one D. The letters outside the diagram indicate the first letter encountered, moving in the direction of the arrow. Keep in mind that after all the letters have been filled in, there will be two blank boxes in each row and column.

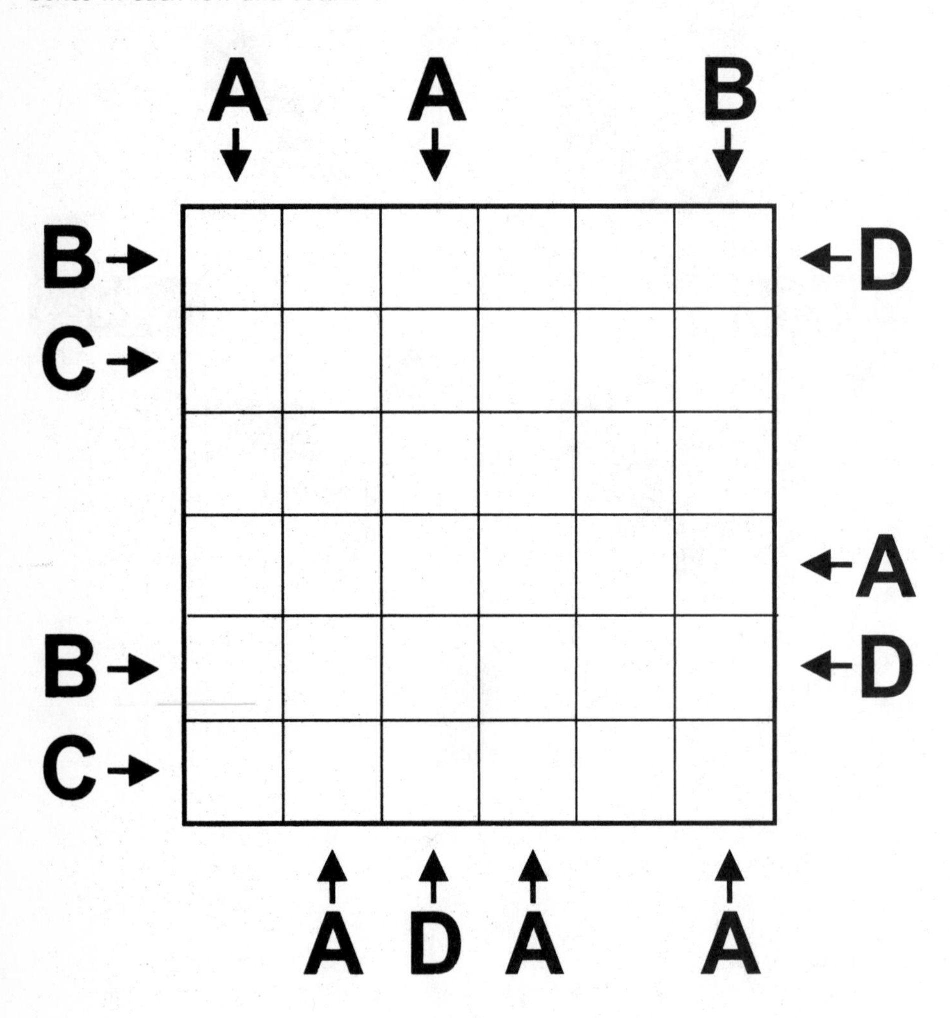

NATIONAL TREASURE

Rearrange the letters in the word CROATIAN to get an article of clothing.

____

★★★★ Sudoku

Fill in the blank boxes so that every row, column, and 3x3 box contains all of the numbers 1 to 9.

4					5		6	1
	1				8			
							7	
	6				1			8
		3				4		
7			9				2	
	4							
			3				5	
3	8		2					9

MIXAGRAMS

Each line contains a five-letter word and a four-letter word that have been mixed together (the order of the letters in each word has not been changed). Unmix the two words on each line and write them in the spaces provided. When you're done, find a two-part answer to the clue by reading down the letter columns in the answers.

CLUE: Court shot

H O B O S O E T H = _ _ _ _ _ + _ _ _ _

A B A F A C A R K = _ _ _ _ _ + _ _ _ _

N I C C U R E L Y = _ _ _ _ _ + _ _ _ _

K I N D U K E L Y = _ _ _ _ _ + _ _ _ _

★★★★★ Themeless Toughie by Daniel R. Stark

ACROSS

1 Tack relative
8 Fillets
15 Vacationing, in a way
16 Comfort zone
17 Tickles
18 Whirlpool alternative
19 Parakeet food
20 Takes a victory lap
22 Select
23 Sherman ___, CA
24 E-zine since '96
25 Half of a matched pair
26 Exploit
27 Hazard a guess
28 Urban unit
29 Successful
31 Selected
32 Band
33 Spender, for one
34 Auto part
37 '58 world's fair site
41 They're off-limits
42 Water hazards
43 Zip
44 Wheels
45 One way to cook
46 Type width
47 Road-sign abbr.
48 Software grouping
49 Stork, e.g.
50 Doris Kearns Goodwin subject
52 Noted
54 Psych up
55 Grandstand cry
56 Sought
57 Endure dog days

DOWN

1 Appears suddenly
2 Loose
3 More streamlined
4 Bosses
5 Get by
6 Combat conclusion
7 Small bird
8 Break
9 Delight
10 Margaret's mom
11 Repeated syllables
12 Puts in order
13 Fight precursor
14 Blended-family member
21 Gave a buzz
24 Resolve
25 Evinces displeasure
27 Places to run
28 ___ set
30 Byrd dog
31 Put into words
33 Income from an auction
34 Misshapen
35 Not unexpected
36 Motives
37 Red Chief, for one
38 Plain
39 Hunter's purchase
40 More bright
42 Fabricated
45 Particle stream, in physics
46 Prospective juror list
48 Ill-humored
49 Judy, to Punch
51 Tai ___
53 Gull's sound

★★★★ One-Way Streets

The diagram represents a pattern of streets. P's are parking spaces, and the black squares are stores. Find the route that starts at a parking space, passes through all stores exactly once, and ends at the other parking space. Arrows indicate one-way traffic for that block only. No block or intersection may be entered more than once.

SOUND THINKING

Common uncapitalized words whose consonant sounds are Z, G, and NG include ZIGGING and ZAGGING. The longest such word has nine letters. What is it?

____

★★ Split Decisions

In this clueless crossword puzzle, each answer consists of two words whose spellings are the same, except for the consecutive letters given. All answers are common words; no phrases or hyphenated or capitalized words are used. Some of the clues may have more than one solution, but there is only one word pair that will correctly link up with all the other word pairs.

TRANSDELETION

Delete one letter from the word REORDERING (!) and rearrange the rest, to get something often seen in a Western movie.

____

★★★★★ Themeless Toughie by Anna Stiga

1	2	3	4	5	6	7	8	■	9	10	11	12	13	14
15								■	16					
17								■	18					
19				■	■	20		21						
22				23	24	■	25			■	■	26		
27						28	■	29		30	31			
■	■	■	■	32			33		■	34				
35	36	37	38		■	39			■	40				
41					■	42			43		■	■	■	■
44					45		■	46			47	48	49	50
51			■	■	52		53	■	54					
55			56	57				58	■	■	59			
60						■	61		62	63				
64						■	65							
66						■	67							

ACROSS

1 Full
9 Kind of rebate
15 Comparatively crisp
16 Elevated
17 Teamwork obstacle
18 Pacifist philosopher
19 Wild talk
20 Emphatic assent
22 Unseen enticements
25 Catch
26 Onetime Hertz owner
27 Medicinal plant
29 Governmental units
32 Jerk
34 Sound starter
35 Lusterless
39 Zip
40 Drop off
41 Son of Jacob
42 Whimsical pursuit
44 Curious
46 What you can do
51 "Look at this!"
52 Smuggle
54 Fun to be with
55 Correspondent's need
59 *"Le surréalisme, c'est moi"* speaker
60 Projected, with "out"
61 On sale, or taken off sale
64 Too bright
65 Air
66 First cloned primate
67 Euro users since 1/1/07

DOWN

1 Luxor Temple sculpture
2 Racing Hall of Famer
3 Engage
4 Introspective query
5 Cash holder
6 Cancún kin
7 Choice word
8 Device with a tumbler
9 *Gidget* setting
10 Composer Menken
11 Player with a click wheel
12 Learned
13 Risky
14 Memo notation
21 Novel nuance
23 Backward
24 Darn
28 Stiffen
30 Sound of sheets
31 Connection with a bend
33 Lose no time
35 Successor of the wax sealer
36 Like
37 Diesel engine's lack
38 British East India Company product
43 Duster
45 Inclines
47 Belgian export
48 Important ingredient in DNA repair
49 *Honor Thy Father* author
50 Deteriorates
53 "Hogwash!"
56 Greek letters
57 A vicuña is on its coat of arms
58 Film-length measure
62 It recognized Israel in '88
63 Speed (up)

★★★★ Your Turn

Entering at the bottom and exiting at the top, find the shortest path through the maze, following these turn rules: You must turn right on red squares, turn left on blue squares, and go straight through yellow squares. Your path may retrace itself and cross at intersections, but you may not reverse your direction at any point.

SAY IT AGAIN

What six-letter word can mean either "shining" or "intelligent"?

_ _ _ _ _ _

★★★★ Star Search

Find the stars that are hidden in some of the blank squares. The numbered squares indicate how many stars are hidden in the squares adjacent to them (including diagonally). There is never more than one star in any square.

							2		
				3	3	3	3		
1		2					2		
		3		3	3		2	2	
2		4		3	3		2	2	
			1	1			2		
			1	1			2		
					2	2			

CHOICE WORDS

Form three six-letter words from the same category, by selecting one letter from each column three times. Each letter will be used exactly once.

G	R	R	O	E	N	_ _ _ _ _ _
M	U	L	M	P	E	_ _ _ _ _ _
S	O	U	L	S	Y	_ _ _ _ _ _

★★★★★ Themeless Toughie by Daniel R. Stark

ACROSS

1 Seriously annoys
8 Awkward
14 Pretty quick
15 Nautical weapon
16 It's free of charge
17 16-year-olds, legally speaking
18 Natural __
19 Denouements
21 Cold kin
22 Oklahoma city
24 Sprinkles lightly
25 Immediate successor
26 *Inside Report* columnist
28 Nathan Hale, circa 1772
29 Tolerated
30 Rumble maker
32 Like SASEs
34 Not owing
36 Chèvre source
37 Out of harm's way
41 More toward spotless
45 Auburn tint
46 Stockholm-based airline
48 Marsh bird
49 Bonsai and ikebana
50 Roughly
52 Firmness of character
53 Canapé topper
54 Supermarket display
56 Olympic flame lighter at Atlanta
57 Tiny aperture
59 Cape waver
61 Necessitates
62 Mentee
63 Conifer creations
64 Stalemate

DOWN

1 Touching
2 Mother of Richard I
3 Slippery
4 Sink
5 Fearsome employer
6 Palm part
7 Party snack
8 Rumble makers
9 Boxer's comments
10 __ tree
11 Bestows
12 Source of direct access
13 Cinched
15 Less than direct
20 Land in the water
23 Muffles
25 Crowd sound
27 Member of suborder Vombatiformes
29 Doldrums
31 Free
33 Dairy unit
35 Asks for
37 More astute
38 Cartland creation
39 Designs
40 Don't play it safe
42 Products of bitterness
43 Play enders, perhaps
44 Sun City citizen
47 Garlicky dish
50 Spreadsheet units
51 Danger signal
54 Dollar, maybe
55 Leave off
58 Yes, in Yokohama
60 Loss leader

★★★★ Number-Out

Shade squares so that no number appears in any row or column more than once. Shaded squares may not touch each other horizontally or vertically, and all unshaded squares must form a single continuous area.

3	6	5	6	4	2
5	3	1	1	1	4
1	2	3	4	5	6
2	4	4	3	1	3
6	4	2	2	2	1
4	5	2	5	3	6

THINK ALIKE

Unscramble the letters in the phrase EVER ONWARD to form two words with the same or similar meanings.

_______________ _______________

★★★★ Line Drawing

Draw three straight lines, each from one edge of the square to another edge (one of which will intersect the other two), so there are two or more words in each of the six regions.

LATHE
TANGO
REDO
REST
BINGO
HALO
RAIN
MINOR
ADMISSION
PALATE
ZOO
COLONEL
PILOT

TWO-BY-FOUR

The eight letters in the word UNFAIRLY can be rearranged to form a pair of common four-letter words in two different ways, if no four-letter word is repeated. Can you find both pairs of words?

_ _ _ _ _ _ _ _

_ _ _ _ _ _ _ _

★★★★★ Themeless Toughie by Merle Baker

1	2	3	4	■	5	6	7	8	9	10	11	12	13	14
15				■	16									
17				■	18									
19				20				■	21					
■	22						■	23						
24						■	25					■	■	■
26					■	27					■	28	29	30
31				■	32					■	33			
34			■	35					■	36				
■	■	■	37					■	38					
39	40	41					■	42						■
43						■	44							45
46						47				■	48			
49										■	50			
51										■	52			

ACROSS

1 An unlikely beginning
5 1 in 21
15 *Sticks and Bones* playwright
16 Annual spectacle
17 Ray of Hollywood
18 Divides into small, hostile units
19 Trick
21 Chinchilla, e.g.
22 Offspring
23 Mass leaders
24 Parish officer
25 Embroidery filaments
26 Put in a stake
27 *My Fair Lady* Tony winner
28 Paper size: Abbr.
31 Places for PFCs
32 Turkish money
33 Ritz alternative
34 German article
35 Raised
36 Palestrina piece
37 Center of power
38 Daughter of Muhammad
39 Far from proud
42 The K in Kmart
43 Like batter
44 Is sparing
46 Play up
48 Stub __
49 They're on stage at the Grammys
50 Counting intervals
51 Admit a mistake
52 An NCO

DOWN

1 Diamond stats
2 Sound sound
3 He's giving up
4 November meteor showers
5 Not coarse
6 Chomsky's namesakes
7 Cruise stop
8 __*War* (Shatner novel)
9 Cardinal kin
10 Danish, in Dijon
11 Eye parts
12 They may be fastened
13 __-A-Kid card
14 Battery elements
20 How hit records go
23 Urge
24 Data-transfer unit
25 Tails opposite
27 Party in Israel
28 Contests
29 Entertainer's intro
30 *La Dolce Vita* composer
32 Royalty payer
33 Tough spots
35 Unqualified success
36 Ginnie __ (bond category)
37 Not conscientious about, perhaps
38 Least inhibited
39 Railing
40 *Flying Dutchman* heroine
41 Set upon
42 Land under two flags
44 Ancient Germanic invader
45 Very recently: Abbr.
47 Euro divs.

★★ Triad Split Decisions

In this clueless crossword puzzle, each answer consists of two words whose spellings are the same, except for the consecutive letters given. All answers are common words; no phrases or hyphenated or capitalized words are used. Some of the clues may have more than one solution, but there is only one word pair that will correctly link up with all the other word pairs.

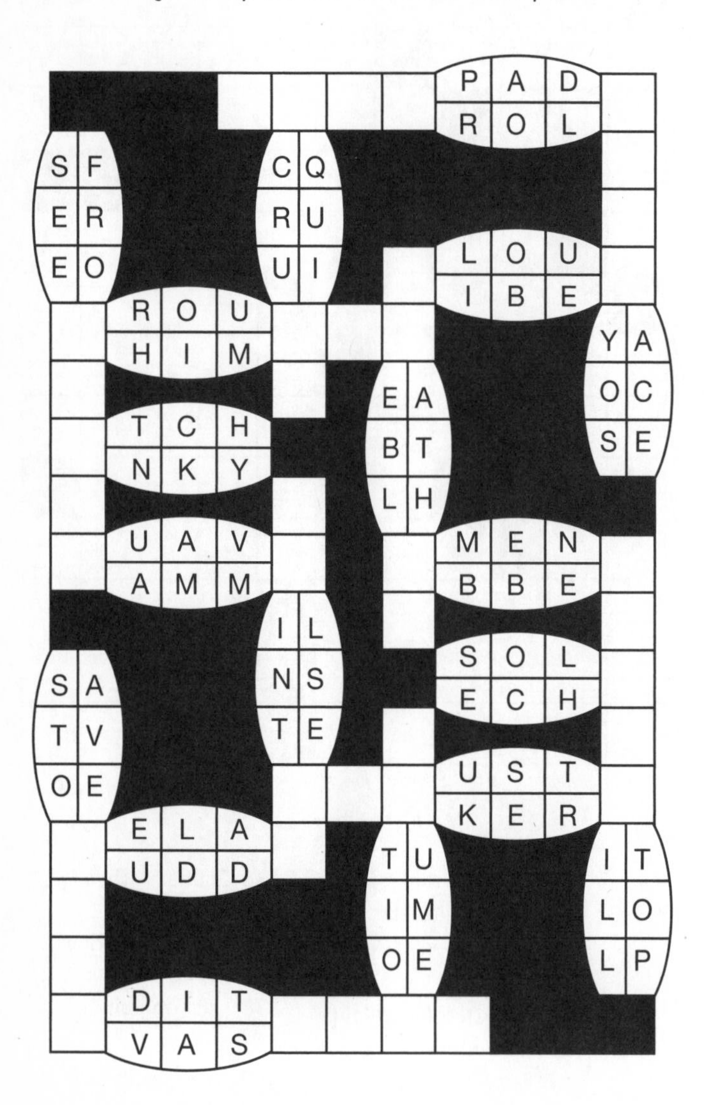

TRANSDELETION

Delete one letter from the word GUARANTEED and rearrange the rest, to get a two-word term for a type of pet.

____

★★★ Piece It Together

Fill in the blue design using pieces with the same shape outlined in black.

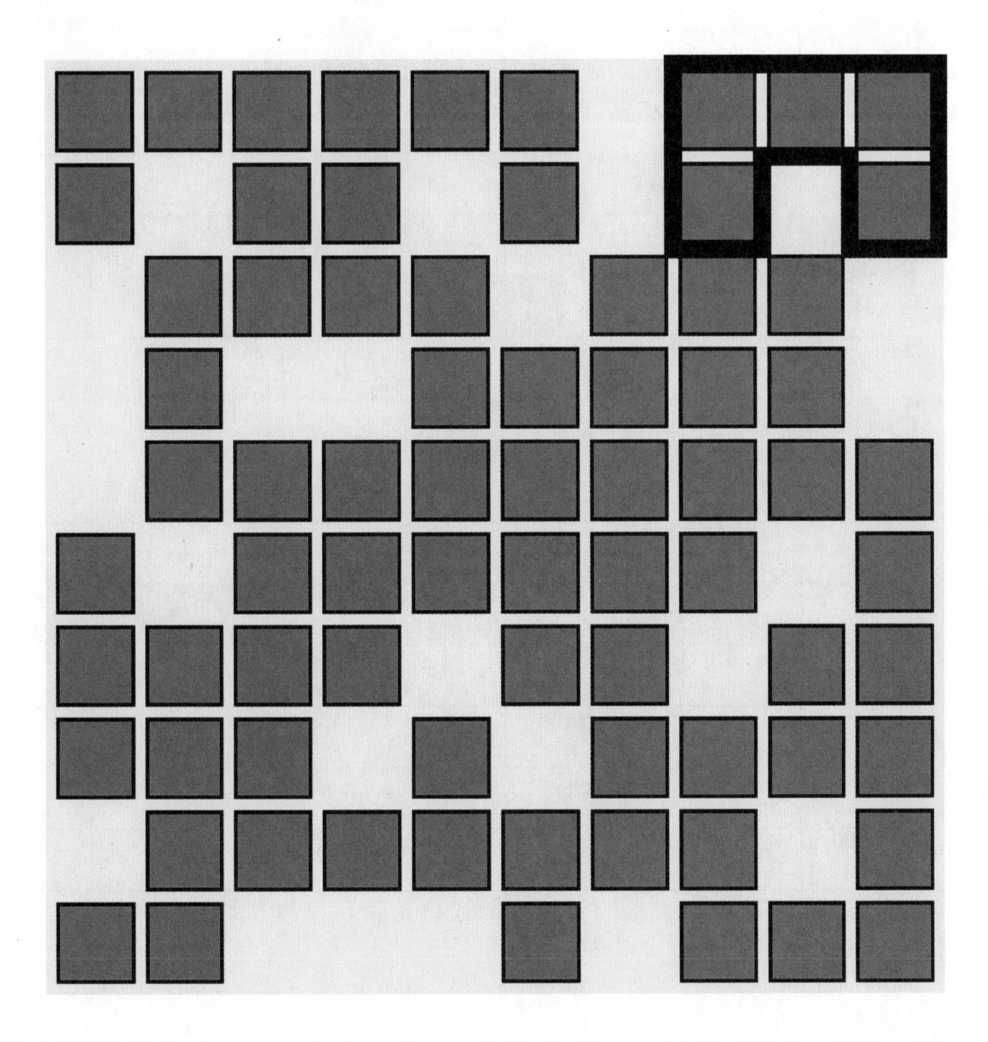

SMALL CHANGE

Change one letter in each of these two words, to form a common two-word phrase.

DOT WATCHER

____

★★★★★ Themeless Toughie by Doug Peterson

1	2	3	4	5	6	7	8	9	■	10	11	12	13	■
14									■	15				16
17									■	18				
19				■	20				■	21				
■	■	■	■	22					23	■	24			
25	26	27	28			■	29			30	■	31		
32					■	33					34			
35					36		■	37						
38							39		■	40				
41			■	42				■	43					
44			45	■	46			47			■	■	■	■
48				49	■	50				■	51	52	53	54
55					■	56				57				
58					■	59								
■	60				■	61								

ACROSS

1 Leader of the pack
10 Leaves impressed
14 Defensive barriers
15 One making assessments
17 Clearings
18 Curriculum follower
19 Minor clash
20 *Dukes of Hazzard* character
21 Treasured instrument
22 Irksome
24 Mideast capital
25 Kingston Trio song subject
29 Sedan state
31 St. with only three counties
32 Muff
33 Viewing period
35 Scoundrel
37 Lawn tool
38 Idling, perhaps
40 Bushed
41 Mick's Yankee teammate
42 Salt's symbol
43 Pieces that are popular
44 "My Cup Runneth Over" singer
46 L.A. neighborhood
48 Count from New Jersey
50 Adjuster's issue
51 Labor Department grp.
55 Service-club members
56 Datebook section
58 Turn out
59 Knockoff
60 __ chair
61 Stout fellow

DOWN

1 Blood type, briefly
2 Certain Finn
3 Appeal
4 Intimate
5 __ rule
6 Fictional phantom
7 With two present
8 Less seaworthy
9 Needed
10 Off-roaders' transport
11 Stands by
12 Takes back legally
13 Coral cousin
16 Calls to action
22 WWI battle site
23 Gutsy
25 Worth pursuing
26 Black Bears' home
27 Fountain selection
28 Single
30 Less windy
33 Crown material
34 Capture, in a way
36 Whack
39 Sinatra standard
43 Satisfy, as demands
45 Cranium feature
47 Up
49 Notice
51 Not roped in by
52 Muddy
53 Tap-dance
54 Colonial poet Bradstreet
57 Untried

PAGE 17

Poor Posture

```
E S S E S ■ P L E A ■ S A M E
C H A R M ■ L E T S ■ E G A D
H A V E A H U N C H ■ N O T I
O W E ■ S O S O ■ H E I G H T
■ ■ ■ U H U H ■ N E M O ■ ■ ■
T A R R E R ■ T E A T R A Y ■
B L A B S ■ C O O P ■ S L O T
A L D A ■ ■ A N N ■ ■ L O D E
R A I N ■ L U G S ■ D U N E S
■ H O S T E S S ■ C A M E L S
■ ■ ■ P O S E ■ H A R P ■ ■ ■
S H A R E S ■ C O R E ■ M R S
A U R A ■ F R O N T S T O O P
G R E W ■ A B L E ■ T A M P A
E T A L ■ T I D Y ■ O N S E T
```

PAGE 18

Track Meet

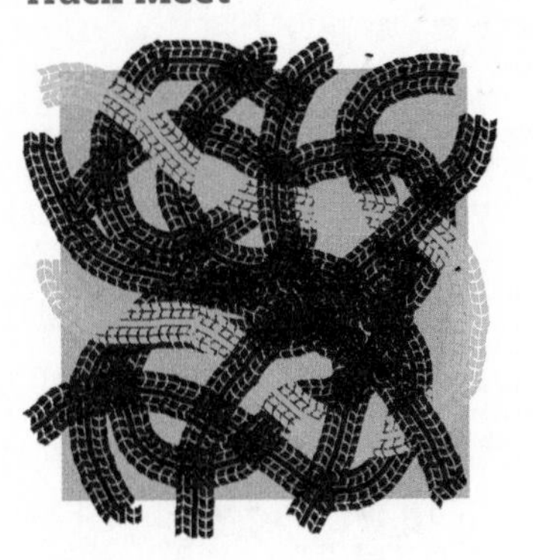

CENTURY MARKS

17, 37, 29, 17

PAGE 19

About Time

```
Y F T Y N E D I T S T D S I S
C E O W E R P L A I P U A O P
D I A R A A J O M H N R S M R
R D O V T D X E C R T A I N I
E D I U R N A L I H E N O N K
T K E E W E I S E S S O O Q G
N H P H E L E G N I N R O M D
I D G N V A U U H R U Y A O D
W I S I E C S K E T S S I E R
I U U N N M U T U A D R C W Y
N R M E I D F N D S E A S O N
T N M V N A I O A P D Y E A Z
E A E E G N F M T E B A C E D
T S R D I A R Y E D A D A W G
```

INITIAL REACTION

History Repeats Itself

PAGE 20

Sudoku

6	3	7	8	5	2	1	9	4
4	9	2	7	1	6	3	5	8
1	8	5	3	4	9	7	2	6
8	2	6	9	3	1	5	4	7
7	4	3	2	8	5	6	1	9
5	1	9	6	7	4	8	3	2
3	6	4	5	9	8	2	7	1
2	7	1	4	6	3	9	8	5
9	5	8	1	2	7	4	6	3

MIXAGRAMS

```
D E R B Y   B E T S
B R E A D   A W A Y
S P I C Y   H A L O
A W A K E   C O K E
```

PAGE 21

Italian Dinners

```
S O U S A ■ E R I N ■ A N T I
O P T I N ■ N A T O ■ R A I D
C E A S E ■ D I E M ■ I S L E
■ C H I C K E N M A R S A L A
■ ■ ■ ■ D I D ■ ■ T U E ■ ■ ■
T E F L O N ■ M A T E ■ L A S
I Q U I T ■ R I F E ■ K E P T
M U S S E L S M A R I N A R A
E A S T ■ E V E R ■ N O S I R
S L Y ■ M O P S ■ L I T T L E
■ ■ ■ S A P ■ ■ P A T ■ ■ ■ ■
V E A L P A R M I G I A N A ■
A X L E ■ R E A L ■ A L O H A
S P U D ■ D A Z E ■ L O S E S
T O M S ■ S P E D ■ S E E M S
```

PAGE 22

Fences

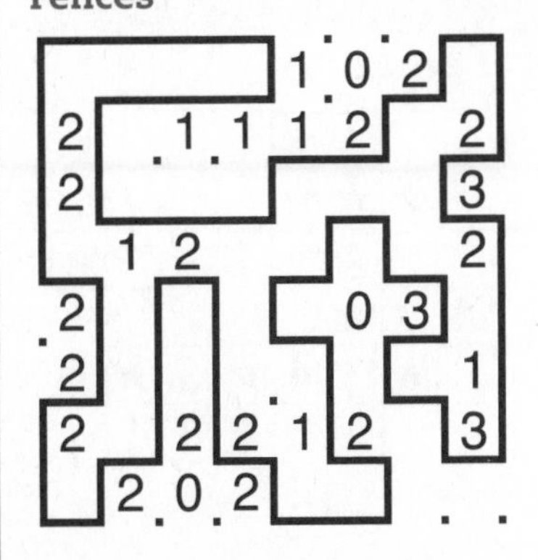

WRONG IS RIGHT

Catalist (should be *catalyst*)

PAGE 23

Line Drawing

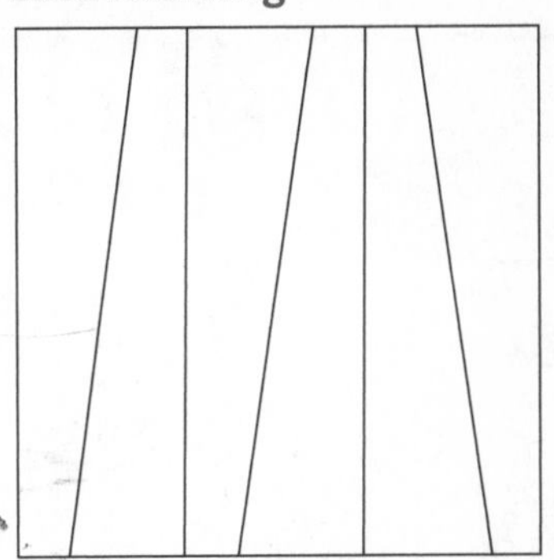

THREE OF A KIND

HE TO<u>OK</u> A PLEA<u>SURE</u> TRIP TO ASPEN <u>IF I NE</u>EDED HIM TO.

PAGE 24

All in the Games

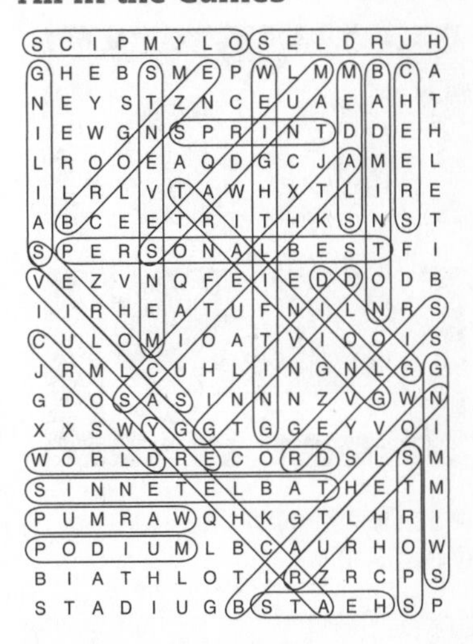

WHO'S WHAT WHERE?

Abilenian

PAGE 25

Outdo Yourself

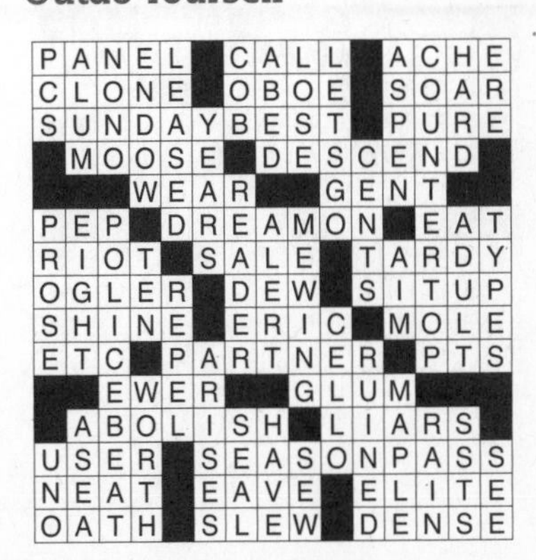

PAGE 26

Number-Out

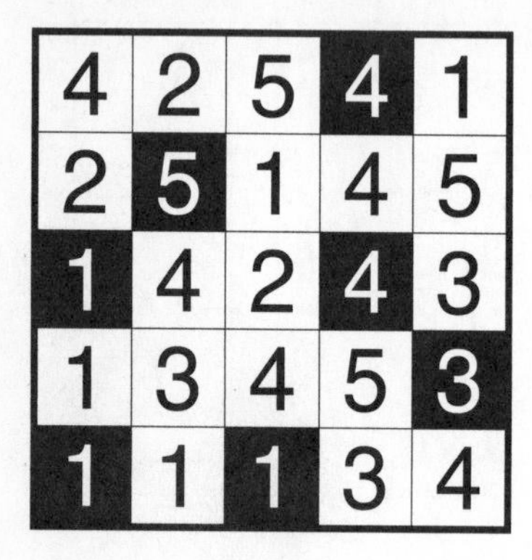

THINK ALIKE

GO, LEAVE

PAGE 27

Go With the Flow

SMALL CHANGE

GYM SHOE

PAGE 28

Like a River

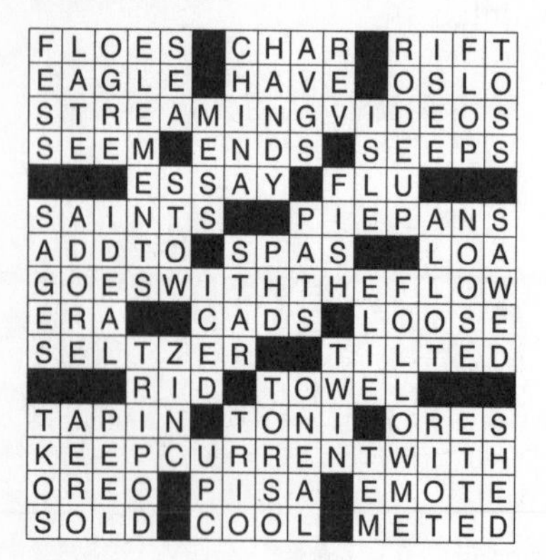

PAGE 29

One-Way Streets

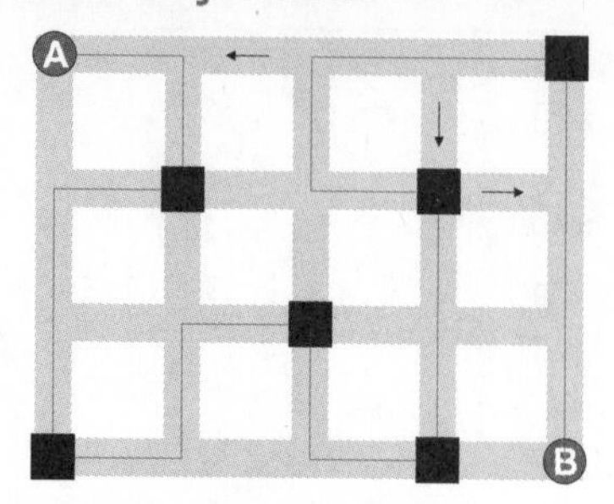

SOUND THINKING

MISCELLANY

PAGE 30

Split Decisions

TRANSDELETION

KENYA

PAGE 31

Star Search

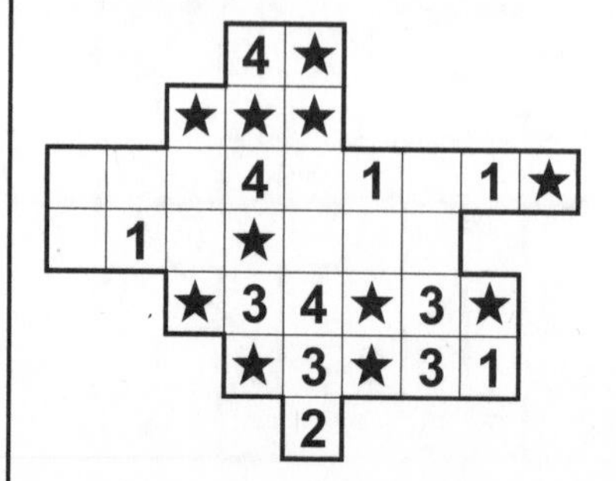

CHOICE WORDS

AUSTIN, DALLAS, LAREDO

PAGE 32

"Many" Words

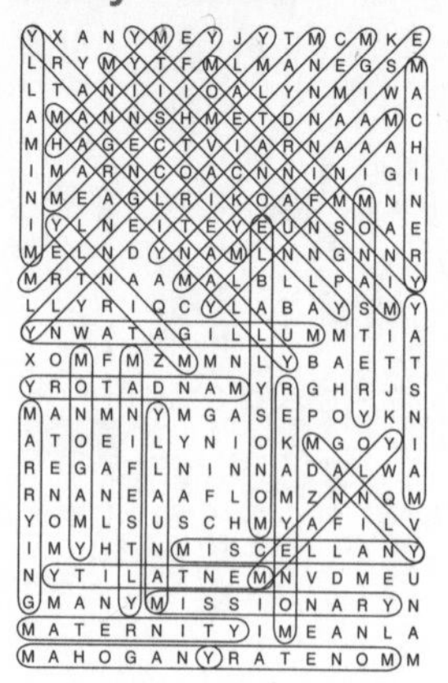

Unlisted word is MANUALLY

IN OTHER WORDS

GRAPEVINE

PAGE 33

Easy as Nails

A	R	C	H		A	B	C	S		G	A	R	B	O
L	A	L	A		L	U	A	U		A	F	O	O	T
O	P	A	L		F	O	R	M		B	L	U	N	T
H	I	S	T	O	R	Y	B	U	F	F		N	E	O
A	D	H	E	R	E			P	L	E	A	D		
			R	E	D	O			U	S	E	F	U	L
J	A	M		S	O	L	A	R		T	R	I	K	E
U	F	O	S			E	R	E			O	L	E	O
M	A	N	O	R		S	T	A	S	H		E	S	S
P	R	E	F	E	R			D	U	O	S			
		Y	A	L	I	E			S	H	A	V	E	S
P	E	C		A	P	P	L	E	P	O	L	I	S	H
A	L	L	O	T		C	O	D	E		S	O	S	O
C	L	I	N	E		O	P	E	N		A	L	A	W
T	A	P	E	D		T	E	N	D		S	A	Y	S

PAGE 34

Hyper-Sudoku

1	6	4	5	9	2	8	3	7
2	8	9	7	3	6	1	5	4
7	3	5	4	1	8	9	2	6
9	2	6	1	8	4	3	7	5
5	1	7	3	2	9	4	6	8
8	4	3	6	5	7	2	9	1
4	7	1	9	6	3	5	8	2
3	5	2	8	7	1	6	4	9
6	9	8	2	4	5	7	1	3

MIXAGRAMS

STROP EACH
GRAVY GALA
PETER ANON
BURRO SAID

PAGE 35

Catfisher

#8

BETWEENER

BAG

PAGE 36

123

3	1	2	1	3	2
2	3	1	3	2	1
1	2	3	2	1	3
3	1	2	1	3	2
2	3	1	3	2	1
1	2	3	2	1	3

SUDOKU SUM

7	3	4
6	1	5
9	2	8

PAGE 37

Beach Bringalongs

F	L	A	K	■	D	I	P	S	■	M	U	T	E	D
L	O	N	E	■	O	R	E	O	■	U	S	H	E	R
E	B	A	Y	■	N	O	R	M	■	D	A	I	R	Y
W	E	T	B	L	A	N	K	E	T	■	B	R	I	E
■	■	■	O	A	T	S	■	■	W	E	L	D	E	R
E	S	C	A	P	E	■	O	L	I	V	E	■	■	■
L	E	A	R	■	■	A	T	O	N	E	■	S	E	A
S	A	N	D	W	I	C	H	I	S	L	A	N	D	S
E	N	E	■	A	D	M	E	N	■	■	S	I	G	H
■	■	■	M	I	L	E	R	■	G	O	A	T	E	E
D	E	L	E	T	E	■	■	F	L	A	W	■	■	■
I	R	A	N	■	R	A	D	I	O	S	H	A	C	K
N	O	R	T	H	■	L	E	N	O	■	O	B	O	E
E	D	G	A	R	■	M	A	A	M	■	L	I	M	P
R	E	E	L	S	■	A	L	L	Y	■	E	T	A	T

PAGE 38

ABC

C	B		A
	C	A	B
A		B	C
B	A	C	

CLUELESS CROSSWORD

C	A	B	B	I	E	S
O	■	U	■	S	■	T
W	I	L	L	O	W	Y
B	■	G	■	L	■	L
O	R	I	G	A	M	I
Y	■	N	■	T	■	S
S	E	G	M	E	N	T

PAGE 39

Find the Ships

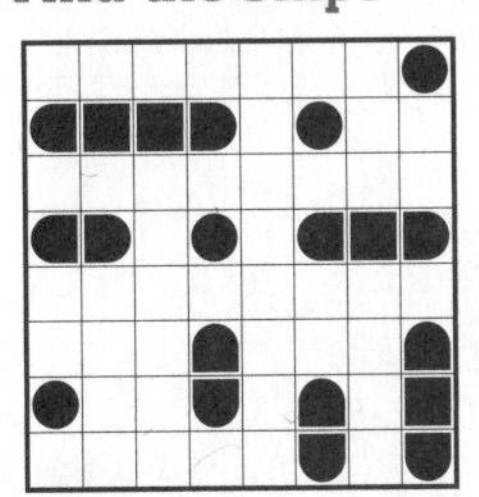

TWO-BY-FOUR

FLAY, CORN

PAGE 40

Leaning

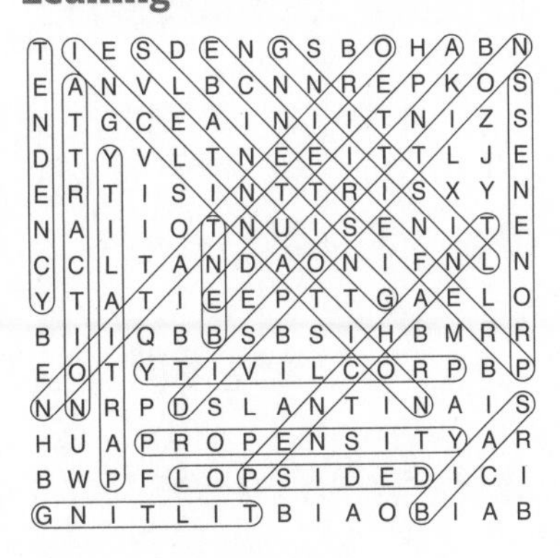

INITIAL REACTION

Faith Will Move Mountains

PAGE 41

Around the House

PAGE 42

Koala Maze

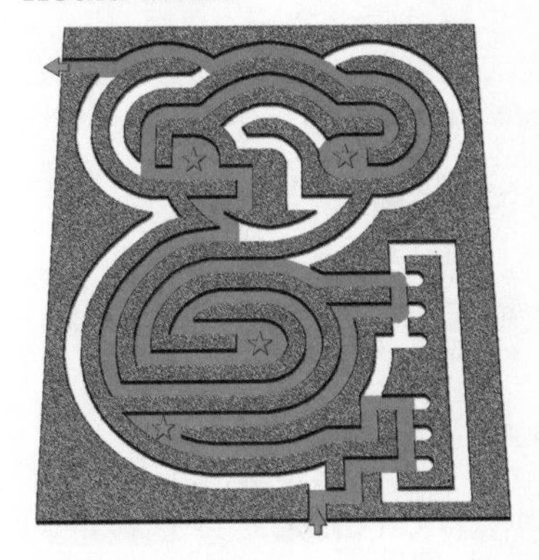

SMALL CHANGE

COAT RACK

PAGE 43

Fences

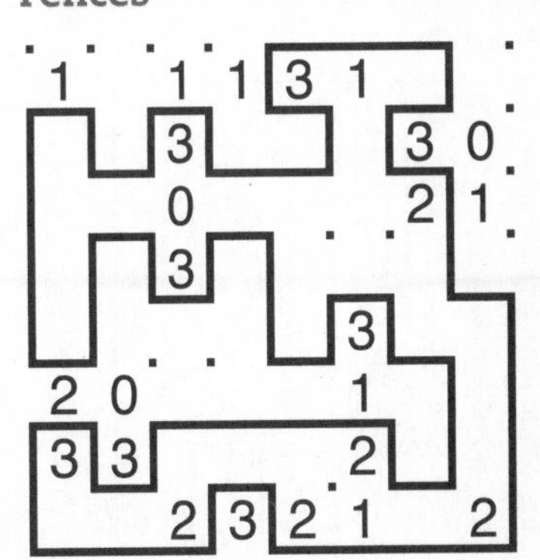

WRONG IS RIGHT

Glossery (should be *glossary*)

PAGE 44

Dinner Date

T	Z	P	P	B	C	D	P	B	M	A	B	W	C	P
C	N	I	W	L	A	U	I	P	T	I	M	A	H	A
P	I	Z	Z	A	A	O	T	S	L	U	N	I	E	S
T	W	Z	E	C	I	T	A	L	I	A	N	T	F	T
B	U	M	D	K	V	P	E	N	E	A	T	E	R	F
E	A	O	I	B	S	E	B	O	Y	R	A	R	M	B
T	I	W	S	O	S	L	A	I	S	R	Y	E	I	J
R	R	T	N	A	R	U	A	T	S	E	R	S	M	B
A	S	E	L	R	X	M	E	A	E	T	T	R	A	B
T	I	A	S	D	B	A	M	V	M	R	M	E	I	N
S	D	G	Q	S	K	I	E	R	O	A	Y	L	E	T
T	H	O	N	H	E	C	N	E	T	T	U	H	E	A
N	L	R	O	I	I	D	G	S	A	S	C	N	A	B
I	A	U	C	V	N	L	A	E	M	T	I	A	N	L
M	S	H	R	M	A	I	N	R	I	W	E	B	F	E
E	E	E	F	F	O	C	D	K	C	O	U	R	S	E
O	S	R	E	S	E	R	V	A	T	I	O	U	K	T

Missing word is TOAST

WHO'S WHAT WHERE?
Tangerine

PAGE 45

Hello, Hello, Hello

T	E	A	R	■	B	I	B	L	E	■	A	C	T	S
H	A	R	E	■	I	D	E	A	S	■	G	O	R	E
A	C	E	S	■	S	E	E	M	S	■	A	R	I	A
W	H	A	T	S	H	A	P	P	E	N	I	N	G	■
■	■	■	■	A	O	L	■	■	N	U	N	■	■	■
S	P	E	D	U	P	■	D	U	C	T	■	H	A	S
P	I	N	E	D	■	T	A	P	E	■	T	A	M	E
I	T	S	N	I	C	E	T	O	S	E	E	Y	O	U
T	A	U	T	■	O	X	E	N	■	V	E	E	R	S
E	S	E	■	A	N	T	S	■	L	E	N	S	E	S
■	■	■	A	B	C	■	■	E	A	R	■	■	■	■
■	H	O	W	S	E	V	E	R	Y	T	H	I	N	G
R	O	M	A	■	P	A	D	R	E	■	A	S	I	A
A	P	E	R	■	T	I	G	E	R	■	R	A	N	G
M	E	N	D	■	S	L	E	D	S	■	D	Y	E	S

PAGE 46

Sudoku

9	6	5	7	3	4	8	2	1
1	3	4	8	9	2	6	5	7
8	7	2	6	1	5	3	9	4
7	1	9	2	4	3	5	8	6
4	2	6	5	7	8	9	1	3
5	8	3	9	6	1	7	4	2
6	9	8	4	2	7	1	3	5
3	4	7	1	5	9	2	6	8
2	5	1	3	8	6	4	7	9

MIXAGRAMS

PANIC ODOR
CRIME AUNT
ACTOR SKID
WHINE SECT

PAGE 47

123

2	3	1	2	1	3
1	2	3	1	3	2
3	1	2	3	2	1
1	3	1	2	3	2
2	1	2	3	1	3
3	2	3	1	2	1

ADDITION SWITCH
1 4 3 + 2 5 8 = 4 0 1

PAGE 48

A Little Light

E	M	B	E	R	■	S	P	A	M	■	B	A	R	B
R	O	U	T	E	■	C	O	P	Y	■	A	L	O	E
R	A	Y	C	H	A	R	L	E	S	■	L	A	C	E
S	T	S	■	E	L	A	L	■	T	H	A	N	K	S
■	■	■	L	A	M	P	■	S	E	A	N	■	■	■
D	E	B	U	T	S	■	A	P	R	I	C	O	T	■
A	L	E	C	S	■	C	L	A	Y	■	E	A	R	L
S	I	L	K	■	■	L	I	T	■	■	B	R	I	E
H	O	L	Y	■	T	O	E	S	■	S	E	E	K	S
■	T	E	S	T	R	U	N	■	S	P	A	D	E	S
■	■	■	T	O	A	D	■	P	O	E	M	■	■	■
H	E	A	R	O	F	■	T	A	P	E	■	A	I	L
A	C	M	E	■	F	L	A	S	H	D	A	N	C	E
S	H	E	A	■	I	O	N	S	■	E	A	T	O	N
H	O	N	K	■	C	U	K	E	■	R	H	I	N	O

PAGE 49

One-Way Streets

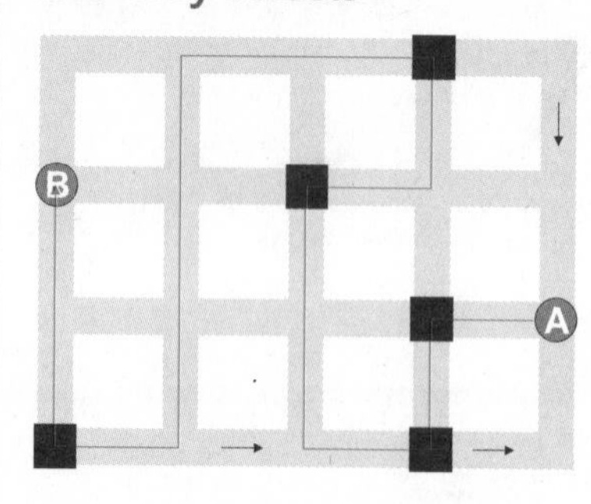

SOUND THINKING
INCLUDE

PAGE 50

Missing Links

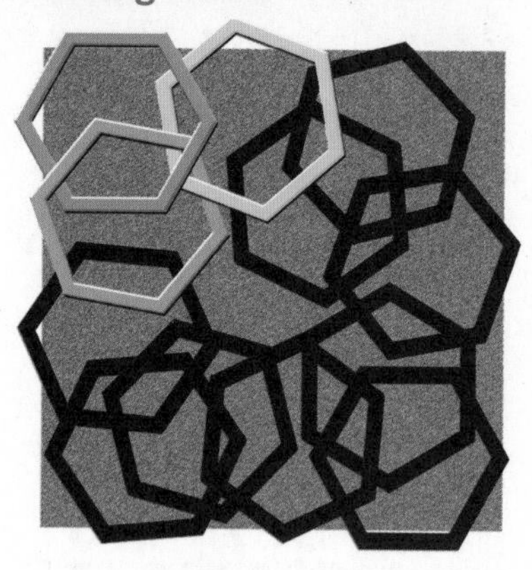

SAY IT AGAIN
DOG

PAGE 51

Star Search

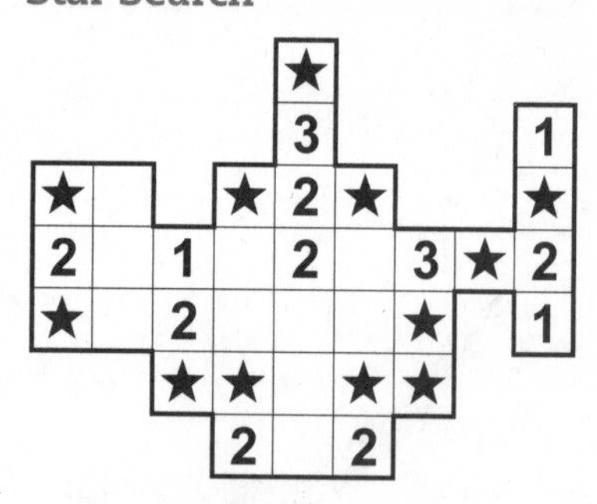

CHOICE WORDS
COMPEL, DEMAND, INSIST

PAGE 52

Cee the USA

S	C	R	A	P	■	C	U	T	S	■	Z	E	S	T
H	O	U	S	E	■	O	H	I	O	■	E	X	P	O
O	A	S	I	S	■	N	O	T	I	■	R	I	O	T
P	L	E	A	T	■	C	H	A	R	L	O	T	T	E
■	■	■	N	O	T	E	■	N	E	O	■	■	■	■
S	E	A	S	■	H	R	S	■	E	S	T	A	T	E
A	T	L	■	P	U	T	T	S	■	T	A	T	A	S
C	H	I	C	A	G	O	I	L	L	I	N	O	I	S
C	A	N	A	L	■	S	N	O	O	T	■	N	N	E
O	N	E	L	A	P	■	T	W	O	■	P	E	T	S
■	■	■	■	T	A	C	■	S	T	I	R	■	■	■
C	L	E	V	E	L	A	N	D	■	R	I	F	L	E
L	U	R	E	■	E	R	O	O	■	I	N	L	A	W
A	S	I	S	■	S	N	O	W	■	S	C	E	N	E
W	H	E	T	■	T	E	N	N	■	H	E	X	E	S

PAGE 53

Paper Chase

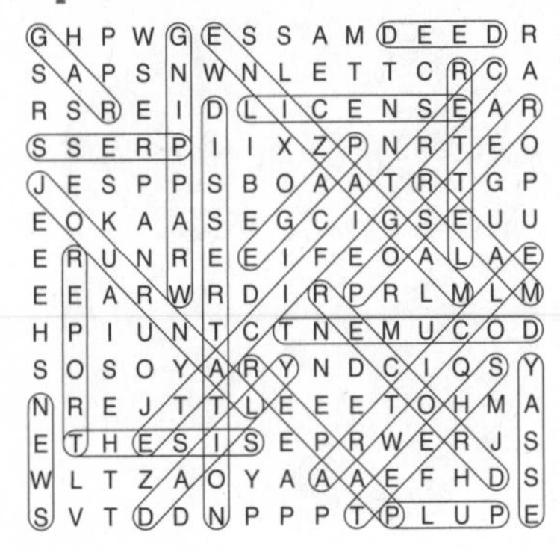

IN OTHER WORDS
LONGEVITY

PAGE 55

Line Drawing

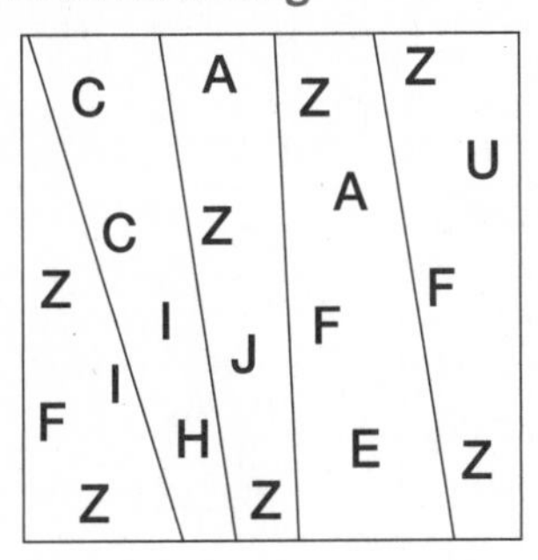

FIZZ, CHIC, JAZZ, FAZE, FUZZ

THREE OF A KIND
NOW I SEE—THE MESSAGE CAME FROM A CRUISE SHIP.

PAGE 56

ABC

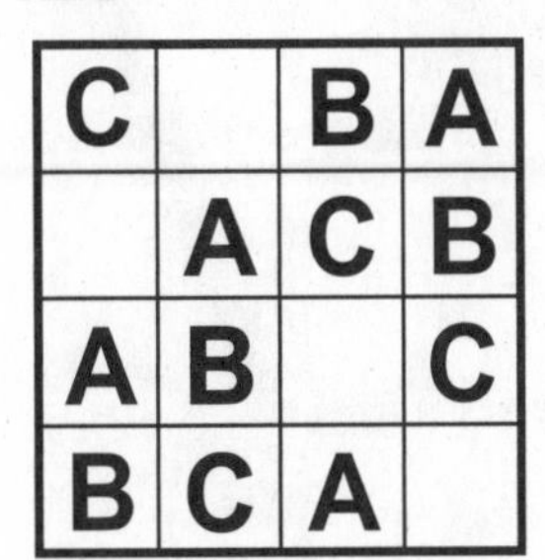

NATIONAL TREASURE
KIWI

PAGE 57

Restaurant Work

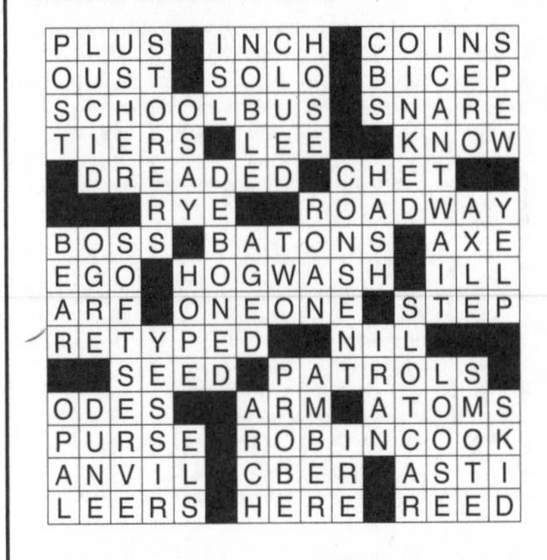

PAGE 58

Five by Five

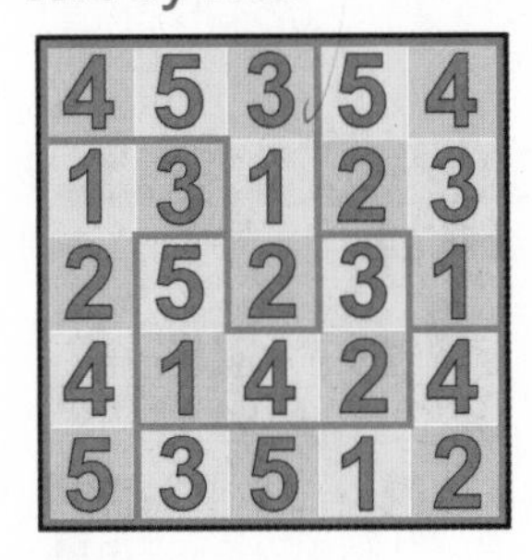

BETWEENER
GUN

PAGE 59

"Dry" to Remember

Unlisted word is SAHARA

INITIAL REACTION
It Takes One To Know One

PAGE 60

Find the Ships

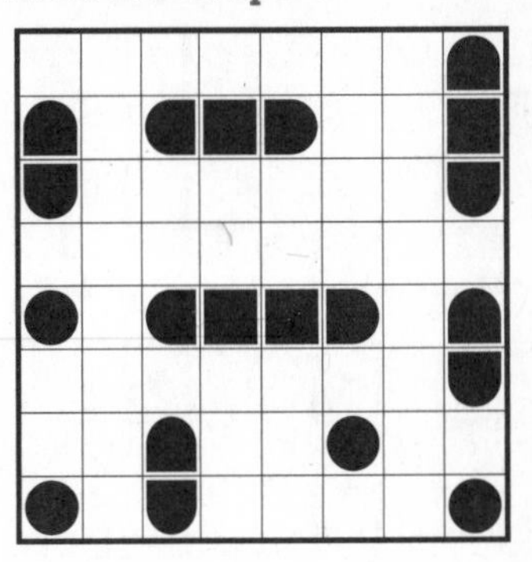

TWO-BY-FOUR
PRIM, UGLY

PAGE 61

Sudoku

9	2	7	4	5	1	6	8	3
1	3	8	6	9	2	4	7	5
5	6	4	7	3	8	1	9	2
2	7	5	9	1	4	8	3	6
3	9	6	2	8	7	5	1	4
8	4	1	5	6	3	9	2	7
4	8	9	3	2	6	7	5	1
6	5	2	1	7	9	3	4	8
7	1	3	8	4	5	2	6	9

MIXAGRAMS
T H R O B   E E R Y
P A N D A   S O D A
F R A N C   P I E R
B R O O K   H O O D

PAGE 62

What's the Skinny?

G	O	A	D	S		A	L	T	O		C	H	A	P
I	D	L	E	S		S	I	R	E		L	E	C	H
L	E	A	N	T	O	S	T	A	R	B	O	A	R	D
A	S	S	T		P	E	E	N		I	S	L	E	S
			A	T	T	N		C	O	D	E			
C	H	I	L	I		T	H	E	M		S	H	O	T
A	I	R		M	I	T	E		A	P	I	E	C	E
S	K	A	T	E	D	O	N	T	H	I	N	I	C	E
T	E	N	U	R	E		C	O	A	L		S	U	N
E	R	I	N		A	H	E	M		E	N	T	R	Y
			A	R	L	O		A	I	D	E			
S	H	A	M	E		R	A	T	S		A	C	M	E
C	O	M	E	S	I	N	F	O	R	A	T	R	I	M
O	P	A	L		M	E	R	E		S	L	A	N	T
W	E	N	T		P	R	O	S		H	Y	M	N	S

PAGE 63

Fences

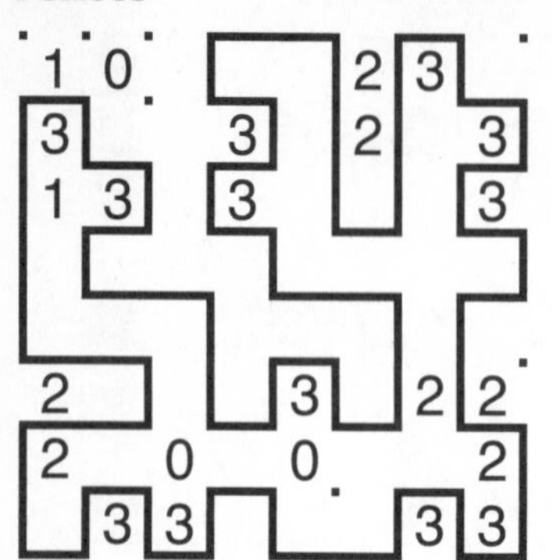

WRONG IS RIGHT

Pasturize (should be *pasteurize*)

PAGE 64

Triad Split Decisions

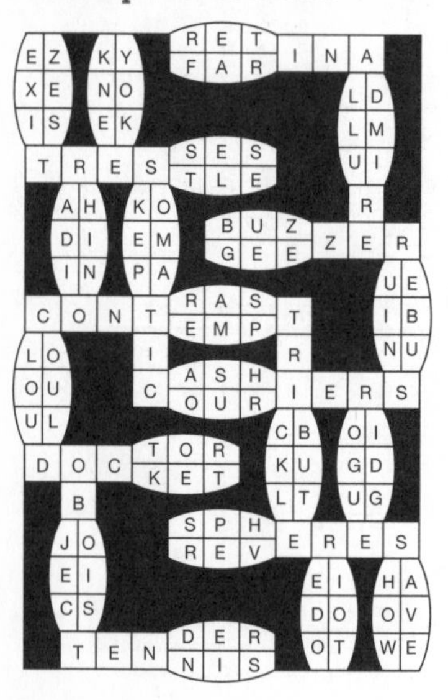

TRANSDELETION

CELLO

PAGE 65

123

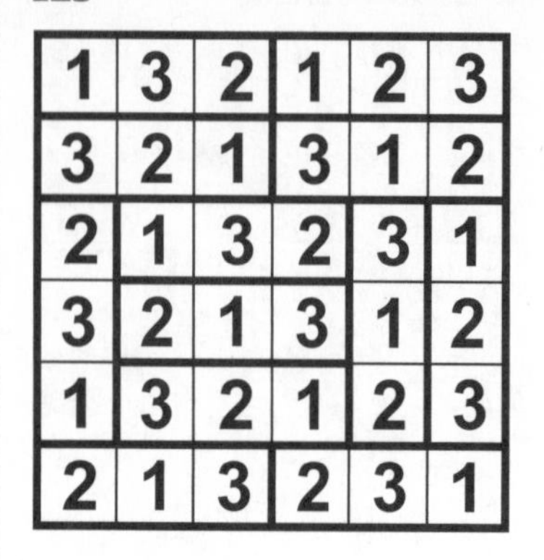

SUDOKU SUM

8	1	7
6	4	2
9	3	5

PAGE 66

Summer Wear

A	L	T	E	R		A	V	I	D		M	A	R	S
T	E	A	S	E		L	O	R	E		O	L	E	O
L	A	M	P	S	H	A	D	E	S		V	E	E	R
A	S	P		T	A	S	K		I	C	I	C	L	E
S	T	A	R	E	D		A	T	R	E	E			
			O	D	O	R		S	E	N	S	E	S	
S	O	A	P		N	E	A	T		T	H	R	E	E
E	M	C	E	E		F	I	R		S	O	L	E	S
T	I	T	H	E		U	R	A	L		R	E	D	S
	T	I	A	R	A	S		P	A	C	T			
			L	I	N	E	S		P	A	S	S	G	O
T	A	S	T	E	S		P	E	S	T		T	E	A
I	S	E	E		W	O	O	D	E	N	T	E	E	S
N	E	A	R		E	N	I	D		A	R	I	S	E
T	A	M	S		R	E	L	Y		P	A	N	E	S

PAGE 67

Number-Out

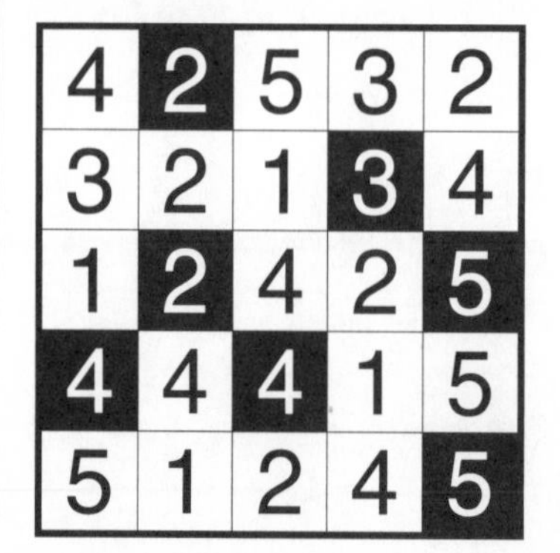

THINK ALIKE

BET, WAGER

PAGE 68

No Three in a Row

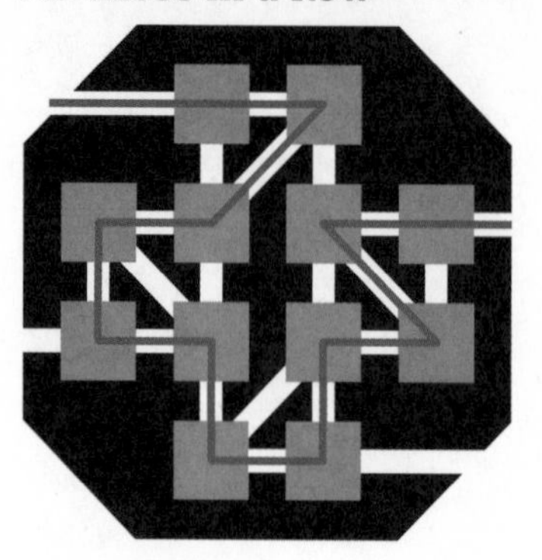

SAY IT AGAIN

HIT

PAGE 69

"Hot" Stuff

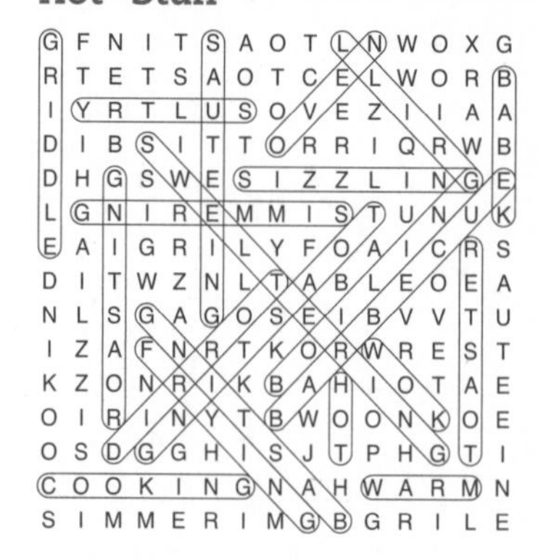

WHO'S WHAT WHERE?

Moose Javian

PAGE 70

Hardware Store

T	O	R	A	H		A	D	D		S	N	A	K	E
E	M	E	R	Y		B	I	O		H	O	L	E	Y
N	A	A	C	P		E	A	R		A	T	O	N	E
E	N	C		H	A	L	L	M	O	N	I	T	O	R
T	I	T	L	E	S			S	A	G				
			I	N	T	R	O		T	H	O	M	A	S
N	O	O	N		R	A	P	S		A	R	O	S	E
E	N	V	E	L	O	P	E	P	R	I	N	T	E	R
S	T	E	N	O		T	R	E	E		A	H	A	B
T	O	R	S	O	S		A	D	A	P	T			
				S	K	I			D	R	E	A	M	S
M	I	C	K	E	Y	M	O	U	S	E		L	O	P
A	S	O	N	E		A	D	S		M	O	L	A	R
A	L	L	E	N		G	E	E		E	L	I	T	E
M	E	T	E	D		E	S	S		D	E	N	S	E

PAGE 71

One-Way Streets

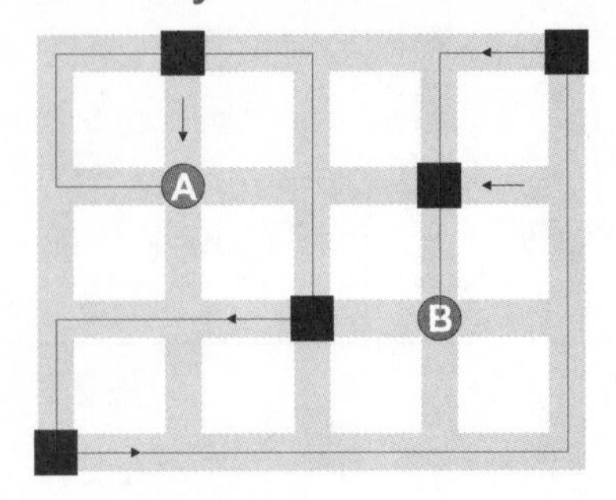

SOUND THINKING
PLAYWRIGHT

PAGE 72

Hyper-Sudoku

7	4	2	3	5	8	1	9	6
3	8	6	2	1	9	5	7	4
5	1	9	7	6	4	3	2	8
2	3	4	5	7	1	6	8	9
8	7	1	9	3	6	4	5	2
9	6	5	8	4	2	7	1	3
6	9	3	1	2	5	8	4	7
1	2	7	4	8	3	9	6	5
4	5	8	6	9	7	2	3	1

CENTURY MARKS
19, 9, 51, 21

PAGE 73

Star Search

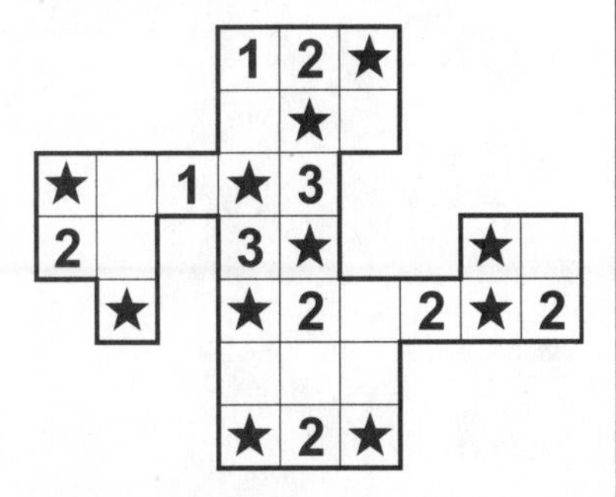

CHOICE WORDS
CARTER, MONROE, REAGAN

PAGE 74

Gossipy

PAGE 75

ABC

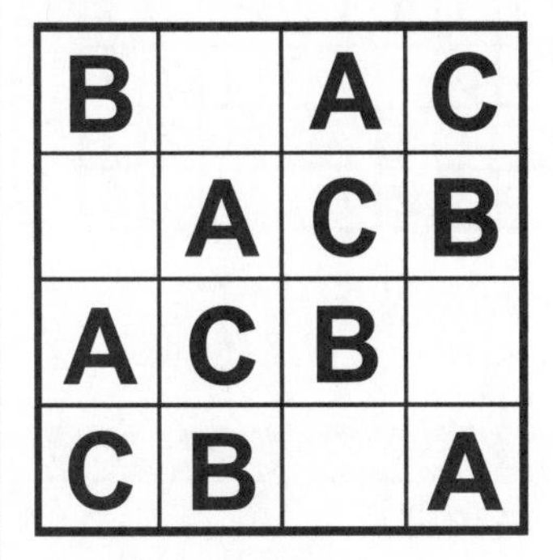

CLUELESS CROSSWORD

PAGE 76

Square Route

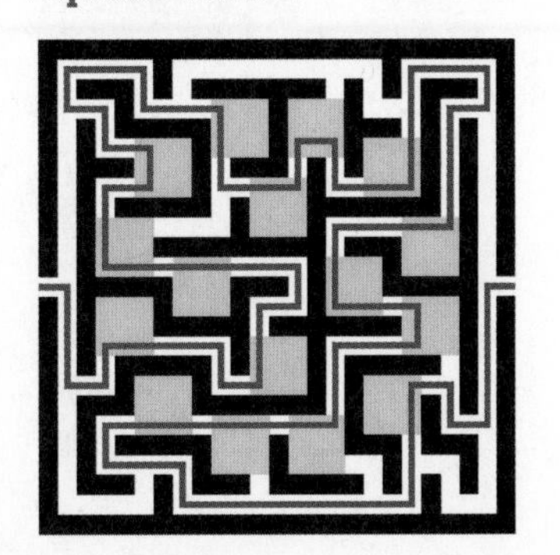

BETWEENER
JAW

PAGE 77

Sudoku

6	1	4	3	7	9	2	8	5
9	2	8	1	6	5	3	4	7
3	7	5	8	2	4	9	1	6
1	5	2	4	9	7	6	3	8
4	6	3	5	1	8	7	9	2
7	8	9	2	3	6	4	5	1
2	9	1	7	5	3	8	6	4
8	3	7	6	4	1	5	2	9
5	4	6	9	8	2	1	7	3

MIXAGRAMS
S H A L E J O B S
R I G I D U N T O
A G L O W M I C E
S H E L L P U N Y

PAGE 78

Dog Day

B	O	S	S	■	A	L	P	S	■	E	G	R	E	T
E	D	I	T	■	R	I	L	E	■	S	N	O	R	E
R	O	L	E	■	T	O	U	T	■	C	O	M	I	C
G	R	O	W	L	I	N	G	S	T	O	M	A	C	H
■	■	■	■	A	S	S	■	■	O	R	E	■	■	■
L	E	T	O	U	T	■	T	E	X	T	■	R	I	P
A	M	O	N	G	■	D	E	L	I	■	S	O	D	A
B	I	R	C	H	B	A	R	K	C	A	N	O	E	S
E	L	S	E	■	A	R	M	S	■	D	U	M	A	S
L	E	O	■	A	M	T	S	■	A	R	G	Y	L	E
■	■	■	O	R	B	■	■	P	R	E	■	■	■	■
T	W	O	P	A	I	R	S	O	F	P	A	N	T	S
H	A	T	E	R	■	A	L	K	A	■	L	E	A	K
U	L	T	R	A	■	G	O	E	R	■	M	A	X	I
G	L	O	A	T	■	S	E	R	F	■	A	R	I	D

PAGE 79

Line Drawing

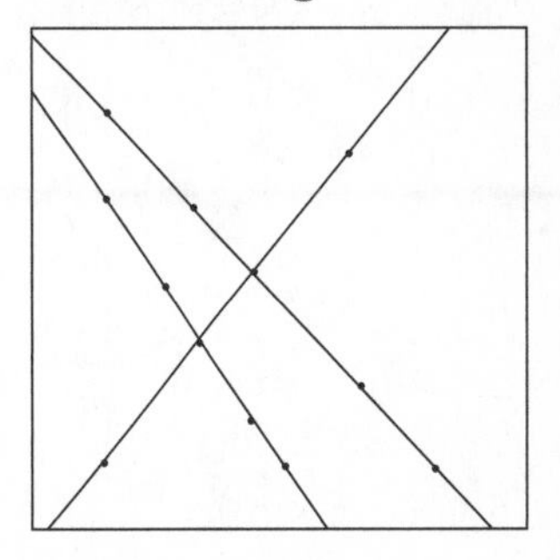

THREE OF A KIND
LAST AUGUST, A NIGHTINGALE FLEW IN MY WINDOW.

PAGE 80

Find the Ships

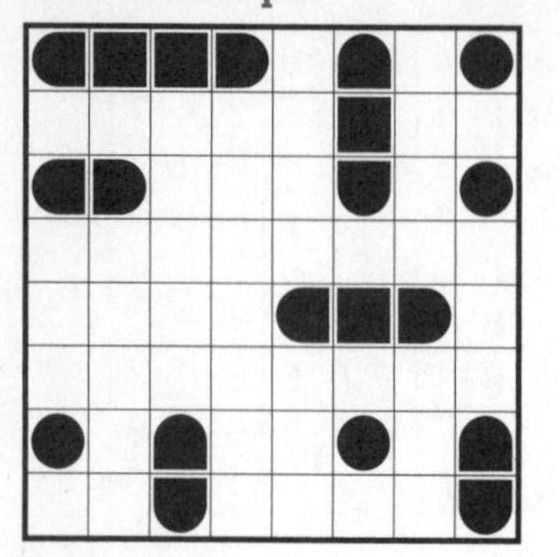

TWO-BY-FOUR

CHIC, DUPE; CUED, CHIP

PAGE 81

Fences

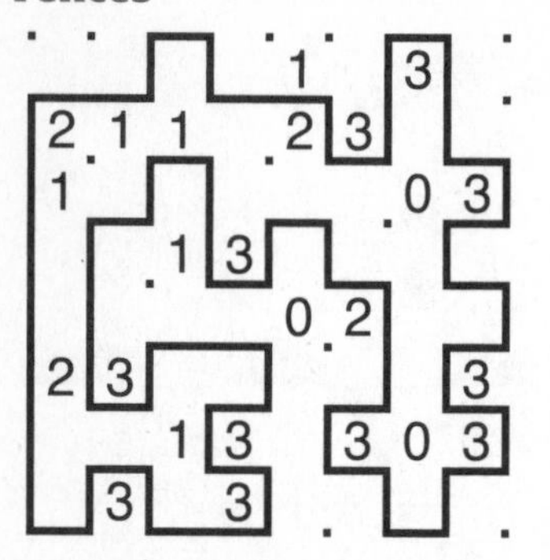

ADDITION SWITCH

2 5 9 + 3 7 3 = 6 3 2

PAGE 82

Swim Meet

T	A	N	G	■	S	A	L	E	M	■	S	M	O	G
A	L	O	E	■	T	R	E	A	D	■	H	E	R	O
L	I	S	T	■	A	M	A	S	S	■	O	M	E	N
K	E	Y	S	T	R	O	K	E	■	L	O	O	S	E
■	■	■	W	O	R	R	Y	■	D	E	E	R	■	■
S	A	F	E	T	Y	■	■	S	A	I	D	Y	E	S
O	R	A	T	E	■	B	E	A	D	S	■	L	I	P
D	I	M	■	■	T	O	L	L	S	■	■	A	D	O
A	S	I	■	T	O	A	S	T	■	L	O	N	E	R
S	E	L	L	O	U	T	■	■	D	E	S	E	R	T
■	■	Y	E	A	R	■	C	A	R	A	T	■	■	■
A	N	T	E	D	■	H	U	M	A	N	R	A	C	E
L	A	I	R	■	S	O	P	U	P	■	I	L	L	S
M	I	M	E	■	P	O	I	S	E	■	C	L	A	P
S	L	E	D	■	A	D	D	E	D	■	H	Y	M	N

PAGE 83

Mental Exercise

Barbara, Home Gym; Cyril, Trampoline; Doreen, Bicycle; Edwin, Dumbbells

SMALL CHANGE

SOFT SPOT

PAGE 84

123

1	3	2	1	2	3	1	3	2
2	1	3	2	3	1	2	1	3
3	2	1	3	1	2	3	2	1
1	3	2	1	2	3	1	3	2
3	2	1	2	3	1	2	1	3
1	3	2	3	1	2	3	2	1
2	1	3	1	3	1	2	3	2
3	2	1	3	2	3	1	2	1
2	1	3	2	1	2	3	1	3

WRONG IS RIGHT

Liason (should be *liaison*)

PAGE 85

Number-Out

1	4	3	3	5
2	3	2	4	1
1	5	5	5	4
3	1	4	5	2
2	2	2	1	5

THINK ALIKE

MOPE, SULK

PAGE 86

Newsworthy

S	A	M	E	■	D	O	N	O	R	■	A	L	S	O
T	R	A	M	■	A	M	I	N	O	■	L	O	O	K
O	G	R	E	■	W	I	N	D	S	■	O	O	P	S
C	U	R	R	E	N	T	E	V	E	N	T	S	■	■
K	E	Y	I	N	■	■	■	D	U	O	■	E	R	E
■	■	■	L	E	A	D	S	■	P	R	E	L	I	M
S	T	L	■	■	L	O	A	N	■	S	T	E	N	O
W	E	A	T	H	E	R	F	O	R	E	C	A	S	T
E	E	R	I	E	■	M	E	N	U	■	■	F	E	E
A	N	G	E	L	S	■	R	O	B	E	S	■	■	■
R	Y	E	■	L	O	S	■	■	■	N	O	I	S	E
■	■	S	P	O	R	T	S	U	P	D	A	T	E	S
P	O	O	L	■	R	A	I	S	E	■	P	A	N	S
J	U	D	O	■	O	L	D	E	N	■	E	L	S	E
S	T	A	Y	■	W	E	E	D	S	■	D	Y	E	S

PAGE 87

Tasmanian Devil Maze

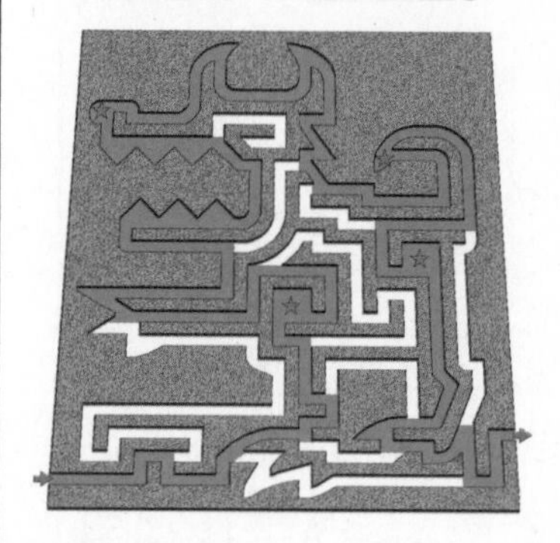

SAY IT AGAIN

JET

PAGE 88

Split Decisions

TRANSDELETION

ORANGE

PAGE 89

Hyper-Sudoku

7	3	1	8	2	6	4	9	5
5	4	8	1	3	9	2	6	7
6	9	2	7	4	5	3	8	1
2	5	3	6	9	1	7	4	8
4	7	9	2	8	3	5	1	6
1	8	6	5	7	4	9	2	3
8	1	4	9	5	7	6	3	2
9	2	7	3	6	8	1	5	4
3	6	5	4	1	2	8	7	9

MIXAGRAMS

RATED WHEY
POSSE RELY
VISTA TALE
VALID STOP

PAGE 90

Evaluations

G	N	A	W		A	M	P	L	E		A	F	A	R
E	A	C	H		R	U	R	A	L		P	I	L	E
A	S	T	I		C	L	I	C	K		P	R	O	D
R	A	I	N	C	H	E	C	K		B	E	S	T	S
			N	O	I	S	E		B	R	A	T		
A	T	T	I	R	E			H	A	I	R	G	E	L
F	I	R	E	D		P	L	A	T	E		R	A	E
R	A	I	D		P	A	I	R	S		D	A	T	A
O	R	A		S	A	L	E	M		S	I	D	E	S
S	A	L	T	I	N	E			S	E	R	E	N	E
		J	E	T	S		T	E	N	E	T			
P	R	U	N	E		F	I	X	E	D	R	A	T	E
L	A	D	S		M	I	N	C	E		O	R	A	L
U	R	G	E		A	N	G	E	R		A	L	P	S
S	E	E	R		P	E	E	L	S		D	O	S	E

PAGE 91

Picture Perfect

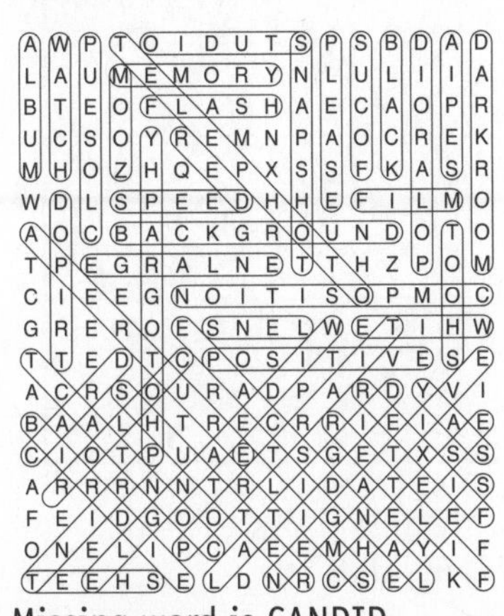

Missing word is CANDID

IN OTHER WORDS

GIRLFRIEND

PAGE 93

One-Way Streets

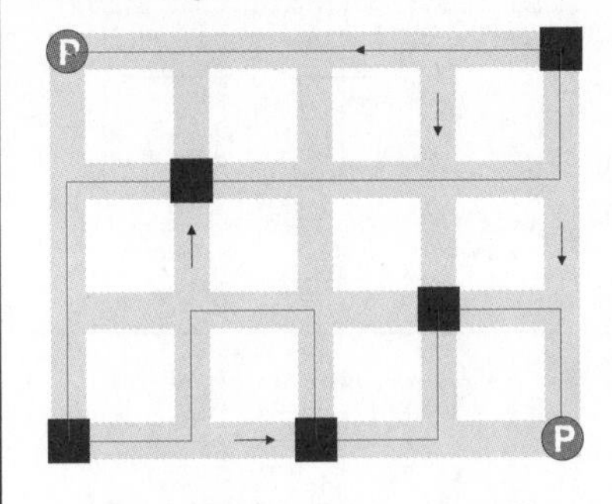

SOUND THINKING

ROADWAY

PAGE 94

Elementary

R	E	G	I	S		B	O	C	A		G	O	O	D
A	D	A	P	T		O	P	E	N		E	B	A	Y
I	G	L	O	O		N	E	C	K		T	O	T	E
L	E	A	D	P	E	N	C	I	L		T	E	S	S
			S	I	T			L	E	V	I			
B	T	U		T	H	A	T		T	I	N	M	A	N
O	H	N	O		E	T	R	E		A	G	I	L	E
S	I	L	V	E	R	M	E	D	A	L	I	S	T	S
S	N	E	E	R		S	E	E	M		N	E	A	T
A	S	T	R	A	Y		S	N	I	P		R	R	S
			A	S	A	P			G	A	S			
C	H	I	C		C	A	R	B	O	N	C	O	P	Y
R	U	S	T		H	I	Y	A		D	O	G	I	E
O	G	L	E		T	R	A	Y		A	O	R	T	A
W	E	E	D		S	S	N	S		S	P	E	A	R

PAGE 95

Tanks a Lot

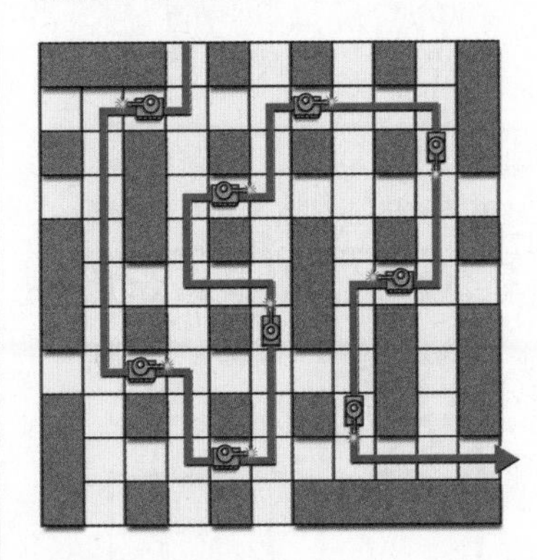

SMALL CHANGE

POT ROAST

PAGE 96

Star Search

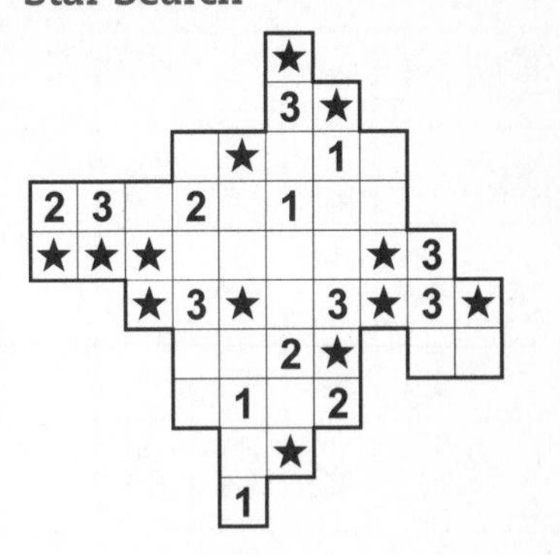

CHOICE WORDS

BUNKUM, DRIVEL, HUMBUG

PAGE 97

Triad Split Decisions

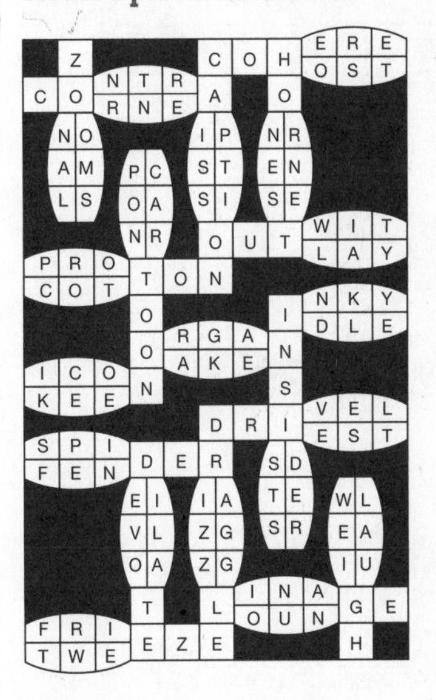

TRANSDELETION

SCYTHE

PAGE 98

Engineering Majors

B	E	R	E	T		S	T	E	M		B	A	R	B
A	D	O	R	E		T	A	P	E		O	B	O	E
H	A	B	I	T		A	X	I	S		B	O	L	L
	M	E	C	H	A	N	I	C	A	L	B	U	L	L
				E	N	D				A	L	T	O	S
D	I	V	E	R	T		S	T	O	N	E			
E	D	E	N			L	U	R	I	D		B	T	U
E	L	E	C	T	R	I	C	A	L	S	T	O	R	M
P	E	R		R	E	T	R	Y			B	O	O	P
			D	O	N	E	E		S	L	A	N	T	S
S	N	A	R	L				T	I	A				
C	I	V	I	L	L	I	B	E	R	T	I	E	S	
O	X	E	N		O	M	A	R		E	N	T	E	R
P	O	R	K		L	A	I	R		S	T	O	R	E
E	N	T	S		A	X	L	E		T	O	N	A	L

PAGE 99

ABC

B	A			C
A		C		B
C	B		A	
	C	A	B	
		B	C	A

NATIONAL TREASURE

OKRA

PAGE 100

Find the Ships

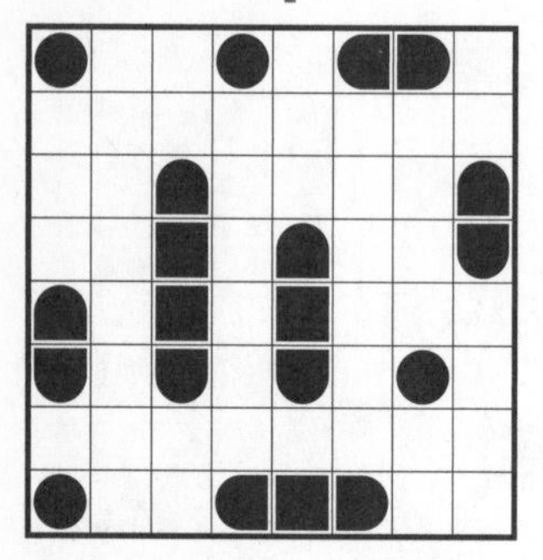

TWO-BY-FOUR

ABLY, AUTO

PAGE 101

Drink Up

C	A	D	R	E		A	N	E	W		S	P	A	S
O	R	I	O	N		L	A	V	A		K	U	R	T
A	R	O	M	A		T	R	O	T		I	N	G	E
S	O	D	A	C	R	A	C	K	E	R		C	O	W
T	W	E	N	T	Y			E	R	I	C	H		
				E	E	L	S		L	O	L	L	E	D
N	O	M	A	D		I	A	G	O		A	I	D	A
A	X	I	S		T	A	B	O	O		S	N	I	T
P	E	L	T		E	R	L	E		T	H	E	T	A
A	N	K	A	R	A		E	R	T	E				
		G	R	E	T	A			S	E	T	O	F	F
P	O	L		C	O	F	F	E	E	T	A	B	L	E
A	H	A	B		W	I	L	Y		I	L	I	A	D
L	I	S	A		E	R	I	E		M	E	T	R	O
M	O	S	T		L	E	T	S		E	S	S	E	N

PAGE 102

Two Pairs

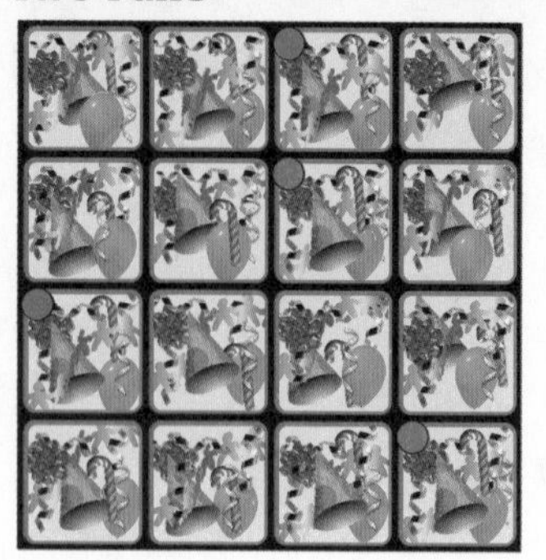

BETWEENER

BASE

PAGE 103

Sudoku

1	7	6	5	2	4	9	8	3
2	9	4	7	8	3	6	1	5
3	5	8	6	9	1	7	2	4
7	2	1	3	6	8	5	4	9
5	8	3	2	4	9	1	7	6
6	4	9	1	5	7	2	3	8
9	1	7	4	3	5	8	6	2
4	6	5	8	1	2	3	9	7
8	3	2	9	7	6	4	5	1

MIXAGRAMS

M O T I F A W E D
P E T A L T A C K
U L T R A C R I B
G A M U T M E S A

PAGE 104

Fences

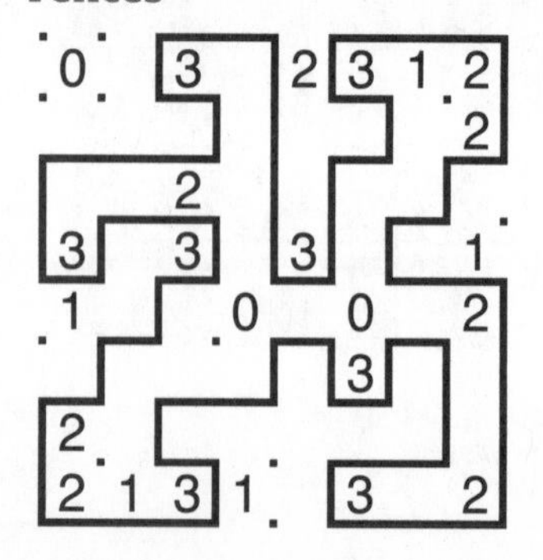

WRONG IS RIGHT

Fragrent (should be *fragrant*)

PAGE 105

Video Store

C	H	I	T	S		C	E	L	T		H	A	S	H
A	A	R	O	N		O	P	I	E		U	C	L	A
D	R	A	M	A	Q	U	E	E	N		S	T	A	Y
S	I	N	E	C	U	R	E		N	A	T	I	V	E
				K	I	T				S	L	O	E	S
E	C	H	O	E	D		D	A	R	K	E	N		
A	L	O	U	D		L	O	B	E	S		L	E	D
T	O	R	T		R	O	V	E	D		M	I	R	A
S	Y	R		R	E	V	E	L		M	A	N	O	R
		O	L	I	V	E	R		S	A	G	E	S	T
S	C	R	A	P				O	E	R				
T	A	S	T	E	S		O	P	E	R	E	T	T	A
A	S	H	E		C	O	M	E	D	Y	T	E	A	M
L	I	O	N		A	D	E	N		M	A	L	L	E
L	O	W	S		M	E	N	S		E	L	L	E	N

PAGE 106

Number-Out

6	4	5	6	1	3
5	6	2	2	2	4
1	3	2	1	6	5
2	1	2	5	2	3
3	5	6	4	3	2
4	3	3	3	5	6

THINK ALIKE

HOT, FIERY

PAGE 107

Hyper-Sudoku

5	2	3	1	9	8	4	7	6
1	6	7	5	2	4	8	9	3
8	4	9	3	7	6	1	2	5
9	8	1	2	6	5	7	3	4
4	7	5	8	3	1	9	6	2
6	3	2	9	4	7	5	1	8
2	5	4	7	1	3	6	8	9
3	1	8	6	5	9	2	4	7
7	9	6	4	8	2	3	5	1

CENTURY MARKS

26, 60, 6, 8

PAGE 108

Looking Tidy

S	H	A	F	T		B	O	O	T	S		S	T	E
S	A	M	O	A		A	L	V	I	N		P	A	S
S	H	A	R	P	C	H	E	E	S	E		R	X	S
			S	E	N	I	O	R		E	D	U	C	E
D	A	N	A		B	A	S	E		R	E	C	O	N
I	T	A	L	I	C			M	A	S	S	E		
D	O	T	E	D		R	O	O	F		I	G	O	R
O	N	T		S	P	E	C	T	R	A		O	L	E
K	E	Y	S		S	I	T	E		E	R	O	D	E
		B	E	G	I	N			E	R	A	S	E	D
T	R	U	E	R		S	T	A	R		T	E	N	S
T	A	M	P	A		T	O	N	I	C	S			
O	O	P		S	M	A	R	T	C	O	O	K	I	E
P	U	P		P	E	T	R	O		G	U	E	S	T
S	L	O		S	T	E	E	N		S	T	R	A	D

PAGE 109

Look Both Ways

INITIAL REACTION

Rome Wasn't Built In A Day

PAGE 110

Sets of Three

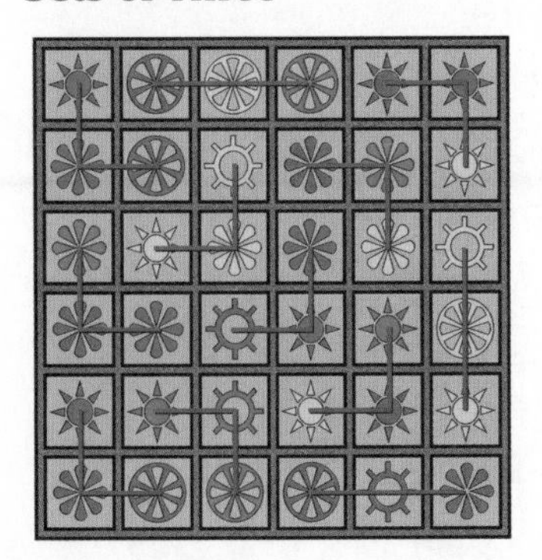

SAY IT AGAIN

LAND

PAGE 111

In Hot Water

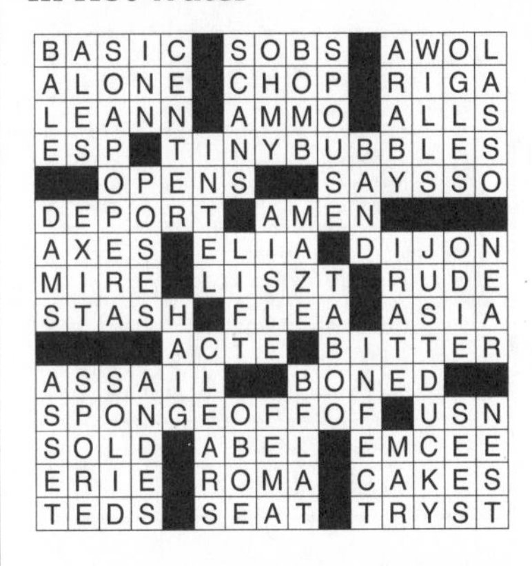

B	A	S	I	C		S	O	B	S		A	W	O	L
A	L	O	N	E		C	H	O	P		R	I	G	A
L	E	A	N	N		A	M	M	O		A	L	L	S
E	S	P		T	I	N	Y	B	U	B	B	L	E	S
		O	P	E	N	S			S	A	Y	S	S	O
D	E	P	O	R	T		A	M	E	N				
A	X	E	S		E	L	I	A		D	I	J	O	N
M	I	R	E		L	I	S	Z	T		R	U	D	E
S	T	A	S	H		F	L	E	A		A	S	I	A
				A	C	T	E		B	I	T	T	E	R
A	S	S	A	I	L			B	O	N	E	D		
S	P	O	N	G	E	O	F	F	O	F		U	S	N
S	O	L	D		A	B	E	L		E	M	C	E	E
E	R	I	E		R	O	M	A		C	A	K	E	S
T	E	D	S		S	E	A	T		T	R	Y	S	T

PAGE 112

One-Way Streets

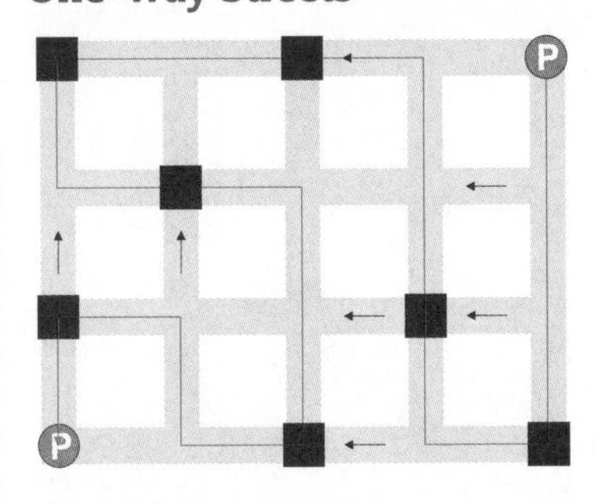

SOUND THINKING

SUBDUE

PAGE 113

123

2	1	2	3	1	3	1	3	2
3	2	3	1	2	1	2	1	3
1	3	1	2	3	2	3	2	1
2	1	3	1	2	3	2	1	3
1	3	2	3	1	2	1	3	2
3	2	1	2	3	1	3	2	1
2	1	3	1	2	3	1	3	2
1	3	2	3	1	2	3	2	1
3	2	1	2	3	1	2	1	3

SUDOKU SUM

4	6	9
8	3	5
1	7	2

PAGE 114

Line Drawing

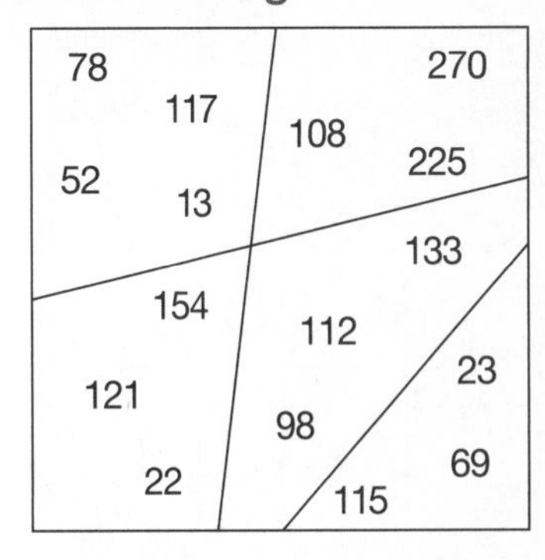

Multiples of 13, multiples of 9, multiples of 11, multiples of 7, multiples of 23

THREE OF A KIND

THEIR KIDS WERE IN DANGER, I LEARNED.

PAGE 115

B-to-B Directory

S	H	I	P	S		S	T	E	M		B	R	A	D
C	U	R	I	E		L	O	D	E		R	E	L	O
A	L	O	N	E		A	D	A	M		I	N	T	O
B	A	N	T	H	E	B	O	M	B		D	E	A	R
				E	S	S			E	D	G	E	R	S
T	I	M	B	R	E		P	A	R	E	E			
E	D	D	I	E		H	E	N		S	C	R	A	P
A	L	S	O			A	N	T			L	I	M	O
K	E	E	L	S		I	C	E		T	U	D	O	R
			O	H	A	R	E		R	O	B	E	R	T
S	T	A	G	E	R			C	A	R				
T	O	R	Y		B	R	E	A	D	C	R	U	M	B
A	W	O	L		O	A	R	S		H	O	N	O	R
F	E	M	A		R	I	M	E		E	L	I	T	E
F	L	A	B		S	L	A	Y		D	E	T	E	R

PAGE 116

Star Search

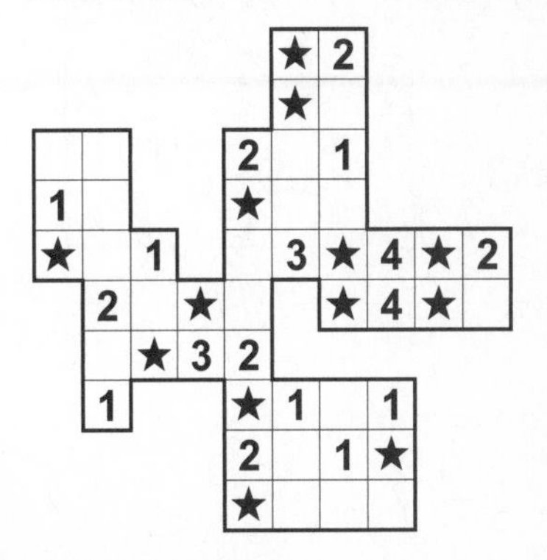

CHOICE WORDS

CHOICE, SUPERB, TIPTOP

PAGE 117

Dicey

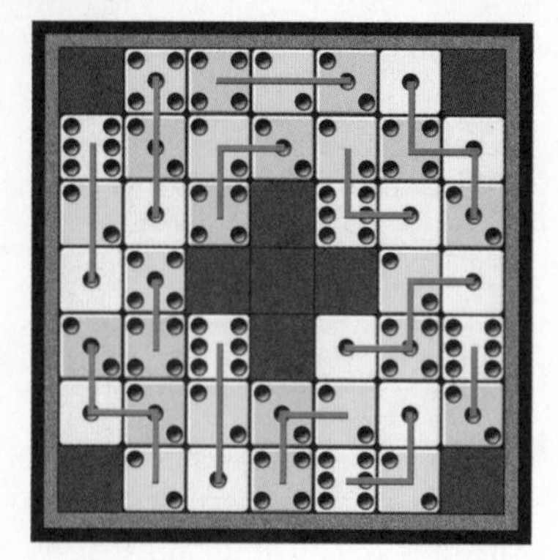

SMALL CHANGE

SAND TRAP

PAGE 118

Followings

G	E	A	R		B	A	S	S		C	E	C	I	L
E	L	L	E		A	L	P	O		A	R	O	S	E
N	E	I	L		K	O	A	N		C	A	R	E	S
I	N	S	I	D	E	T	R	A	C	K		N	E	T
E	A	T	E	R	S			R	O	L	E	S		
			F	O	A	L	S		N	E	C	T	A	R
A	P	E		P	L	A	I	D		D	R	A	N	O
M	A	Y	A		E	N	T	E	R		U	L	N	A
E	V	E	N	T		D	U	K	E	S		K	E	N
N	E	S	T	E	D		P	E	S	T	S			
		H	E	R	O	N			P	E	A	R	L	S
B	O	A		S	W	A	L	L	O	W	T	A	I	L
A	N	D	R	E		M	A	I	N		E	M	M	A
S	T	O	O	L		E	K	E	D		E	B	B	S
H	O	W	D	Y		D	E	N	S		N	O	S	H

PAGE 119

Hyper-Sudoku

4	6	7	3	9	8	2	1	5
5	2	3	7	6	1	8	9	4
9	8	1	4	2	5	7	6	3
7	9	5	6	8	4	3	2	1
6	1	4	2	7	3	9	5	8
2	3	8	1	5	9	4	7	6
8	7	6	5	4	2	1	3	9
1	4	2	9	3	6	5	8	7
3	5	9	8	1	7	6	4	2

MIXAGRAMS

MEDIA A LONG G
ASKEW W MAMA A
POLKA A CALM M
GOOFY Y POLE E

PAGE 120

ABC

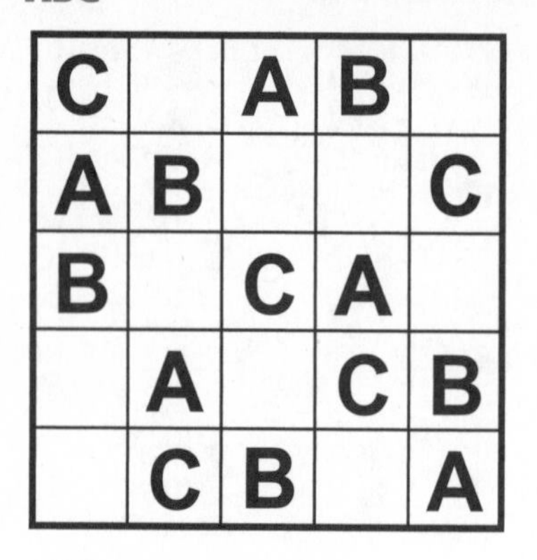

NATIONAL TREASURE

BAAING

PAGE 121

Two Pair

L	O	D	E	S		D	O	L	E		S	T	E	M
A	G	I	L	E		E	V	I	L		T	H	A	I
G	R	E	E	N	S	F	E	E	S		A	R	T	S
S	E	M	E	S	T	E	R		A	G	R	E	E	S
				O	A	R				E	V	E	R	Y
M	I	S	E	R	Y		N	O	B	L	E	S		
P	A	W	N	S		H	O	W	L	S		P	O	P
A	M	E	S		T	I	B	E	T		T	E	L	E
A	B	E		A	N	D	E	S		S	W	E	D	E
		P	A	S	T	E	L		G	L	I	D	E	R
F	I	S	T	S				P	I	E				
R	O	W	E	N	A		M	A	G	E	N	T	A	S
O	N	E	S		F	R	E	E	S	P	E	E	C	H
D	I	E	T		A	I	L	S		O	M	A	H	A
O	A	K	S		R	O	D	E		N	O	S	E	D

PAGE 122

Knot or Not?

Knot: 1 and 4, Not: 2 and 3

BETWEENER

CHOP

PAGE 123

Find the Ships

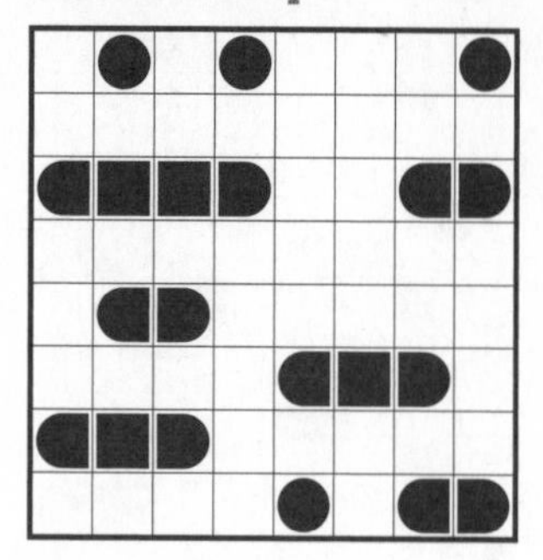

TWO-BY-FOUR

ZERO, OMIT; OOZE, TRIM; ZOOM, TIER (or TIRE or RITE); ORZO, EMIT (or MITE or TIME or ITEM)

PAGE 124

Triad Split Decisions

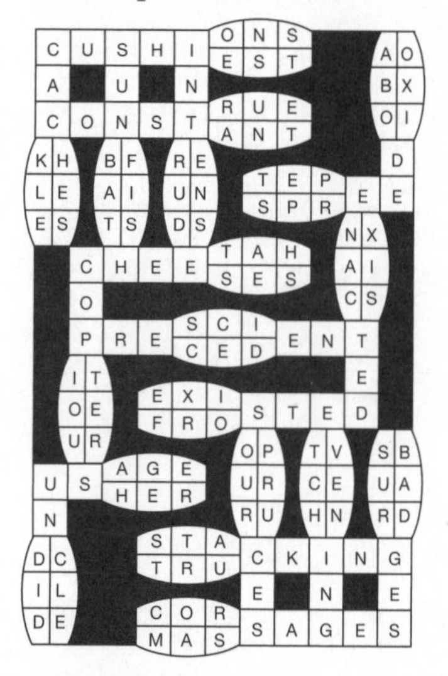

TRANSDELETION

PRIEST

PAGE 125

Street Smarts

S	U	B	S		R	E	G	A	L		E	T	C	H
C	H	I	A		A	D	O	B	E		R	E	L	Y
O	H	B	Y	T	H	E	W	A	Y		A	S	A	P
T	U	L	S	A		N	E	S	T		S	T	Y	E
T	H	E	Y	R	E		R	E	E	L	E	D		
			E	A	R	P				E	R	R	O	R
O	A	F	S		N	E	W	A	G	E		I	M	P
P	R	O		P	I	L	A	T	E	S		V	I	M
E	G	O		L	E	T	S	O	N		S	E	T	S
D	O	D	G	E				P	E	S	T			
		C	L	A	M	O	R		S	P	A	S	M	S
W	H	O	A		I	P	O	D		A	L	L	A	H
H	O	U	R		M	E	M	O	R	Y	L	A	N	E
I	N	R	E		I	R	A	N	I		E	V	I	L
P	E	T	S		C	A	N	T	O		D	E	A	L

PAGE 126

123

1	3	2	1	2	3	1	2	3
2	1	3	2	3	1	2	3	1
3	2	1	3	1	2	3	1	2
1	3	2	1	2	3	1	2	3
3	2	1	3	1	2	3	1	2
2	1	3	2	3	1	2	3	1
1	3	2	1	2	3	1	2	3
2	1	3	2	3	1	2	3	1
3	2	1	3	1	2	3	1	2

WRONG IS RIGHT

Treatice (should be *treatise*)

PAGE 127

Fences

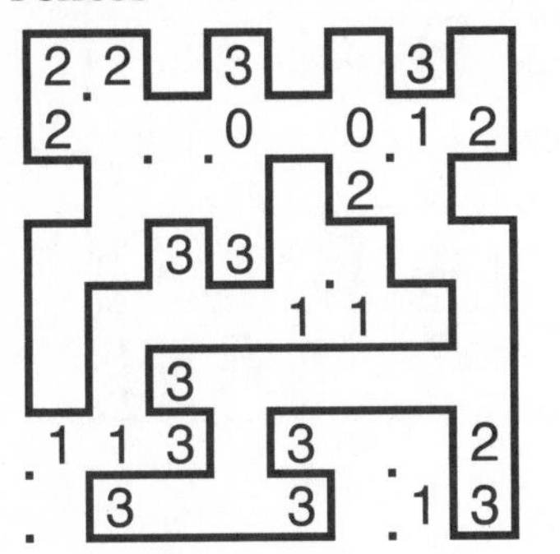

ADDITION SWITCH

3 3 7 + 4 7 9 = 8 1 6

PAGE 128

Thriller

C	R	U	M	B		R	A	F	T	S		T	A	R
P	A	P	E	R		A	U	R	A	L		I	R	E
O	N	C	L	O	U	D	N	I	N	E		C	I	A
				K	N	O	T		S	N	A	K	E	D
P	R	O	T	E	I	N				D	I	L	L	Y
R	E	V	E	R	T		R	E	V	E	R	E		
O	P	E	N	S		M	A	Y	O	R		D	B	A
S	O	R	T		D	O	Z	E	N		S	P	I	N
E	S	T		S	I	L	O	S		P	A	I	N	T
		H	I	T	T	E	R		D	O	I	N	G	S
C	R	E	P	E				C	A	R	D	K	E	Y
R	E	M	O	R	A		M	A	S	T				
A	D	O		I	N	H	O	G	H	E	A	V	E	N
W	Y	O		L	O	I	R	E		R	A	I	S	E
L	E	N		E	N	D	E	D		S	H	E	E	T

PAGE 129

Cockatoo Maze

SAY IT AGAIN

MINE

PAGE 131

At the Theater

T	E	K	C	I	T	Q	C	R	M	O	V	I	E	S
R	E	S	T	R	A	I	L	E	R	E	E	Z	M	T
D	I	C	S	O	U	N	D	T	R	A	C	K	O	R
A	R	A	I	T	J	S	R	S	S	N	A	P	T	A
P	D	O	T	F	C	G	E	U	R	R	M	Z	I	I
O	O	V	C	R	F	C	E	B	A	O	E	I	O	L
S	T	P	E	P	U	O	V	K	T	C	N	D	N	E
T	E	E	D	R	O	C	X	C	S	P	I	U	T	E
E	N	Q	T	O	T	P	E	O	N	O	C	T	L	O
R	S	A	U	J	G	I	M	L	B	P	E	S	I	U
B	I	E	L	E	Y	R	S	B	S	R	F	D	F	F
N	V	E	A	C	L	W	K	I	E	I	U	I	I	I
S	E	R	U	T	C	I	P	H	N	T	A	L	L	L
R	E	E	I	O	S	O	S	H	S	G	M	X	I	F
F	S	T	A	R	A	U	E	R	E	I	M	E	R	P

Missing answer is CANDY

WHO'S WHAT WHERE?

Taoseno

PAGE 132

Hyper-Sudoku

4	7	2	9	6	3	1	8	5
8	6	9	7	1	5	2	3	4
3	1	5	8	2	4	9	7	6
5	2	3	4	9	8	6	1	7
7	8	6	1	3	2	4	5	9
9	4	1	5	7	6	8	2	3
2	3	7	6	4	1	5	9	8
6	9	8	2	5	7	3	4	1
1	5	4	3	8	9	7	6	2

MIXAGRAMS

EARTH SWAP
KARMA SIZE
SPIEL ETCH
BRIEF USES

PAGE 133

On the Job

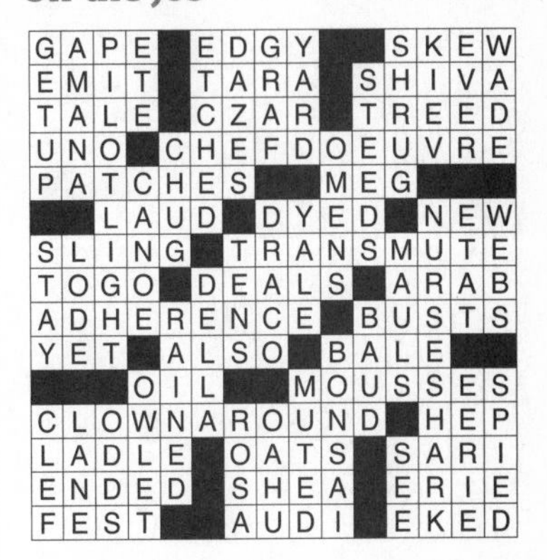

G	A	P	E		E	D	G	Y			S	K	E	W
E	M	I	T		T	A	R	A		S	H	I	V	A
T	A	L	E		C	Z	A	R		T	R	E	E	D
U	N	O		C	H	E	F	D	O	E	U	V	R	E
P	A	T	C	H	E	S			M	E	G			
		L	A	U	D		D	Y	E	D		N	E	W
S	L	I	N	G		T	R	A	N	S	M	U	T	E
T	O	G	O		D	E	A	L	S		A	R	A	B
A	D	H	E	R	E	N	C	E		B	U	S	T	S
Y	E	T		A	L	S	O		B	A	L	E		
			O	I	L			M	O	U	S	S	E	S
C	L	O	W	N	A	R	O	U	N	D		H	E	P
L	A	D	L	E		O	A	T	S		S	A	R	I
E	N	D	E	D		S	H	E	A		E	R	I	E
F	E	S	T			A	U	D	I		E	K	E	D

PAGE 134

One-Way Streets

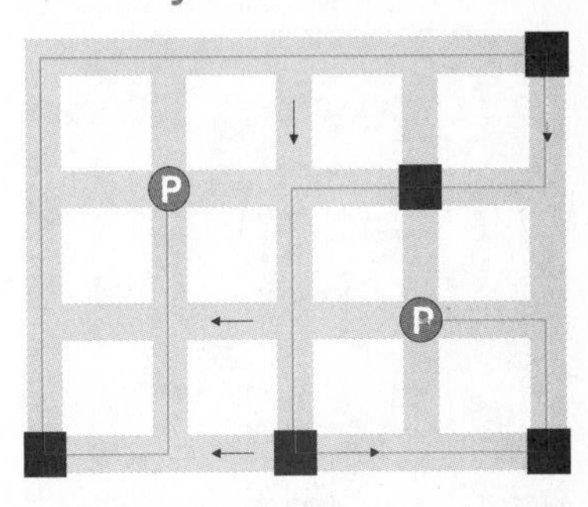

SOUND THINKING

ETHNIC

PAGE 135

Star Search

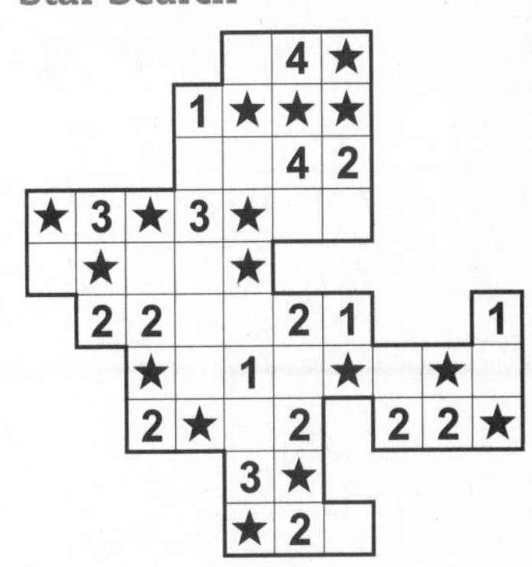

CHOICE WORDS

BATBOY, INNING, UMPIRE

PAGE 136

Three-Peats

B	O	F	F	S	■	O	W	E	S	■	T	A	P	E
A	P	I	A	N	■	P	E	L	E	■	A	B	E	L
B	A	R	B	A	R	E	L	L	A	■	R	E	A	L
A	R	M	■	R	E	N	T	■	M	O	T	T	L	E
S	T	A	B	L	E	S	■	G	I	L	A	■	■	■
■	■	■	O	E	D	■	T	O	L	E	R	A	T	E
E	M	E	N	D	■	F	O	R	E	■	S	W	A	T
V	E	R	B	■	H	A	R	E	S	■	A	L	T	O
E	L	M	O	■	A	L	A	N	■	S	U	S	A	N
S	T	A	N	D	I	S	H	■	T	A	C	■	■	■
■	■	■	N	I	L	E	■	N	O	V	E	N	A	S
R	E	G	I	N	A	■	K	O	N	A	■	E	S	P
O	G	R	E	■	C	I	N	C	I	N	N	A	T	I
A	G	A	R	■	A	R	E	A	■	T	U	T	O	R
R	Y	N	E	■	B	A	W	L	■	S	T	O	R	E

PAGE 137

Color Paths

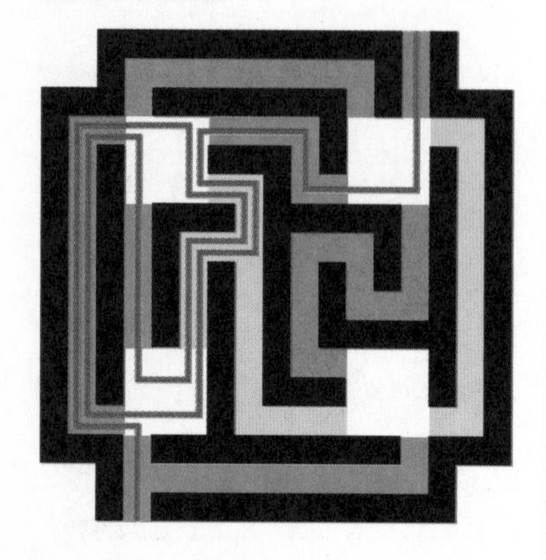

SMALL CHANGE

TOWN CRIER

PAGE 138

Sudoku

2	8	3	4	6	9	5	1	7
5	6	9	8	7	1	2	3	4
1	7	4	3	5	2	8	9	6
4	2	5	9	3	8	7	6	1
7	9	1	5	4	6	3	2	8
8	3	6	2	1	7	4	5	9
3	1	8	6	2	4	9	7	5
6	4	2	7	9	5	1	8	3
9	5	7	1	8	3	6	4	2

CENTURY MARKS

37, 15, 36, 12

PAGE 139

Veggie Plate

T	A	N	S	■	B	L	A	S	E	■	C	O	N	E
O	R	B	S	■	R	I	L	L	E	■	O	N	Y	X
P	E	A	S	H	O	O	T	E	R	■	P	I	P	E
I	N	E	■	O	N	T	H	E	■	W	O	O	D	S
C	A	R	R	O	T	T	O	P	■	R	U	N	■	■
■	■	■	I	D	E	A	■	S	U	I	T	S	M	E
D	O	B	B	S	■	■	M	I	S	T	■	K	E	Y
U	K	E	S	■	P	L	A	N	S	■	P	I	N	E
E	R	A	■	D	O	O	R	■	■	S	A	N	D	S
T	A	N	G	E	L	O	■	U	S	E	R	■	■	■
■	■	S	I	N	■	P	E	P	P	E	R	P	O	T
R	I	T	Z	Y	■	H	A	D	A	T	■	I	C	H
A	D	A	M	■	P	O	T	A	T	O	R	A	C	E
P	O	L	O	■	E	L	I	T	E	■	O	N	U	S
T	S	K	S	■	G	E	N	E	S	■	W	O	R	E

PAGE 140

Split Decisions

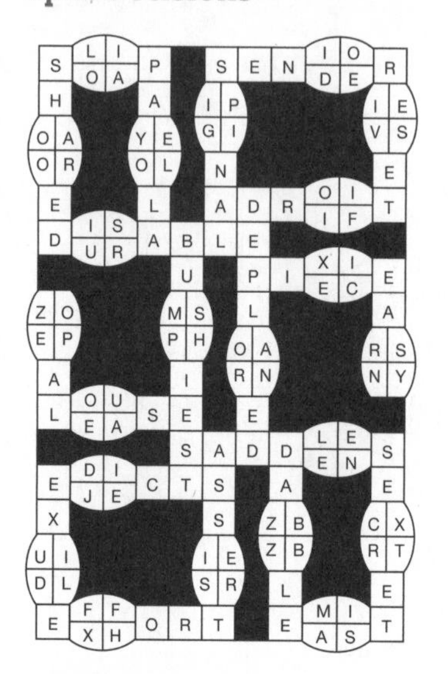

TRANSDELETION

TEQUILA

PAGE 141

Number-Out

3	1	5	2	4	3
5	**2**	2	**2**	1	**1**
4	3	1	6	**6**	2
1	2	**4**	4	6	5
4	6	4	**1**	5	1
2	4	3	5	**5**	6

THINK ALIKE

CEASE, STOP

PAGE 142

Searches

C	O	G	S	■	A	C	H	E	■	P	L	A	T	O
U	C	L	A	■	B	R	O	M	■	T	U	N	E	D
S	T	O	R	E	R	O	O	M	■	B	L	O	N	D
H	A	S	A	L	O	O	K	A	R	O	U	N	D	■
Y	D	S	■	M	A	N	■	■	E	A	S	Y	■	■
■	■	■	D	I	D	■	C	H	A	T	■	M	O	A
T	H	E	I	R	■	L	A	I	C	■	P	O	L	S
R	U	M	M	A	G	E	S	T	H	R	O	U	G	H
A	L	E	S	■	O	N	E	S	■	A	S	S	A	Y
P	A	R	■	E	A	T	S	■	B	Y	E	■	■	■
■	■	G	E	N	T	■	■	Z	A	G	■	R	P	M
■	B	E	A	T	S	T	H	E	B	U	S	H	E	S
H	E	N	R	I	■	R	O	B	I	N	H	O	O	D
R	A	C	E	R	■	I	N	R	E	■	A	N	N	O
S	U	E	D	E	■	M	E	A	D	■	M	E	S	S

PAGE 143

ABC

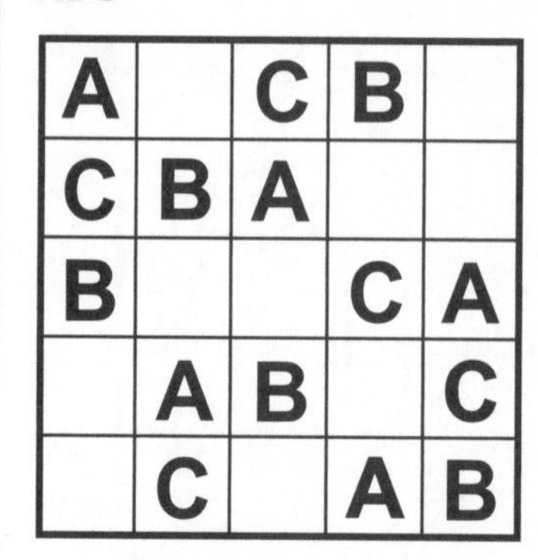

A		C	B	
C	B	A		
B			C	A
	A	B		C
	C		A	B

CLUELESS CROSSWORD

S	H	I	A	T	S	U
T	■	S	■	E	■	T
A	N	T	I	Q	U	E
N	■	H	■	U	■	N
D	I	M	W	I	T	S
E	■	U	■	L	■	I
E	N	S	N	A	R	L

PAGE 144

Looped Path

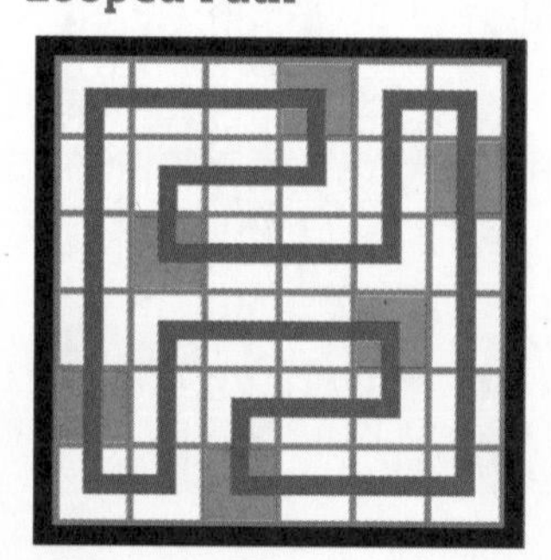

BETWEENER

FROG

PAGE 145

Line Drawing

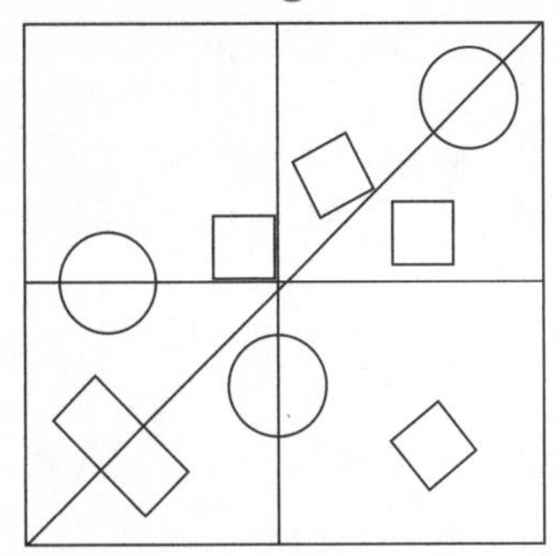

THREE OF A KIND

FOR MOST AMERICANS, SKIN DIVING REQUIRES DILIGENT LESSONS.

PAGE 146

Toppings

S	C	A	B	■	I	M	P	S	■	G	O	A	P	E
T	A	L	E	■	N	C	A	A	■	E	L	B	O	W
A	N	T	E	■	T	I	N	T	■	T	A	S	T	E
S	O	A	P	B	O	X	D	E	R	B	Y	■	■	■
H	E	R	E	A	T	■	A	D	A	Y	■	C	O	D
■	■	■	D	R	A	M	■	■	N	O	M	O	R	E
A	H	A	■	B	L	A	S	T	I	N	G	C	A	P
C	A	S	E	■	■	R	I	O	■	■	M	O	L	T
T	R	I	P	L	E	C	R	O	W	N	■	A	S	H
O	R	D	A	I	N	■	■	T	A	O	S	■	■	■
R	Y	E	■	E	R	A	S	■	S	P	A	R	T	A
■	■	■	B	O	Y	Z	N	T	H	E	H	O	O	D
N	E	G	E	V	■	T	A	K	E	■	A	V	I	D
A	G	I	L	E	■	E	F	O	R	■	R	E	L	O
P	O	L	A	R	■	C	U	S	S	■	A	S	S	N

PAGE 147

Find the Ships

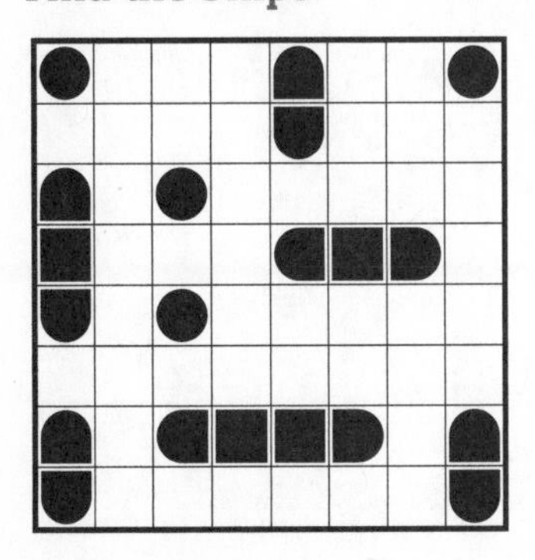

TWO-BY-FOUR

INFO, DIET (or EDIT or TIED or TIDE)

PAGE 148

Hyper-Sudoku

2	7	8	5	4	9	1	3	6
4	9	6	7	1	3	8	5	2
3	1	5	2	8	6	4	7	9
6	4	3	8	5	1	2	9	7
9	2	1	6	3	7	5	4	8
8	5	7	4	9	2	3	6	1
7	8	2	3	6	5	9	1	4
5	6	9	1	2	4	7	8	3
1	3	4	9	7	8	6	2	5

MIXAGRAMS

ABLER HORN
SALVE ONCE
ANGLE CITE
EKING STAY

PAGE 149

Name of the Game

P	O	L	L	■	S	C	A	M	■	D	A	F	F	Y
A	L	O	E	■	C	O	C	O	■	E	C	O	L	E
R	I	N	D	■	A	L	T	O	■	G	R	O	U	T
I	V	E	G	O	T	A	S	E	C	R	E	T	■	■
S	I	R	E	D	■	■	■	D	U	E	■	L	I	B
H	A	S	■	D	U	N	K	■	D	E	V	O	T	E
■	■	■	E	E	R	I	E	R	■	■	O	N	C	E
T	H	E	P	R	I	C	E	I	S	R	I	G	H	T
H	O	S	E	■	■	E	L	O	P	E	D	■	■	■
R	E	C	E	D	E	■	S	T	A	N	■	F	A	N
U	S	A	■	O	R	E	■	■	■	T	A	L	L	Y
■	■	L	E	T	S	M	A	K	E	A	D	E	A	L
I	R	A	T	E	■	O	V	E	N	■	M	E	M	O
T	O	T	A	L	■	T	E	N	D	■	I	C	O	N
S	W	E	L	L	■	E	R	O	S	■	T	E	S	S

PAGE 150

Fences

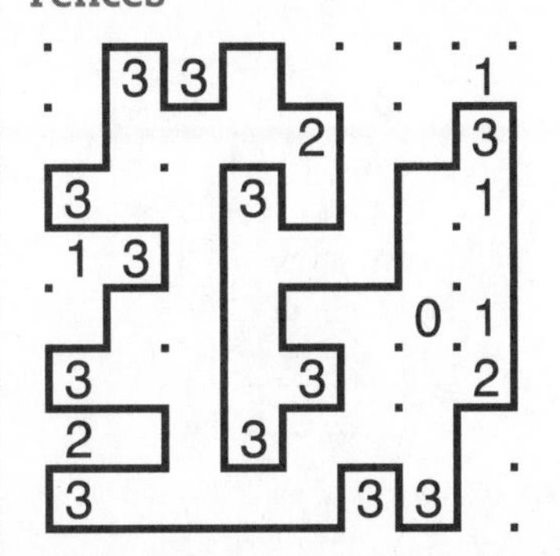

WRONG IS RIGHT

Pomagranate (should be *pomegranate*)

PAGE 151

Dotty

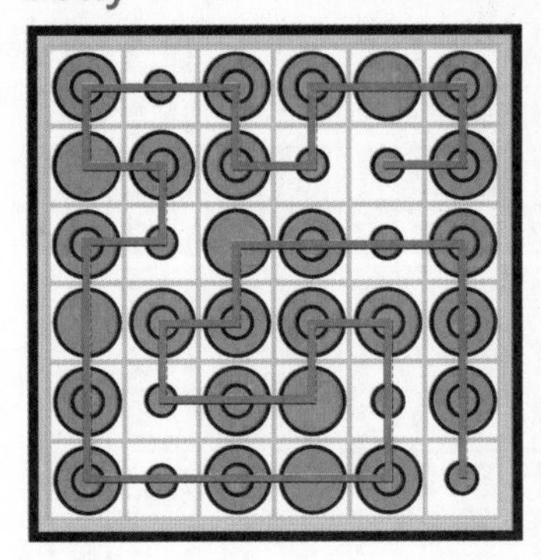

SAY IT AGAIN

PLANE

PAGE 152

Number-Out

6	4	5	2	1	2
3	1	4	2	3	3
5	2	2	2	6	3
2	5	3	6	4	3
1	4	3	1	2	5
4	2	6	3	5	4

THINK ALIKE

JUMP, LEAP

PAGE 153

Sparklers

T	W	I	N	■	S	T	A	I	D	■	C	H	E	W
R	A	C	E	■	C	A	N	D	O	■	H	A	L	E
A	S	E	C	■	I	N	T	E	R	■	I	N	I	T
J	A	C	K	O	F	D	I	A	M	O	N	D	S	■
A	B	A	■	P	I	E	■	■	I	N	A	B	I	T
N	I	P	A	T	■	M	A	T	T	E	■	O	O	H
■	■	■	B	I	D	■	B	I	O	■	S	O	N	Y
■	V	O	L	C	A	N	I	C	R	O	C	K	S	■
P	A	V	E	■	N	O	D	■	Y	O	U	■	■	■
A	G	E	■	I	N	N	E	S	■	M	T	W	T	F
W	A	R	C	R	Y	■	■	I	S	P	■	H	A	R
■	B	R	E	A	K	I	N	G	T	H	E	I	C	E
T	O	A	D	■	A	D	A	N	O	■	A	N	K	A
A	N	T	E	■	Y	O	D	E	L	■	S	E	E	K
O	D	E	S	■	E	L	A	T	E	■	E	D	D	Y

PAGE 154

123

2	1	3	2	1	3	1	3	2
3	2	1	3	2	1	2	1	3
1	3	2	1	3	2	3	2	1
2	1	3	2	1	3	1	3	2
3	2	1	3	2	1	2	1	3
1	3	2	1	3	2	3	2	1
2	1	3	2	1	3	1	3	2
1	3	2	1	3	2	3	2	1
3	2	1	3	2	1	2	1	3

SUDOKU SUM

5	8	6
3	1	9
7	2	4

PAGE 155

Find the Ships

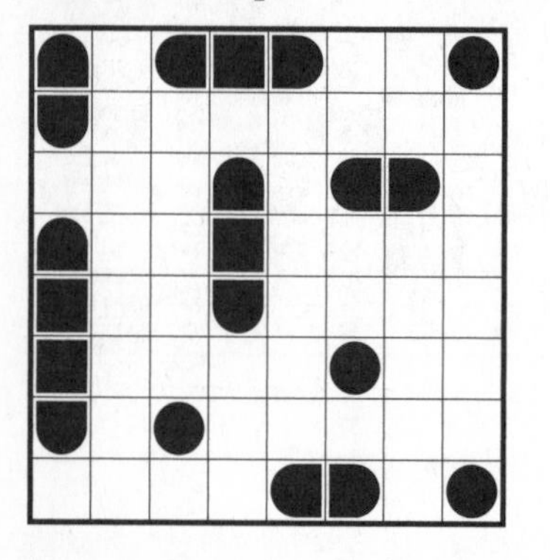

TWO-BY-FOUR

FAIL, COIF (or FOCI)

PAGE 156

Weather Report

S	H	A	W	■	M	A	T	E	Y	■	T	W	O	S
C	O	R	E	■	A	G	I	L	E	■	H	I	R	T
R	A	I	N	C	H	E	C	K	S	■	I	N	C	A
A	R	E	T	H	A	■	■	S	O	M	E	D	A	Y
M	D	S	■	E	L	I	S	■	R	I	F	F	■	■
■	■	■	F	R	O	S	T	I	N	G	■	A	L	T
P	O	S	E	R	■	A	R	N	O	■	B	L	A	H
R	U	N	N	Y	■	B	A	D	■	H	A	L	V	E
I	Z	O	D	■	M	E	N	U	■	A	S	S	A	Y
M	O	W	■	C	O	L	D	C	A	S	H	■	■	■
■	■	W	E	A	R	■	S	E	W	S	■	J	E	T
T	S	H	I	R	T	S	■	■	A	L	C	O	V	E
S	W	I	G	■	I	C	E	B	R	E	A	K	E	R
P	A	T	H	■	S	A	L	A	D	■	P	E	N	S
S	T	E	T	■	E	M	M	Y	S	■	E	R	T	E

PAGE 157

Chef's Special

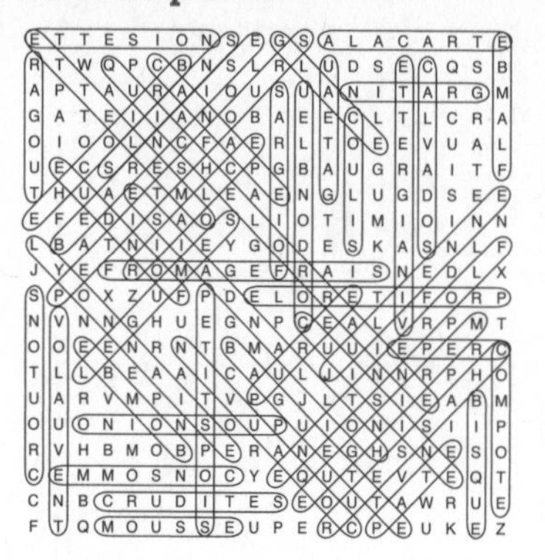

IN OTHER WORDS

MULTIYEAR

PAGE 158

Alternating Tiles

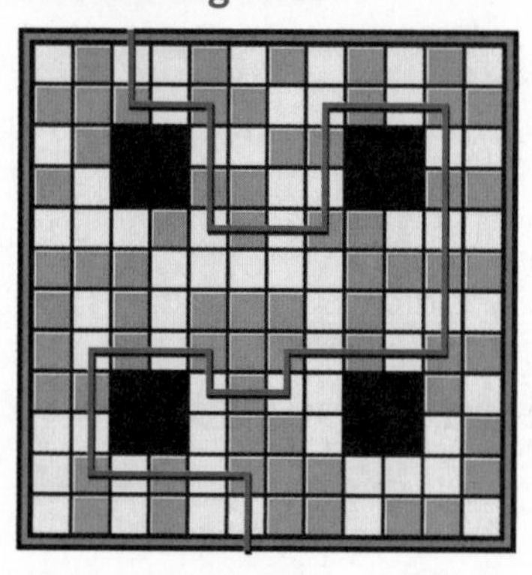

SMALL CHANGE

MAD HATTER

PAGE 159

Star Search

					2	★			
			1		4	★	2	1	
★	3			★	★				★
★	★		1	4	★		1		2
	★			4	★		★		★
	1	2		★	★	★	★	3	
			★		5	★			
			1		2	★	2		

CHOICE WORDS

ARTERY, AVENUE, STREET

PAGE 160

Sign Language

E	L	I	Z	A	■	N	A	R	C	■	I	N	K	Y
A	U	D	I	T	■	O	S	H	A	■	N	A	N	A
S	T	O	P	M	O	T	I	O	N	■	T	I	E	R
Y	E	L	P	■	M	C	A	N	■	H	E	L	E	N
■	■	■	O	P	A	L	■	D	O	U	R	■	■	■
F	R	A	■	O	N	E	W	A	Y	G	L	A	S	S
J	E	R	E	M	I	A	H	■	S	O	O	T	H	E
O	N	O	R	■	■	R	A	W	■	■	C	R	U	D
R	E	M	A	D	E	■	C	H	E	C	K	I	N	G
D	E	A	D	E	N	D	K	I	D	S	■	A	T	E
■	■	■	I	N	T	O	■	T	G	I	F	■	■	■
J	U	I	C	Y	■	T	R	E	E	■	R	O	O	T
A	L	V	A	■	Y	I	E	L	D	C	U	R	V	E
G	N	A	T	■	O	M	N	I	■	B	I	Z	E	T
S	A	N	E	■	M	E	T	E	■	S	T	O	N	E

PAGE 161

Sudoku

7	3	4	1	9	8	5	2	6
5	6	2	3	4	7	9	1	8
9	8	1	6	5	2	4	7	3
1	4	6	9	7	3	2	8	5
2	9	7	5	8	1	3	6	4
3	5	8	2	6	4	1	9	7
4	2	3	7	1	6	8	5	9
6	1	5	8	3	9	7	4	2
8	7	9	4	2	5	6	3	1

MIXAGRAMS

ETHER LUGE
CRIMP LURE
LURCH BAIT
KEYED SITE

PAGE 162

One-Way Streets

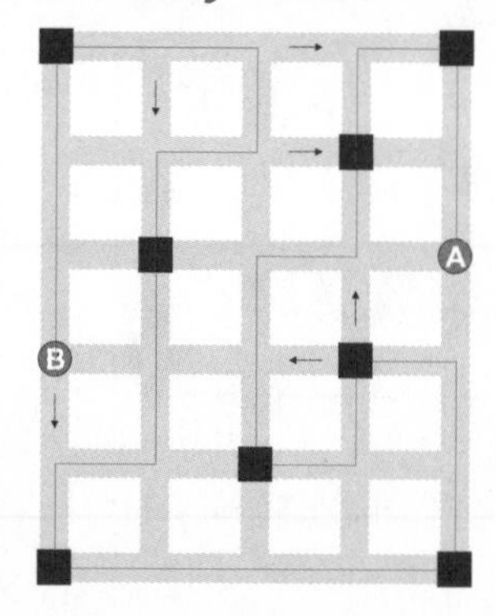

SOUND THINKING

OVERNIGHT

PAGE 163

ABC

B	A			C
	C	B	A	
		A	C	B
A		C	B	
C	B			A

NATIONAL TREASURE

NATURALS

PAGE 164

Making the Cut

D	B	A	C	K	■	L	A	P	P	■	L	E	A	N
A	L	P	H	A	■	A	C	R	E	■	E	L	S	E
K	A	R	A	T	E	C	H	O	P	■	F	L	A	T
A	Z	O	R	E	S	■	I	M	P	■	T	A	P	S
R	E	N	T	■	T	O	E	■	E	L	F	■	■	■
■	■	■	■	■	A	D	S	■	R	E	L	I	C	S
A	R	T	S	■	T	O	T	S	■	T	A	R	O	T
W	H	O	P	P	E	R	■	E	N	S	N	A	R	E
E	E	R	I	E	■	S	A	N	E	■	K	N	E	W
D	A	N	C	E	R	■	P	O	W	■	■	■	■	■
■	■	■	E	R	E	■	P	R	E	■	F	A	M	E
T	H	O	R	■	F	D	A	■	S	A	L	M	O	N
I	O	T	A	■	F	I	R	S	T	R	O	U	N	D
E	P	I	C	■	E	V	E	R	■	C	A	S	T	E
D	E	S	K	■	D	E	L	I	■	S	T	E	E	D

PAGE 165

Wheels and Cogs

Two steaks

BETWEENER

PASTE

PAGE 166

Find the Ships

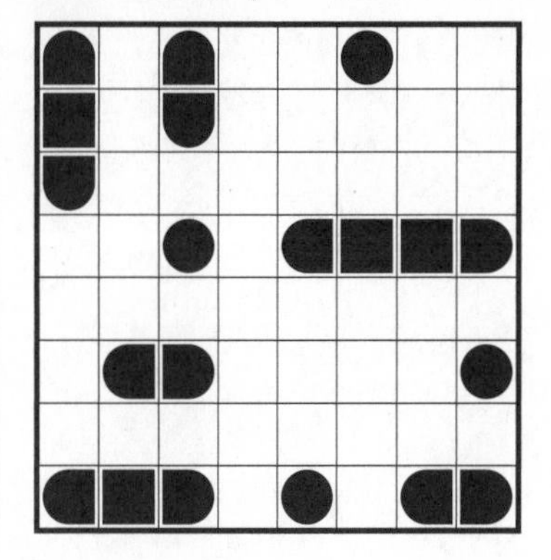

TWO-BY-FOUR

HEMP, PLAT: HELP, TAMP

PAGE 167

123

3	1	2	3	2	1	3	1	2
2	3	1	2	1	3	2	3	1
1	2	3	1	3	2	1	2	3
3	1	2	3	2	1	3	1	2
2	3	1	2	3	2	1	3	1
3	1	2	3	1	3	2	1	2
1	2	3	1	2	1	3	2	3
2	3	1	2	1	3	2	3	1
1	2	3	1	3	2	1	2	3

ADDITION SWITCH

4 7 8 + 4 2 8 = 9 0 6

PAGE 169

Scare Off

C	A	Y	■	A	H	E	A	D	■	P	U	G	E	T
A	M	A	■	S	E	L	M	A	■	E	P	O	C	H
L	A	C	■	C	A	R	E	S	A	N	D	W	O	E
I	N	H	O	R	R	O	R	■	M	A	I	N	L	Y
F	A	T	C	I	T	Y	■	B	U	L	K	■	■	■
■	■	R	O	B	S	■	N	E	S	T	E	G	G	S
S	H	A	M	E	■	H	O	K	E	Y	■	R	A	E
P	U	C	E	■	P	U	M	A	S	■	E	E	G	S
A	G	E	■	Q	A	N	D	A	■	U	V	E	A	S
R	E	S	O	U	R	C	E	■	S	P	I	N	■	■
■	■	■	L	A	S	H	■	R	E	S	T	A	G	E
A	M	P	E	R	E	■	H	E	L	I	A	C	A	L
C	E	S	A	R	C	H	A	V	E	Z	■	R	U	E
T	A	S	T	E	■	P	R	U	N	E	■	E	N	G
I	N	T	E	L	■	S	P	E	E	D	■	S	T	Y

PAGE 170

Fences

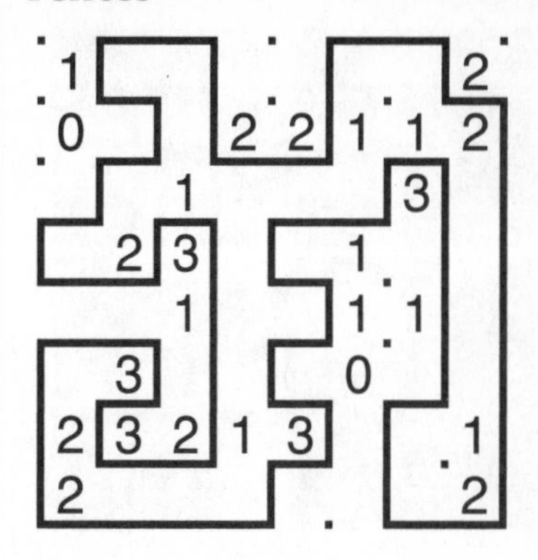

WRONG IS RIGHT

Ascerbic (should be *acerbic*)

PAGE 171

Number-Out

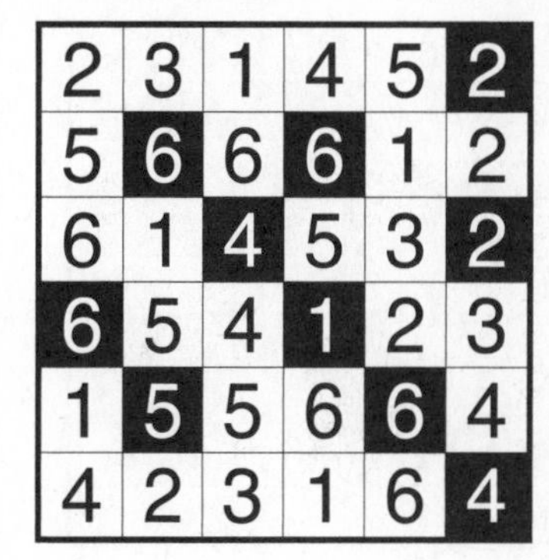

2	3	1	4	5	2
5	6	6	6	1	2
6	1	4	5	3	2
6	5	4	1	2	3
1	5	5	6	6	4
4	2	3	1	6	4

THINK ALIKE

COW, BOVINE

PAGE 172

Differing Opinions

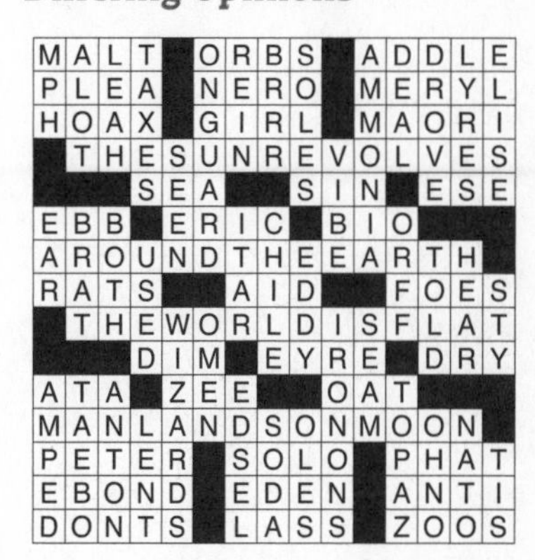

M	A	L	T	■	O	R	B	S	■	A	D	D	L	E
P	L	E	A	■	N	E	R	O	■	M	E	R	Y	L
H	O	A	X	■	G	I	R	L	■	M	A	O	R	I
■	T	H	E	S	U	N	R	E	V	O	L	V	E	S
■	■	■	S	E	A	■	■	S	I	N	■	E	S	E
E	B	B	■	E	R	I	C	■	B	I	O	■	■	■
A	R	O	U	N	D	T	H	E	E	A	R	T	H	■
R	A	T	S	■	■	A	I	D	■	■	F	O	E	S
■	T	H	E	W	O	R	L	D	I	S	F	L	A	T
■	■	■	D	I	M	■	E	Y	R	E	■	D	R	Y
A	T	A	■	Z	E	E	■	■	O	A	T	■	■	■
M	A	N	L	A	N	D	S	O	N	M	O	O	N	■
P	E	T	E	R	■	S	O	L	O	■	P	H	A	T
E	B	O	N	D	■	E	D	E	N	■	A	N	T	I
D	O	N	T	S	■	L	A	S	S	■	Z	O	O	S

PAGE 173

Straight Ahead

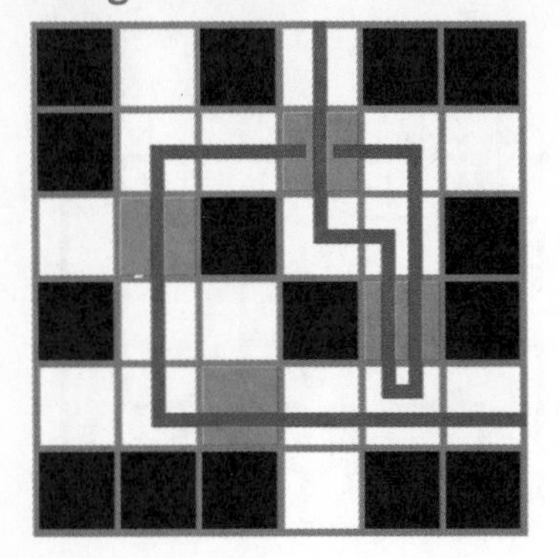

BETWEENER

SAUCE

PAGE 174

Hyper-Sudoku

3	2	6	9	7	4	8	5	1
9	4	8	1	5	3	6	7	2
1	7	5	2	6	8	4	9	3
4	3	9	6	8	5	1	2	7
5	8	7	3	2	1	9	6	4
6	1	2	7	4	9	3	8	5
7	9	3	5	1	6	2	4	8
2	6	4	8	3	7	5	1	9
8	5	1	4	9	2	7	3	6

MIXAGRAMS

HEAVE TRIP
ENTRY DOER
AHEAD ROCK
DIVAN SMOG

PAGE 175

Wow!

INITIAL REACTION

The Pen Is Mightier Than The Sword

PAGE 176

Platter Chatter

S	C	A	B	■	U	S	E	R	S	■	S	T	A	G
L	A	C	E	■	N	A	T	A	L	■	L	I	M	A
O	R	C	A	■	F	A	R	M	A	N	I	M	A	L
P	R	E	S	S	U	R	E	P	L	A	T	E	■	■
P	I	S	T	O	N	■	■	S	O	D	■	L	I	T
Y	E	S	■	I	N	S	O	■	M	I	M	O	S	A
■	■	■	F	L	Y	I	N	G	S	A	U	C	E	R
O	M	O	O	■	■	K	E	Y	■	■	I	K	E	A
D	O	D	G	E	C	H	A	R	G	E	R	■	■	■
D	A	Y	G	L	O	■	M	O	O	R	■	C	H	A
S	T	S	■	I	M	A	■	■	A	T	E	O	U	T
■	■	S	A	T	E	L	L	I	T	E	D	I	S	H
P	R	E	D	E	S	T	I	N	E	■	U	N	T	O
S	C	U	D	■	T	A	S	T	E	■	C	O	L	M
T	A	S	S	■	O	R	A	L	S	■	E	P	E	E

PAGE 177

Triad Split Decisions

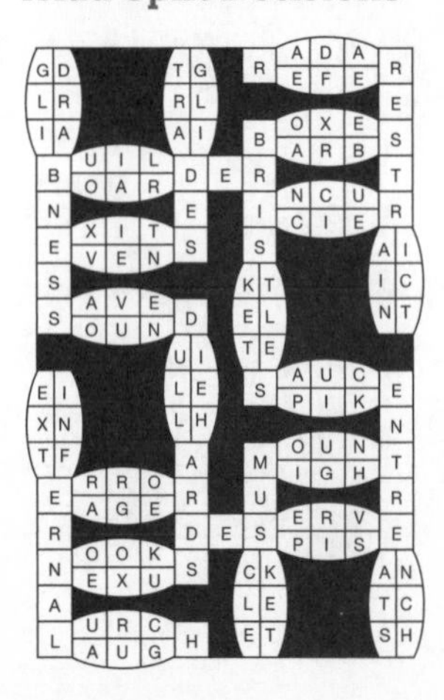

TRANSDELETION

GALLEON

PAGE 178

One-Way Streets

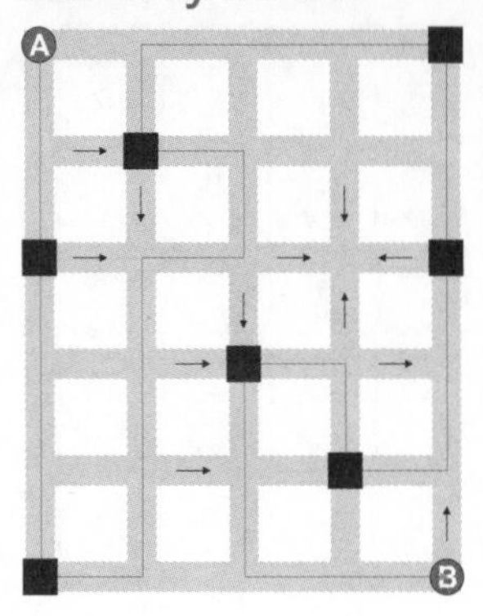

SOUND THINKING

ONE

PAGE 179

Relatively Speaking

S	P	L	A	T	■	M	A	R	S	■	T	H	A	W
D	I	A	N	A	■	U	T	A	H	■	V	O	L	E
I	T	S	T	R	U	E	T	H	A	T	I	W	A	S
■	■	■	E	P	P	S	■	S	N	I	D	E	S	T
A	M	E	N	■	E	L	M	■	K	O	O	■	■	■
B	O	R	N	I	N	I	O	W	A	■	L	E	N	S
A	R	M	A	N	D	■	D	I	R	E	■	M	O	P
S	L	I	E	R	■	B	U	T	■	V	I	O	L	A
E	E	N	■	E	V	I	L	■	S	E	N	T	O	N
D	Y	E	S	■	I	C	A	N	T	S	P	E	A	K
■	■	■	H	I	S	■	R	U	E	■	E	D	D	Y
O	C	T	A	V	I	A	■	A	M	O	R	■	■	■
F	O	R	M	Y	T	W	I	N	S	I	S	T	E	R
F	L	O	E	■	E	R	I	C	■	L	O	W	L	Y
S	A	Y	S	■	D	Y	N	E	■	S	N	A	K	E

PAGE 180

Sequence Maze

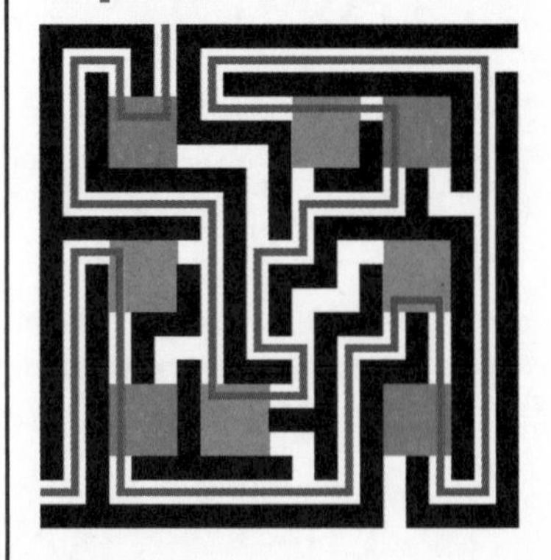

SAY IT AGAIN

STATE

PAGE 181

Star Search

			1	1	1	1			
			★			★			
			1		2				
					2	★	2		1
			4	★	3			★	2
	2	★	★	★		3	★	★	2
		★	6	★	★		★		1
		★	3						
					1				
			1	★					

CHOICE WORDS

ALCOVE, LOUNGE, PARLOR

PAGE 182

Sudoku

7	4	2	1	3	8	6	9	5
9	5	8	4	7	6	3	2	1
3	1	6	5	2	9	4	8	7
1	8	4	7	5	2	9	3	6
6	3	9	8	1	4	5	7	2
5	2	7	6	9	3	8	1	4
4	9	1	3	6	7	2	5	8
8	7	3	2	4	5	1	6	9
2	6	5	9	8	1	7	4	3

CENTURY MARKS

31, 28, 19, 22

PAGE 183

Ex Factors

L	E	A	F		M	E	G	A		B	A	Y	E	D
O	S	S	O		O	L	A	V		A	G	O	R	A
N	A	T	O		R	O	S	E		R	I	G	I	D
G	U	I	L	D	A	P	P	R	E	N	T	I	C	E
				A	S	E			L	E	A			
L	I	T	M	U	S		L	A	D	Y		T	E	T
A	L	I	E	N		H	A	L	E		A	R	L	O
V	O	L	S	T	E	A	D	O	R	S	T	A	M	P
E	V	E	S		N	I	L	E		W	A	L	E	S
R	E	D		T	I	R	E		C	A	N	A	R	Y
			P	E	A			S	A	M				
T	H	R	E	E	C	E	N	T	P	I	E	C	E	S
H	A	U	N	T		Z	E	R	O		T	A	X	I
A	L	I	N	E		R	O	U	T		C	R	A	M
T	O	N	E	R		A	N	T	E		H	E	M	P

PAGE 184

ABC

A		B		C
B		C		A
	C	A	B	
	A		C	B
C	B		A	

CLUELESS CROSSWORD

P	R	E	T	Z	E	L
A		C		I		O
T	H	O	U	G	H	T
E		N		Z		U
L	O	O	F	A	H	S
L		M		G		E
A	B	Y	S	S	E	S

PAGE 185

Find the Ships

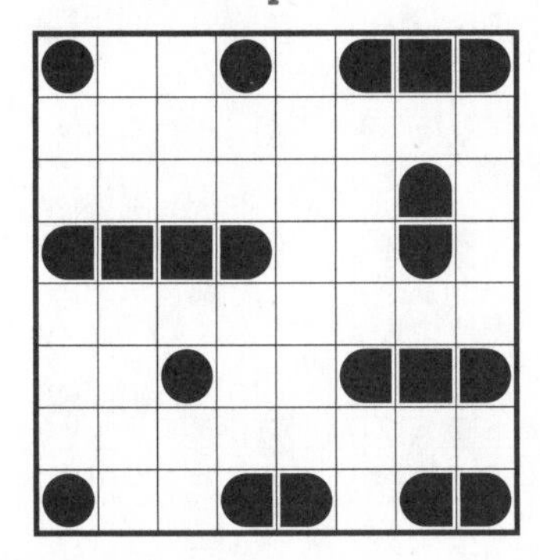

TWO-BY-FOUR

WIRE, EVER (or VEER)

PAGE 186

Greenland

S	T	A	R	E		P	A	P	A	L		K	E	G
T	A	T	E	R		O	H	A	R	A		E	R	A
O	L	I	V	E	B	R	A	N	C	H		L	I	Z
M	I	L	E		L	E	S	T	A	T		L	E	E
P	A	T	A	K	I			E	D	I	F	Y		
			L	I	M	E	A	D	E		I	R	A	S
L	B	J		O	P	A	L		S	C	R	I	P	T
O	R	A	L	S		T	O	P		Z	E	P	P	O
S	U	D	O	K	U		H	I	V	E		A	S	P
S	T	E	P		P	E	A	C	O	C	K			
		P	E	S	T	S			W	H	O	M	P	S
J	K	L		K	E	T	T	L	E		D	I	O	N
A	A	A		E	M	E	R	A	L	D	I	S	L	E
I	N	N		E	P	E	E	S		R	A	D	A	R
L	E	T		T	O	M	E	S		S	K	O	R	T

PAGE 187

Dot to Dot

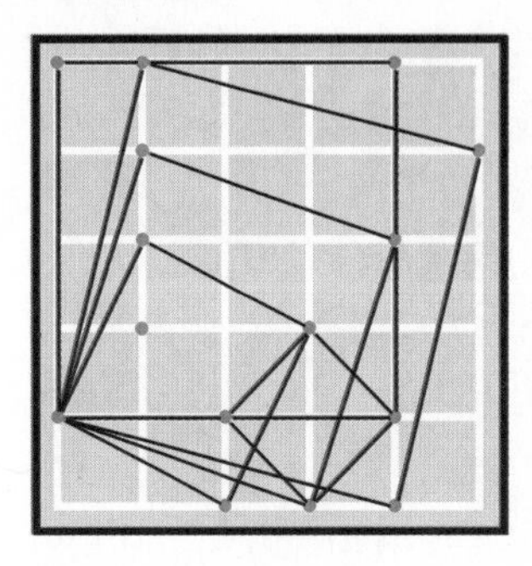

SMALL CHANGE

PRIME MOVER

PAGE 188

123

3	1	2	1	2	3	2	3	1
2	3	1	2	3	1	3	1	2
1	2	3	1	2	3	1	2	3
2	3	1	3	1	2	3	1	2
1	2	3	2	3	1	2	3	1
3	1	2	3	1	2	1	2	3
2	3	1	2	3	1	2	3	1
3	1	2	3	1	2	3	1	2
1	2	3	1	2	3	1	2	3

SUDOKU SUM

4	7	2
1	3	9
8	6	5

PAGE 189

Fences

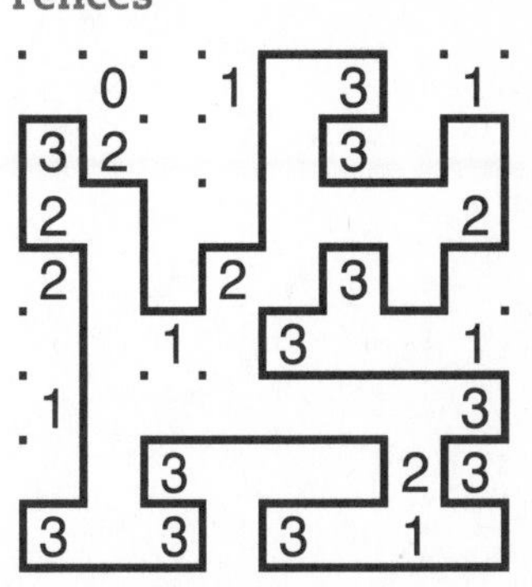

WRONG IS RIGHT

Chickory (should be *chicory*)

PAGE 190

Around the Clock

B	A	S	K	■	U	P	N	■	S	N	A	P	U	P
L	U	T	E	■	P	L	O	■	A	L	L	O	T	S
I	R	O	N	S	O	U	T	■	Y	E	L	L	A	T
M	O	R	N	I	N	G	G	L	O	R	Y	■	■	■
P	R	E	Y	S	■	S	O	A	K	■	■	D	O	H
S	A	D	■	■	D	I	O	R	■	G	L	O	A	T
■	■	■	N	O	O	N	D	A	Y	L	I	G	H	T
R	E	V	I	E	W	■	■	■	E	A	T	S	U	P
E	V	E	N	I	N	G	S	H	A	D	E	■	■	■
P	E	T	A	L	■	O	P	U	S	■	■	A	S	U
O	R	O	■	■	C	O	R	N	■	S	A	L	O	N
■	■	■	M	I	D	N	I	G	H	T	B	L	U	E
I	N	D	O	O	R	■	N	E	E	D	L	E	R	S
C	O	O	L	T	O	■	G	R	E	■	E	L	E	C
I	N	S	E	A	M	■	Y	S	L	■	R	E	D	O

PAGE 191

Hyper-Sudoku

4	3	1	8	9	6	7	2	5
8	7	6	5	3	2	4	1	9
5	9	2	1	4	7	8	3	6
1	4	8	3	2	9	6	5	7
2	5	7	6	8	4	1	9	3
9	6	3	7	1	5	2	4	8
3	8	5	2	6	1	9	7	4
7	1	4	9	5	8	3	6	2
6	2	9	4	7	3	5	8	1

MIXAGRAMS

E B B E D   D O Z E
T O R S O   A V I D
A W O K E   L E N S
C L E A N   A R T S

PAGE 192

Split Decisions

TRANSDELETION

CERULEAN

PAGE 193

The A List

N	A	D	A	■	R	A	S	A	■	S	A	G	A	■
A	S	A	N	■	A	R	C	S	■	W	A	R	N	S
H	A	N	K	S	T	R	A	M	■	A	M	A	N	A
■	P	L	A	T	T	■	N	A	S	T	■	H	A	M
■	■	■	R	A	R	A	■	R	A	S	C	A	L	S
A	S	F	A	R	A	S	■	A	L	A	R	M	■	■
T	A	R	■	S	P	C	A	■	■	T	A	N	G	S
A	D	A	M	■	S	H	A	N	A	■	W	A	A	C
D	A	N	A	S	■	■	H	A	L	F	■	S	L	A
■	■	K	R	A	F	T	■	G	A	L	A	H	A	D
B	A	C	K	B	A	R	■	S	N	A	G	■	■	■
R	C	A	■	B	A	A	L	■	A	G	H	A	S	■
A	L	P	H	A	■	C	A	R	L	S	A	G	A	N
M	A	R	A	T	■	T	V	A	D	■	S	R	A	S
■	M	A	S	H	■	S	A	N	A	■	T	A	R	A

PAGE 194

Solitaire Poker

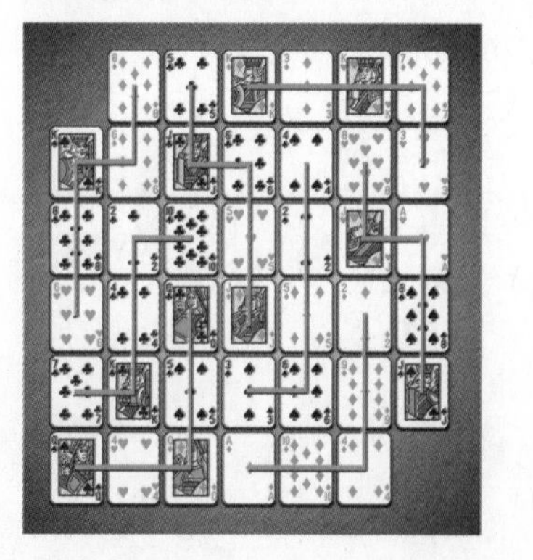

BETWEENER

TIGHT

PAGE 195

Number-Out

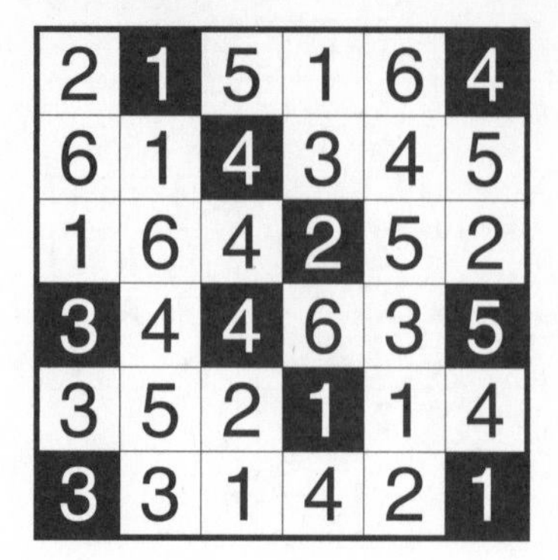

2	1	5	1	6	4
6	1	4	3	4	5
1	6	4	2	5	2
3	4	4	6	3	5
3	5	2	1	1	4
3	3	1	4	2	1

THINK ALIKE

FATHER, DAD

PAGE 196

One-Way Streets

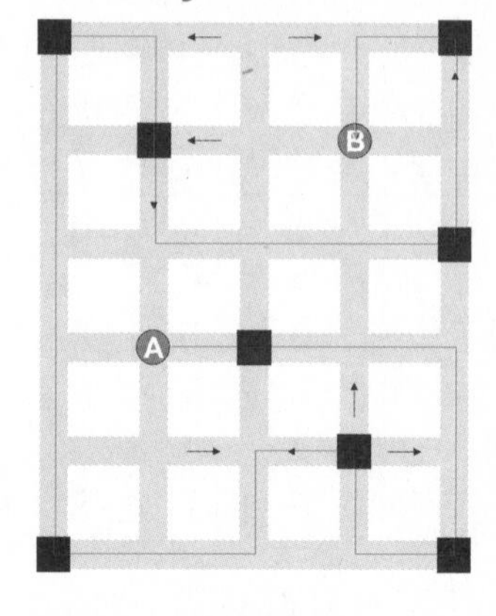

SOUND THINKING

UNION

PAGE 197

Aural Antonyms

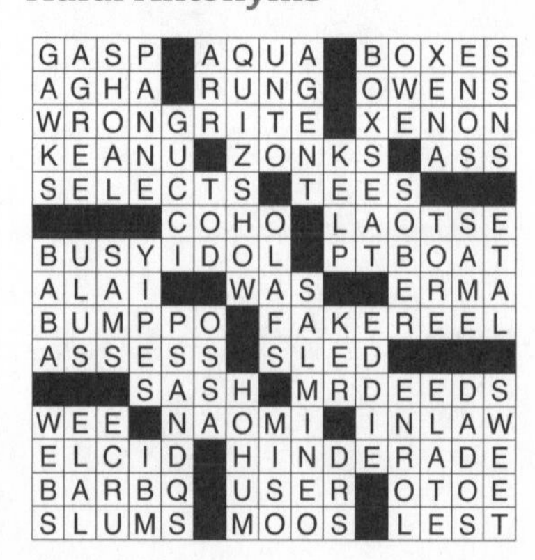

G	A	S	P	■	A	Q	U	A	■	B	O	X	E	S
A	G	H	A	■	R	U	N	G	■	O	W	E	N	S
W	R	O	N	G	R	I	T	E	■	X	E	N	O	N
K	E	A	N	U	■	Z	O	N	K	S	■	A	S	S
S	E	L	E	C	T	S	■	T	E	E	S	■	■	■
■	■	■	■	C	O	H	O	■	L	A	O	T	S	E
B	U	S	Y	I	D	O	L	■	P	T	B	O	A	T
A	L	A	I	■	■	W	A	S	■	■	E	R	M	A
B	U	M	P	P	O	■	F	A	K	E	R	E	E	L
A	S	S	E	S	S	■	S	L	E	D	■	■	■	■
■	■	■	S	A	S	H	■	M	R	D	E	E	D	S
W	E	E	■	N	A	O	M	I	■	I	N	L	A	W
E	L	C	I	D	■	H	I	N	D	E	R	A	D	E
B	A	R	B	Q	■	U	S	E	R	■	O	T	O	E
S	L	U	M	S	■	M	O	O	S	■	L	E	S	T

PAGE 198

Sudoku

3	5	4	2	9	6	8	7	1
8	7	2	5	1	3	6	9	4
9	6	1	4	7	8	3	2	5
6	1	9	7	8	2	4	5	3
7	3	5	1	6	4	2	8	9
2	4	8	3	5	9	7	1	6
5	8	6	9	3	7	1	4	2
4	9	7	6	2	1	5	3	8
1	2	3	8	4	5	9	6	7

MIXAGRAMS

C A N A L L O B E
I D O L S F L E X
E A G E R D U D S
A M I S S F R E T

PAGE 199

Star Search

				2		1			
		1		★	★				
1	★		3		★	4	★	2	
			★	★			★		
				2		1		1	
						1			1
		2	★	2	★				★
		★					2	★	2
		2	★	★			★		
			2	2	2	★	2		

CHOICE WORDS

CARROT, RADISH, TURNIP

PAGE 200

River Heads

C	L	A	M	P	■	S	H	O	D	■	S	P	A	R
H	O	N	O	R	■	P	O	L	A	■	H	O	L	E
A	G	O	R	A	■	U	B	E	R	■	O	D	I	N
D	O	N	N	Y	B	R	O	O	K	■	R	I	S	E
■	■	■	■	E	A	T	■	■	E	S	T	A	T	E
A	P	I	A	R	Y	■	F	I	N	E	S	T	■	■
P	A	N	G	S	■	L	A	T	E	N	■	R	A	W
S	I	D	E	■	S	I	R	E	D	■	M	I	N	E
E	D	U	■	S	T	E	A	M	■	V	I	S	T	A
■	■	S	T	R	A	N	D	■	F	A	L	T	E	R
A	C	T	I	O	N	■	■	U	R	N	■	■	■	■
W	A	R	T	■	C	A	M	P	A	I	G	N	E	R
A	R	I	A	■	H	I	E	S	■	L	L	A	M	A
R	O	A	N	■	E	D	I	E	■	L	I	M	I	T
E	L	L	S	■	D	E	N	T	■	A	B	E	T	S

PAGE 201

Tractor Maze

SAY IT AGAIN

TABLE

PAGE 202

Pathfinder

SILICON, URANIUM, ZINC, MERCURY, TIN, IRON, TUNGSTEN, CALCIUM, NICKEL, ARGON, PHOSPHORUS, NITROGEN, NEON, POTASSIUM, RADIUM, HYDROGEN, PLATINUM, GOLD, SODIUM

WHO'S WHAT WHERE?

Emirian

PAGE 203

ABC

	C		A	B
B	A		C	
C	B	A		
		C	B	A
A		B		C

CLUELESS CROSSWORD

P L U M B E R
I R O E
L A C O N I C
G H A E
R E I G N E D
I N Z E
M U S T A R D

PAGE 204

Themeless Toughie

S	A	F	E	B	E	T	■	G	A	S	M	A	I	N
T	R	U	D	E	A	U	■	A	R	T	I	S	T	E
L	E	N	D	E	R	S	■	T	A	U	N	T	E	D
■	■	■	A	F	L	C	I	O	■	A	T	O	M	S
A	D	E	S	■	D	A	D	■	D	R	J	■	■	■
N	E	A	■	C	O	L	O	R	A	T	U	R	A	S
O	N	T	H	E	M	O	N	E	Y	■	L	O	S	T
R	A	S	E	S	■	O	T	S	■	C	E	S	T	A
A	L	I	D	■	E	S	K	I	M	O	P	I	E	S
K	I	N	G	S	R	A	N	S	O	M	■	T	R	I
■	■	■	E	P	A	■	O	T	C	■	K	A	N	S
R	A	F	F	I	■	A	W	A	K	E	N	■	■	■
A	L	L	U	D	E	S	■	N	E	V	A	D	A	N
I	P	A	N	E	M	A	■	C	R	E	V	I	C	E
D	E	W	D	R	O	P	■	E	S	S	E	N	C	E

PAGE 206

Find the Ships

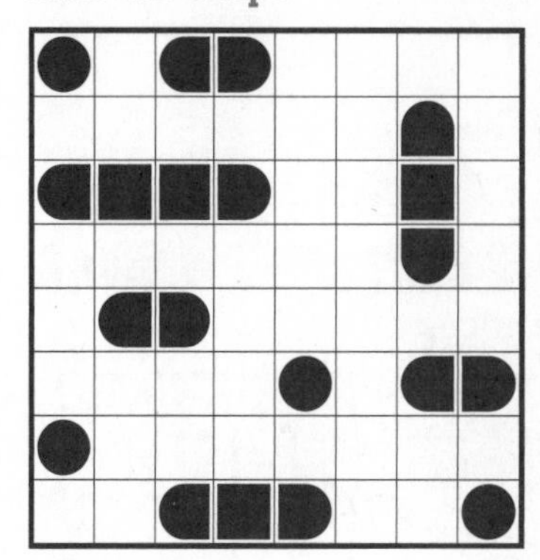

TWO-BY-FOUR

AXLE (or AXEL), TUBA (or ABUT or TABU)

PAGE 207

Hyper-Sudoku

4	2	7	8	5	3	1	9	6
9	3	8	6	2	1	4	5	7
6	5	1	7	4	9	2	3	8
5	4	9	2	1	7	8	6	3
7	1	6	4	3	8	5	2	9
3	8	2	9	6	5	7	1	4
8	7	5	1	9	6	3	4	2
1	6	4	3	7	2	9	8	5
2	9	3	5	8	4	6	7	1

BETWEENER

HAMMER

PAGE 208

Themeless Toughie

P	I	A	N	I	S	T	S	■	K	E	E	P	A	T
U	N	S	O	C	I	A	L	■	O	L	E	O	L	E
F	T	K	N	O	X	K	Y	■	V	I	L	L	A	S
F	R	E	O	N	■	E	N	P	A	S	S	A	N	T
S	O	W	S	■	C	O	E	R	C	E	■	N	F	C
■	■	■	■	R	O	U	S	E	S	■	H	E	R	A
I	T	S	Y	B	I	T	S	Y	■	L	U	G	E	S
R	E	T	A	I	N	■	■	■	D	E	G	R	E	E
I	T	E	M	S	■	S	O	L	E	N	O	I	D	S
S	E	A	S	■	R	O	B	I	N	S	■	■	■	■
H	A	M	■	D	E	F	T	L	Y	■	S	A	L	A
I	T	I	N	E	R	A	R	Y	■	D	E	M	O	N
S	E	R	E	N	E	■	U	P	C	O	M	I	N	G
M	T	O	S	S	A	■	D	A	R	L	I	N	G	S
S	E	N	S	E	D	■	E	D	I	T	S	O	U	T

PAGE 209

Plate Class

#2

SMALL CHANGE

STRING BEAN

PAGE 210

Fences

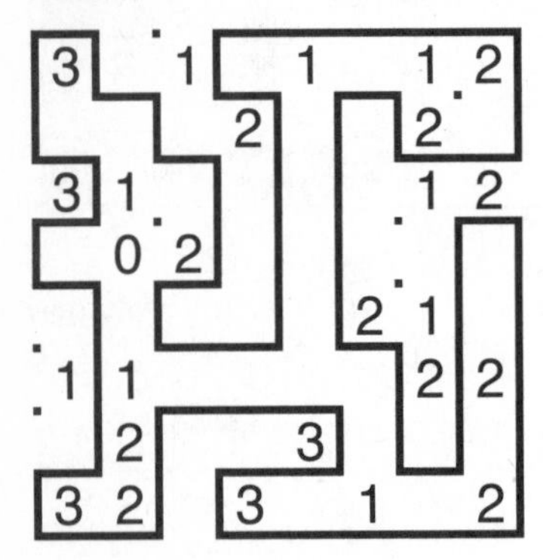

ADDITION SWITCH

5 9 7 + 1 8 9 = 7 8 6

PAGE 211

Themeless Toughie

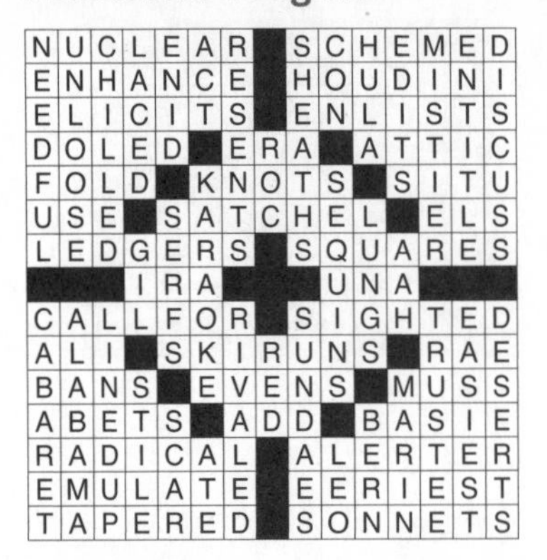

PAGE 212

123

3	1	2	3	2	1	3	1	2
1	2	3	1	3	2	1	2	3
2	3	1	2	1	3	2	3	1
3	1	2	3	2	1	3	1	2
1	2	3	1	3	2	1	2	3
2	3	1	2	1	3	2	3	1
3	1	2	3	2	1	3	1	2
2	3	1	2	1	3	2	3	1
1	2	3	1	3	2	1	2	3

WRONG IS RIGHT

Syncronize (should be *synchronize*)

PAGE 213

Number-Out

3	2	**1**	4	5	**6**
5	**3**	2	**5**	1	4
2	6	1	5	**6**	3
4	**1**	5	**5**	6	1
1	5	**3**	3	2	6
2	3	6	1	**3**	5

THINK ALIKE

LABOR, WORK

PAGE 214

Themeless Toughie

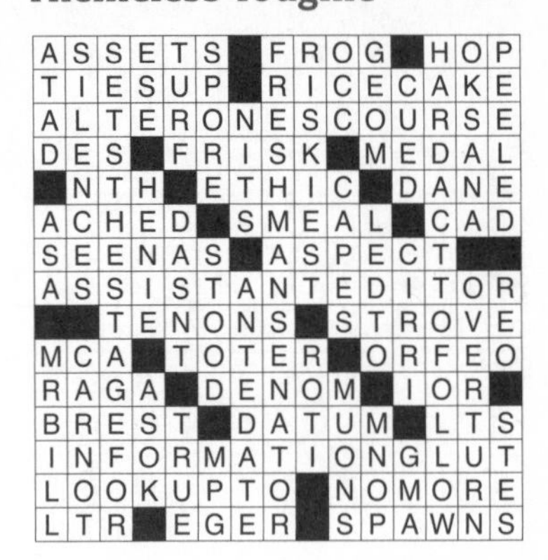

PAGE 215

Mythological Jigsaw

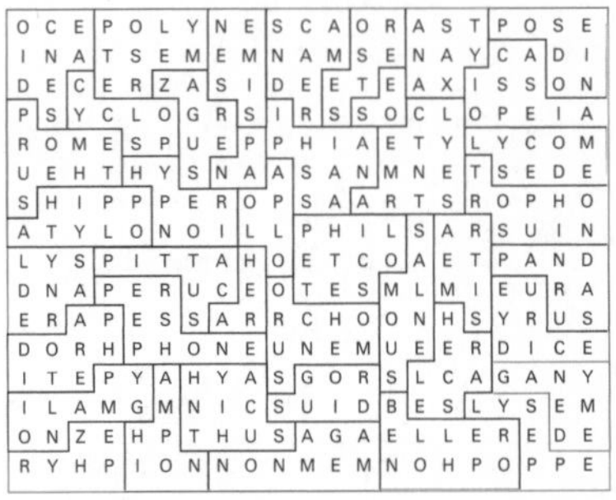

O C E P O L Y N E S C A O R A S T P O S E
I N A T S E M E M N A M S E N A Y C A D I
D E C E R Z A S I D E E T E A X I S S O N
P S Y C L O G R S I R S S O C L O P E I A
R O M E S P U E P P H I A E T Y L Y C O M
U E H T H Y S N A A S A N M N E T S E D E
S H I P P P E R O P S A A R T S R O P H O
A T Y L O N O I L L P H I L S A R S U I N
L Y S P I T T A H O E T C O A E T P A N D
D N A P E R U C E O T E S M L M I E U R A
E R A P E S S A R R C H O O N H S Y R U S
D O R H P H O N E U N E M U E E R D I C E
I T E P Y A H Y A S G O R S L C A G A N Y
I L A M G M N I C S U I D B E S L Y S E M
O N Z E H P T H U S A G A E L L E R E D E
R Y H P I O N N O N M E M N O H P O P P E

IN OTHER WORDS

OBSEQUIOUS

PAGE 216

Sequence Maze

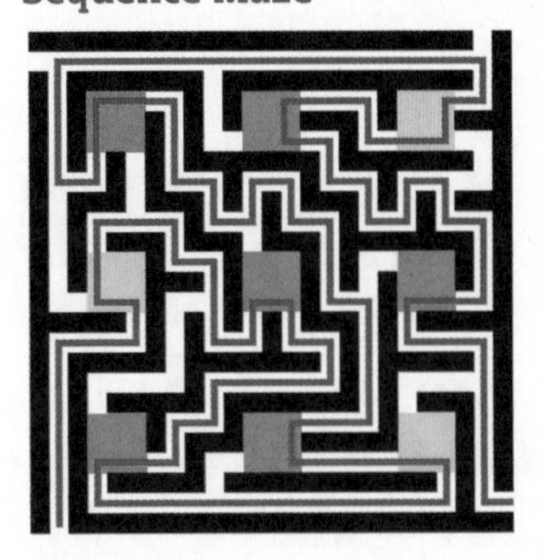

SAY IT AGAIN

ATTEND

PAGE 217

Themeless Toughie

P	E	A	T	B	O	G		A	D	J	U	S	T	S
O	N	L	E	A	V	E		P	R	E	P	P	I	E
S	T	A	R	T	I	N	G	P	I	T	C	H	E	R
T	E	M	P	E		T	R	E	E	S		E	R	E
D	R	O	S	S		L	E	A	D		F	R	A	N
O	E	D			P	E	A	R		A	L	I	C	E
C	R	E	A	T	E		S	E	T	B	A	C	K	
			N	A	N	C	Y	D	R	E	W			
	R	A	N	C	H	O	S		I	T	S	E	L	F
M	E	T	O	O		A	P	E	X			N	E	O
A	L	L	Y		A	L	O	U		S	E	G	A	R
M	E	A		H	U	M	O	R		C	R	A	N	E
M	A	N	D	A	R	I	N	O	R	A	N	G	E	S
A	R	T	I	S	A	N		P	U	N	I	E	S	T
S	N	A	P	P	L	E		A	T	T	E	S	T	S

PAGE 218

ABCD

	B	A	C	D	
		C	D	A	B
A	D		B		C
D	C	B	A		
B	A			C	D
C		D		B	A

NATIONAL TREASURE

RAINCOAT

PAGE 219

Sudoku

4	3	2	7	9	5	8	6	1
5	1	7	6	3	8	9	4	2
8	9	6	4	1	2	5	7	3
9	6	4	5	2	1	7	3	8
1	2	3	8	6	7	4	9	5
7	5	8	9	4	3	1	2	6
2	4	9	1	5	6	3	8	7
6	7	1	3	8	9	2	5	4
3	8	5	2	7	4	6	1	9

MIXAGRAMS

B O O T H H O S E
A B A C K A F A R
C U R L Y N I C E
K I N K Y D U E L

PAGE 220

Themeless Toughie

P	U	S	H	P	I	N		D	E	B	O	N	E	S
O	N	L	E	A	V	E		E	L	E	M	E	N	T
P	L	E	A	S	E	S		M	A	S	S	A	G	E
S	E	E	D	S		T	R	O	T	S		T	A	P
O	A	K	S		S	L	A	T	E		H	E	R	S
U	S	E		O	P	I	N	E		C	O	N	D	O
T	H	R	I	V	I	N	G		C	H	O	S	E	N
			G	A	N	G		P	O	E	T			
G	R	I	L	L	E		B	R	U	S	S	E	L	S
N	O	N	O	S		C	R	O	C	S		V	I	M
A	U	T	O		P	O	A	C	H		P	I	C	A
R	T	E		S	U	I	T	E		W	A	D	E	R
L	I	N	C	O	L	N		E	M	I	N	E	N	T
E	N	T	H	U	S	E		D	E	F	E	N	S	E
D	E	S	I	R	E	D		S	W	E	L	T	E	R

PAGE 221

One-Way Streets

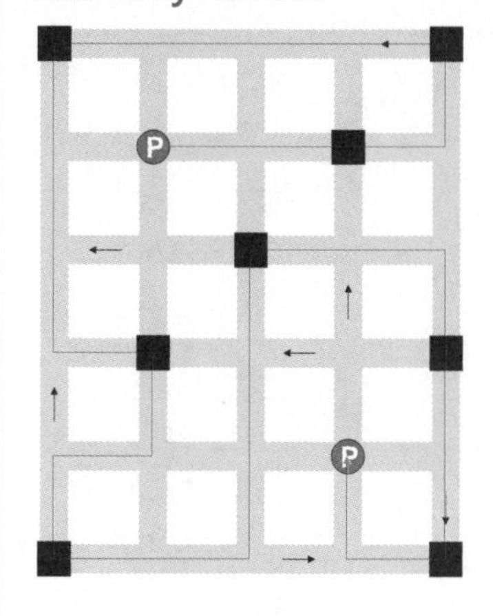

SOUND THINKING

EASYGOING

PAGE 222

Split Decisions

TRANSDELETION

DERRINGER

PAGE 223

Themeless Toughie

S	A	T	I	A	T	E	D		M	A	I	L	I	N
C	R	U	S	T	I	E	R		A	L	P	I	N	E
A	C	R	I	M	O	N	Y		L	A	O	T	S	E
R	A	N	T			Y	E	S	I	N	D	E	E	D
A	R	O	M	A	S		R	U	B			R	C	A
B	O	N	E	S	E	T		B	U	R	E	A	U	S
				T	W	E	R	P		U	L	T	R	A
M	A	T	T	E		N	I	L		S	L	E	E	P
A	S	H	E	R		S	P	O	R	T				
S	T	R	A	N	G	E		T	A	L	E	N	T	S
O	H	O			R	U	N		G	E	N	I	A	L
N	O	T	E	P	A	P	E	R			D	A	L	I
J	U	T	T	E	D		R	E	P	R	I	C	E	D
A	G	L	A	R	E		T	E	L	E	V	I	S	E
R	H	E	S	U	S		S	L	O	V	E	N	E	S

PAGE 224

Your Turn

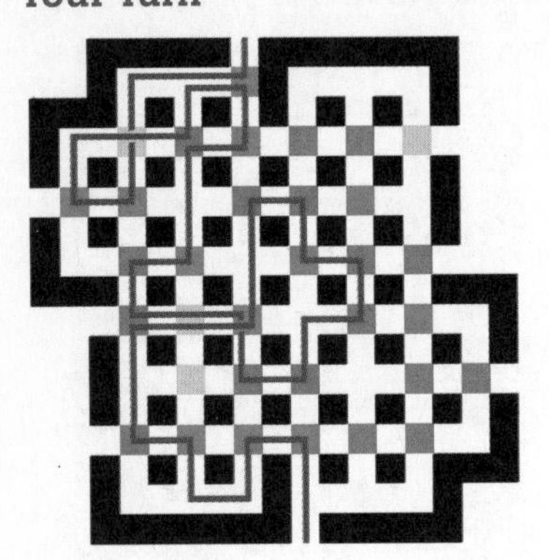

SAY IT AGAIN

BRIGHT

PAGE 225

Star Search

					★		2	★	
			★	3	3	3	3	★	
1		2			★	★	2		
★		3	★	3	3		2	2	★
2	★	4	★	3	3	★	2	2	★
		★			★	★			
			1	1			2		
			1	1		★	2		
				★	2	2	★		

CHOICE WORDS

GRUMPY, MOROSE, SULLEN

PAGE 226

Themeless Toughie

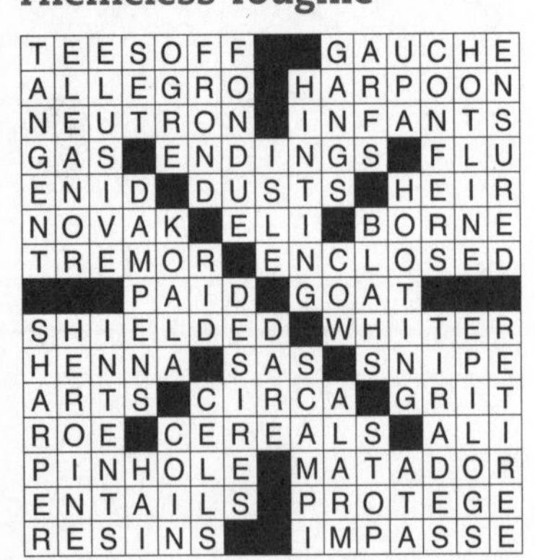

PAGE 227

Number-Out

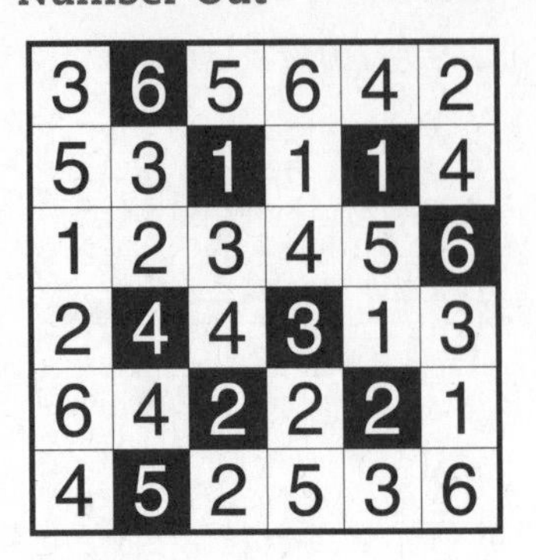

THINK ALIKE

WANDER, ROVE

PAGE 228

Line Drawing

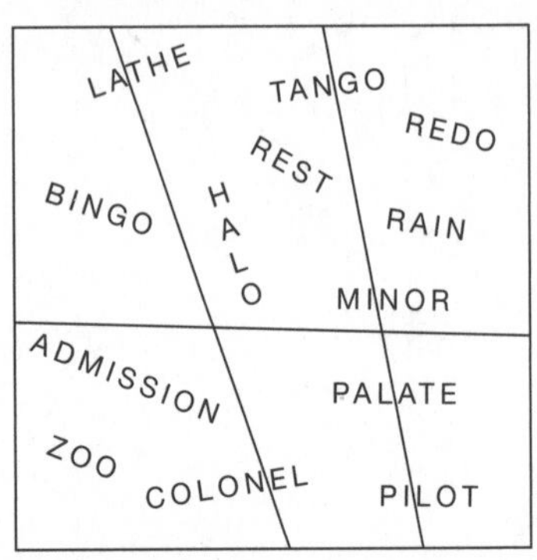

TWO-BY-FOUR

RUIN, FLAY; FURY, NAIL (or LAIN)

PAGE 229

Themeless Toughie

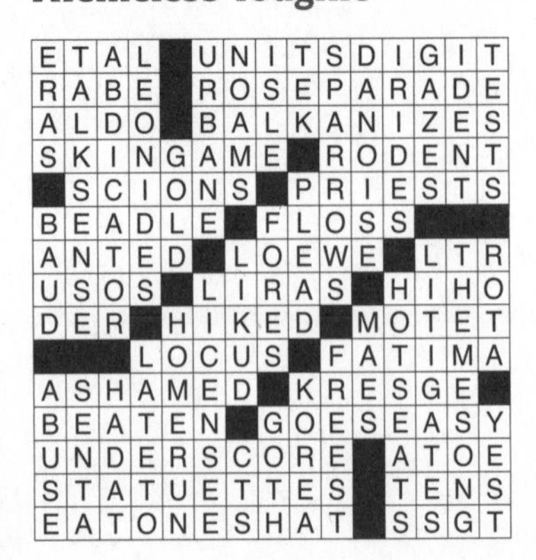

PAGE 230

Triad Split Decisions

TRANSDELETION

GREAT DANE

PAGE 231

Piece It Together

SMALL CHANGE

DOG CATCHER

PAGE 232

Themeless Toughie

ALPHAMALE AWES
PALISADES TAXER
OPENAREAS VITAE
SPAT LUKE STRAD
VEXING SANA
DOOLEY ETAT DEL
ERROR PRIMETIME
SOANDSO AERATOR
INNEUTRAL SPENT
ROG NACL REESES
AMES BELAIR
BASIE LOSS OSHA
LIONS AFTERNOON
ENDUP IMITATION
EASY NEROWOLFE